The Book of the Great Northern

THE MAIN LINE

AN ENGINEERING COMMENTARY
Part Two: Welwyn North to Doncaster

Peter J Coster

C.Eng, MICE, MCIT

IRWELL PRESS Ltd.

ISBN 978 1 906919 31 3

Preface

With the second book of the pair examining the engineering and operation of the GNR main line from Kings Cross to Doncaster over the years, we turn our attention away from the metropolis towards the countryside. I have not repeated the preface of Part One, but the comments apply equally to Part Two. This is not a detailed history of the GN main line, but an engineering and operational commentary.

However, it would not be possible nowadays to write a reflective account of this nature without acknowledging the enormous archive of historical material from the many authors who have already written on this subject and I am happy to do so. As I wrote in Part One, the definitive work was that of Charles H Grinling, "The History of the Great Northern Railway". Then there was the work of such as John Wrottesley, R A H (Bob) Weight, F A S Brown, E A J Neve, W A Tuplin and others, latterly Dr Ben Brooksbank. To all these I give my grateful thanks.

While my knowledge of the GN main line is good, it is not infallible, and where there is doubt over any issue or caption, I have said so. Anecdotes were part of the working railway at all levels and I have included a selection where it seemed apposite, as I recall them together with my own memories. Comments and clarification should be forwarded to Irwell Press in the usual way. My grateful thanks go to friends and colleagues over the years, particularly Ken Haysom, formerly Assistant Chief Civil Engineer on the Southern Region of BR and previously Divisional Engineer at Kings Cross.

This has been assembled for your interest, nostalgia and perhaps even amusement. This is my tribute to generations of "GN men and women" who built and ran a good railway that I remember with admiration and fondness.

Peter J Coster,
Pendoggett Farm,
St. Kew, Bodmin,
Cornwall.

First published in the United Kingdom in 2011
by Irwell Press Limited, 59A, High Street, Clophill,
Bedfordshire MK45 4BE
Printed by Konway Press

Contents

A view of what appears to be the up side of the viaduct. The slight rake or inclination of the piers up to arch springing level is clearly visible as are the tie-bars and plates.

CHAPTER TEN

Welwyn North, Knebworth, Langley Junction and Stevenage

We resume our imaginary trip as guests of the GNR, as the gleaming 'Klondyke' and her inspection saloon return from Hatfield. No doubt the directors and officials would have been discussing plans to build a new station to serve the new Garden City, which came to fruition in 1926. The suburban service was worked until the introduction of diesel traction by 0-6-2Ts, by firstly the Ivatt N1s and then Gresley's N2s hauling the twin four car articulated sets, the 'quad-arts'of immortal memory. Occasionally one of Hatfield's 'Swedies', ex-GE N7 0-6-2Ts, broke the N2 monopoly, coming into Kings Cross on a Dunstable service. The services terminated progressively further north; New Barnet, then Potters Bar, and then Hatfield. Some services continued to Welwyn Garden City, but the steam age facilities were not so good as at Hatfield.

Welwyn Garden City was the northern limit of the inner suburban electrification, first proposed in the early 1900s, and which eventually came to fruition in the 1970s. Stabling sidings were laid north of the station on the down side. A new concrete flyover was constructed, to allow up trains to start from the down platform and cross to the up slow without blocking the main lines. The electric service was introduced in November 1976, using the connections referred to earlier at Finsbury Park with the Northern City Line. As mentioned the layout at Kings Cross was relaid completely, the electrification progressed on to Royston, and the outer suburban area was switched over the electric operation in February 1978.

The inner suburban service was, and at the time of writing still is operated by 30 years old Class 313 dual-voltage three car EMUs, running on 25Kv as far as the changeover point at Drayton Park, and DC third rail from there to Moorgate. These were the first EMUs with airbag suspension, and there were some initial problems with a greater sway on curves than the fixed equipment engineers had anticipated, demonstrating the truth that we all came to learn, that the pantograph is a remarkably effective tool for dewiring the OLE (overhead line equipment), i.e. bringing down the contact wire! The time cannot be far away when the 313s will be replaced.

A mile or so further north, the additional tracks stopped at the site of the old Digswell signalbox, south of Welwyn or Digswell viaduct. The signalbox was replaced in the early 1930s with power operated points and operation transferred to Welwyn North. The signals were then operated manually from across the viaduct. Between the high ground north of Welwyn Garden City and that north of Welwyn (later) North lay the valley of the River Mimram, which was crossed by Welwyn Viaduct. Welwyn Viaduct is one of the most famous bridgeworks we have, certainly on the GN. It is structurally unremarkable by comparison with the major railway bridges, but it is long, high and a fine example of a railway viaduct. It is no doubt one of the most hard-worked in terms of the speed and frequency of line occupation. It is 520 yards long and consists of 40 arches of 30ft span; its maximum height is 98ft, and the width between parapets is 26ft. Each pier has a 'rake' of 1 in 40 both laterally and longitudinally; in other words the piers taper with height. It was built in brick, fired from local clay, and later clad in hard engineering blue bricks. It is one of most famous and well-loved examples of railway engineering.

The cost of bridging a gap, by viaduct, is only justified when the alternative option of an embankment is estimated to cost more, or with increasing height and consequent land purchase, or simply judged impracticable. The construction of the viaduct was reasonably straightforward in principle, but in practice a huge undertaking. The design was prepared by Lewis Cubitt, and it has his classical simplicity: one might contrast Welwyn with another more flamboyant and much-loved outstanding engineering work, the Ouse Valley Viaduct

An up express headed by (probably) an A1 Pacific crosses Welwyn viaduct.

Welwyn North c1926

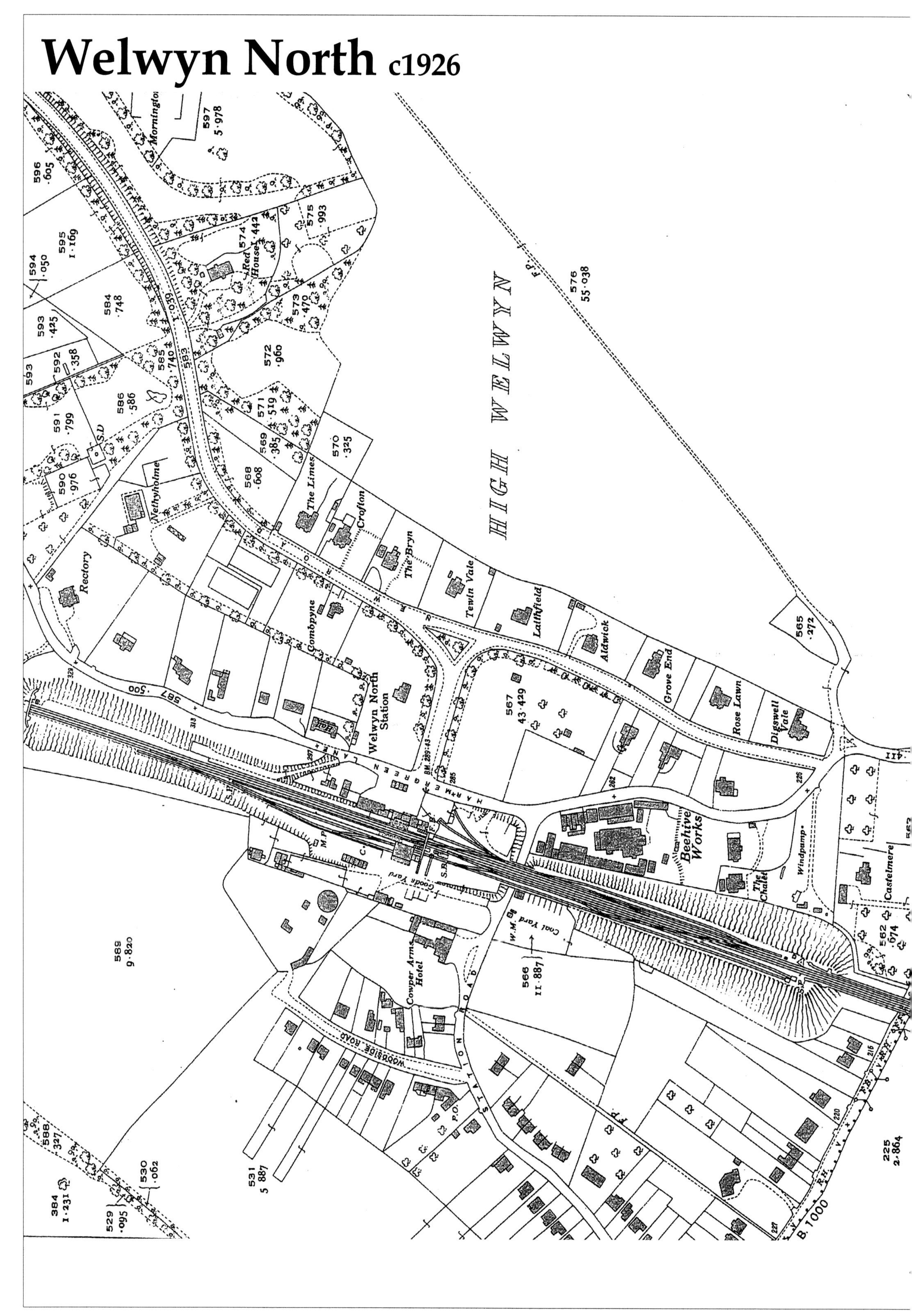

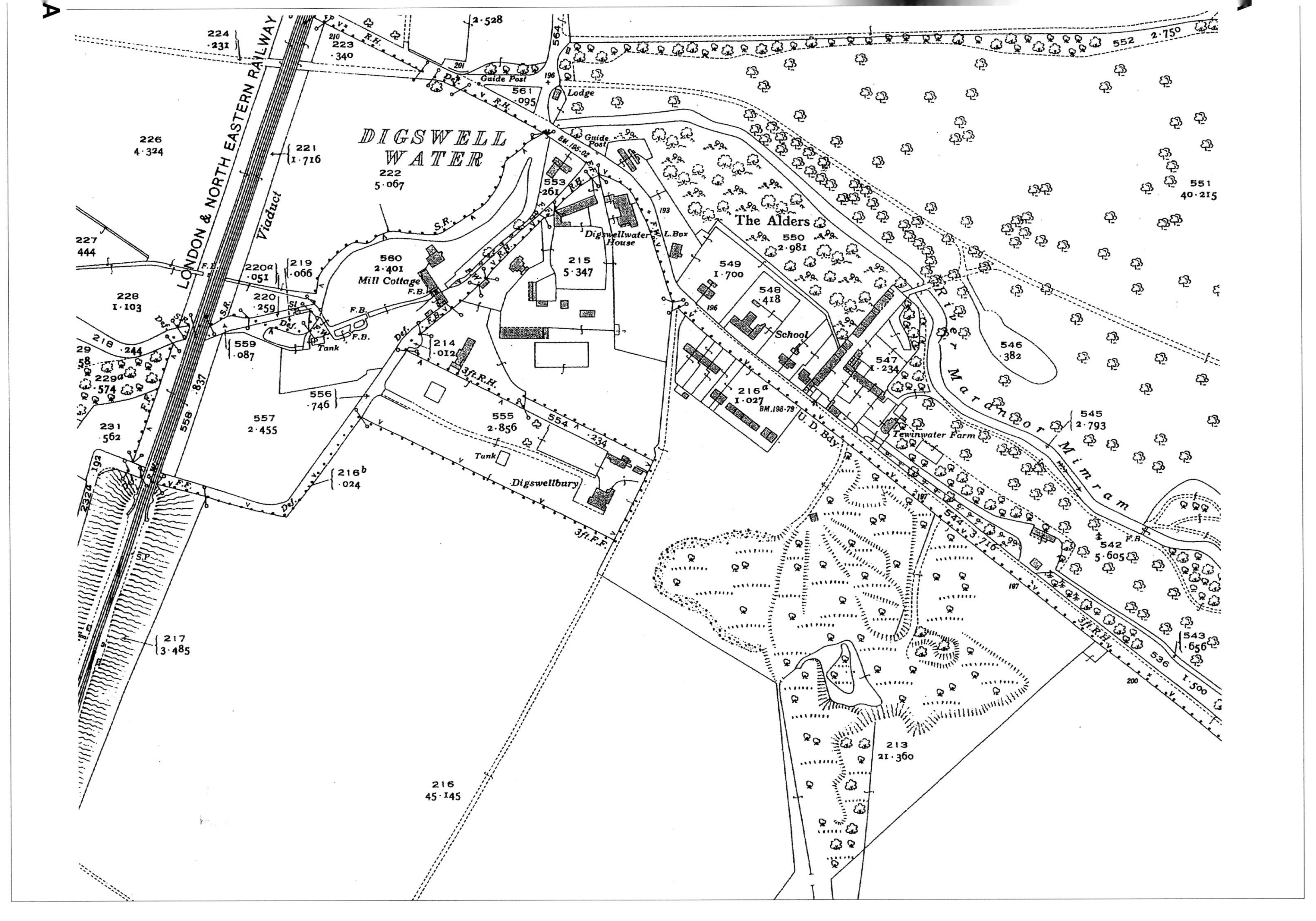

A
DIGSWELL WATER
River Maran or Mimram
The Alders
School
Tewinwater Farm
Digswellwater House
Digswellbury
Mill Cottage
Lodge
Guide Post
L. Box
U. D. Bdy.
Tank
Viaduct
LONDON & NORTH EASTERN RAILWAY

The down Elizabethan on Welwyn Viaduct with A4 No.60011 EMPIRE OF INDIA on 24th June 1959. Once again the slight rake of the piers is apparent.

The down Elizabethan on 8th July 1959 at the north end of the viaduct, headed by A4 No.60027 MERLIN. Major structures such as the viaduct were fitted with an additional pair of rails as guard rails in order that any damage from a derailed or defective vehicle should be avoided or at least minimised.

A selection of vintage vehicles at Welwyn North on the up side, 6th December 1963.

Back to the older 'Italianate' GN style; the up side entrance at Welwyn North on 6th December 1963.

near Haywards Heath. The contractor for much of the work of building the GNR was Thomas Brassey.

The first task would have been to establish and construct solid foundations, for they had to bear the enormous weight of the viaduct and passing traffic. Every pier had to be firm, for differential settlement was the Achilles' heel of viaduct construction. The piers would then have been set out and an army of bricklayers set to work constructing them. The piers are cellular; that is, not solid. As they grew, they would have been linked with scaffolding both for access and to ensure stability, until the height reached that of the arch springing. The height of each pier from its foundation varied, but the level of the arch springings was the same. The piers are 'cellular'; that is, not solid. The alignment of the pier heads would have been carefully monitored, for even with master bricklayers, in something like 400 brick courses it is difficult to keep to line and level without some overriding control. And, of course, each arch was the same semi-circular span of 30ft.

***Left.* The GNR booking hall often had an ornate screen with the booking positions as here at Welwyn North on 6th December 1963.**

***Below.* Part of a typical GN/LNER waiting room at Welwyn North. How times have changed!**

With each lift of scaffolding, there was the (literally) supporting task of erecting working platforms safely and providing enough room for the bricklayers to work accurately inside and outside the pier walls. Then the centring was erected, the name given to the semicircular wooden formwork that sat on the scaffolding between the piers. Its function was to support the 'green' brickwork until it had developed sufficient strength. The arch rings of brickwork were erected on the centring, comprising up to five concentric brickwork rings, possibly interlocked to avoid separation. Once the rings were in position, the spandrel walls (the viaduct walls above and between the arch rings) would have been built up between the arch rings, and the parapet walls built through.

The strength of a viaduct is its continuity, and a lack of continuity is its great weakness. It was necessary to avoid too great an eccentric loading on each pier, which occurred when building one arch ring and not its neighbour. The result would have been raised bending stresses in the pier, which, if not controlled, were likely to cause cracking or worse. It would have been essential, in order to avoid constructing all 40 arches simultaneously and at the same pace, to provide strong temporary timber supports between the piers at the head. Once the parapets were complete, the task of backing the arches would be completed and the track laid. The space between two arches sharing the same pier was filled with backing, low grade concrete and rubble to hold the arches in position without distortion. Some viaducts have access passages from manholes at track level, to inspect drainage and the insides of piers.

Early on, the condition of the spandrels gave concern, perhaps through bulging and/or cracking, and tie bars and plates have been added. At 90ft without the aid of skyhooks, it must have been a task rather more complex than it might appear. Drilling a 3in hole 30ft long and offering up a 32ft bar with a rail crane at that height is a nice game played slowly, and I would imagine – it is a task I have never had to face – that the work was largely carried out from the viaduct using half length bars and threaded couplers. It would have required each of the piers to be scaffolded, to get at the tie plates and securing nuts, and probably a trench excavated under the tracks to position the bars.

The valley of the Mimram was a very pretty sight, but in recent years the invasion of houses from the south has largely ruined this attractive rural scene. In the early 1950s when fog was far more common than now, there was a tale circulating among the signalmen which, if true, made the hair stand on end. It is another anecdote that I cannot vouch for, indeed it seems most unlikely, but experience of the railway is that one cannot rely on the ordinary and must expect the unlikely. A train of coal empties had been waiting on the down goods at Digswell in extremely thick fog, and after the down stopping service had passed, it was let into the two track section. As the passenger train had stopped at Welwyn North, until the Welwyn North signalman had received 'train out of section', he would have let the freight forward from signal to signal, and the coal empties drew eventually to a halt at the home signal, which was just off the north end of the viaduct. The driver was waiting for the home signal to clear, when he was astonished to see the guard outside the cab, enquiring what the delay was. Thinking that they were in Welwyn North platform, the guard had walked along it to the engine to find out what was going on. Only it wasn't the platform.

Welwyn North was one of those places that appealed to the photographer and the modeller. In railway terms, it was a pretty little place in almost unspoilt countryside in GNR days. It had two platform faces, a small goods yard south of the station on the down side, and a footbridge placed to perfection for the photographer. North of the station lay Welwyn South Tunnel (446 yards) and some 4-500 yards beyond was Welwyn North Tunnel (1,046 yards). The gap between the two tunnels was another popular location for photographers and some wonderful work was produced in the steam era. The tunnels were bored through the chalk of the eastern end of the Chiltern Hills, and the line rose through the tunnels and over the short Woolmer Green Viaduct to the summit near the 24th milepost in a deep cutting. Once again, the impressive portals have that stamp of classical simplicity of Lewis Cubitt. As the bank could be charged at speed, it was of little

The ornate footbridge at the south end of the platform at Welwyn North on 6th December 1963. That's the goods shed to the left.

The up platform at Welwyn North on 6th December 1963. The platform wall has been renewed in standard concrete blocks.

consequence but the unbraked freight, starting from rest at Digswell, could be a long while before tucking its tail in at Woolmer Green.

The latter was the point at which two tracks became four again, although until comparatively recently the down slow turn-in was situated on the left-hand curve and ensured a poor ride at speed. I believe the left-hand curve was a transition curve, and the use of the turn-in affected the riding on the down main. The turn-in alignment also involved negative cant which was undesirable. The main to slow connection has been moved northwards on to the straight to give a smoother ride.

The Welwyn bottleneck has been a conundrum for the operators for decades. Slow-moving freight is a thing of the past, but the speed of expresses has increased considerably, restoring the status quo in speed difference. The operation has changed, that change accelerating rapidly in the last few decades, so that the 500 ton expresses of the steam era have been replaced by the multiple unit railway, with its often small trains running at far greater frequencies. The three or four main services and non-stop Peterborough and Cambridge line services each hour clash with the services stopping at Welwyn North. Line capacity is at a premium, and rail use is increasing, exacerbating an already fraught situation. The New Line, which we shall discuss shortly, at first sight is the extra pair of tracks so sorely needed. However it has its own frequent service of inner suburban trains terminating at Hertford North and calling at almost all ten stations, added to which is a service continuing beyond to rejoin the main line at Langley. The platforms face on to the double track line and there is no means of passing stopping services. There is little line capacity to spare and access from the south involves a heavy TSR. There would be little comparison between the speeds permitted on the main line and the New Line.

The options appear to be to widen the existing viaduct, to construct a second crossing of the Mimram valley, to re-engineer the New Line to increase capacity, or the two options beloved of the Department of Transport, 'do as little as possible to achieve the objective' and 'do nothing'. Railways were victims of their own success over the years, as most stations seeded local communities, and the growth of housing round the stations usually prevented expansion of the railway. Any deliberation over the future needed to be informed by a close inspection of the viaduct itself, first of all.

Widening the existing viaduct or building another would also be enormously expensive. There is of course another short viaduct at the north end of the bottleneck that would need widening. Works of outstanding engineering importance ought to be altered only as a last resort; some of the treatment meted out to St.Pancras for instance gives me pause for thought about the effectiveness of the guardians of our heritage.

Adapting a 150 year old viaduct for quadrupling would not be wise. Replication alongside in blue brick – even just as a facing to a concrete structure - would be phenomenally expensive and a bricklayer's charter. A completely new structure would be dramatically different and therefore ill at ease alongside, pointing to a new alignment to the east diverging near the old junction for Hertford, with new tunnels towards Woolmer Green. Quadrupling the stations of the New Line, plus possibly another bore through Ponsbourne, would be expensive and not a little messy and the resulting alignment much slower. Perhaps it might be worth considering an incremental approach instead, looking at quadrupling through Welwyn North and widening the south end of the South Tunnel, or extending the widening through the tunnel section.

Moving north we come to the village of Knebworth, now nearly South Stevenage. Knebworth was a two island platform station, exactly 25 miles from Kings Cross. From the summit south of the station there was a dip down to Langley Junction followed by a slight rise to Stevenage, then 27 miles of almost unbroken downgrade to the banks of the Bedfordshire Ouse at Offord. Knebworth was the location of the new Control office when it was evacuated at the start of the Second World War. It was always a place where it was better

The fairly rudimentary down platform shelter on 6th December 1963, goods shed and goods yard behind.

Welwyn North, looking south, with the signalbox beyond the footbridge in 1957. Out there, the viaduct beckons.

A general view of Welwyn North, with a down Leeds express headed by a new Brush Type 4 (Cl.47) approaching on 6th December 1963. In the first year or so of their existence they were often termed 'Hawker Siddeley' Type 4s, after the parent company of Brush Ltd.

Looking north from the footbridge at Welwyn North towards Welwyn South Tunnel.

The view south from Welwyn South tunnel portal showing the straight line to and beyond Welwyn Garden City on 30th March 1943. At a guess, the photograph has been taken to record the down side failure in the cutting slope. The tunnels were bored largely through chalk, and the failure appears to have been a slide in the surface material and not a slip.

The massive and imposing tunnel portal at Welwyn South in 1957. The first impression is of over-engineering, but who would not be proud of such a magnificent structure?

An up express, probably from South Yorkshire, emerges from Welwyn South tunnel behind A1 No.60119 PATRICK STIRLING in summer 1958.

The historic occasion on 30th June 1938 with Stirling Single No.1 and her vintage train, crossing the small viaduct at Woolmer Green on the two track section. See also Part One, page 214.

Thompson A2/3 No.60523 SUN CASTLE heads an up parcels train out of Welwyn South tunnel in the late 1950s.

Knebworth c1926

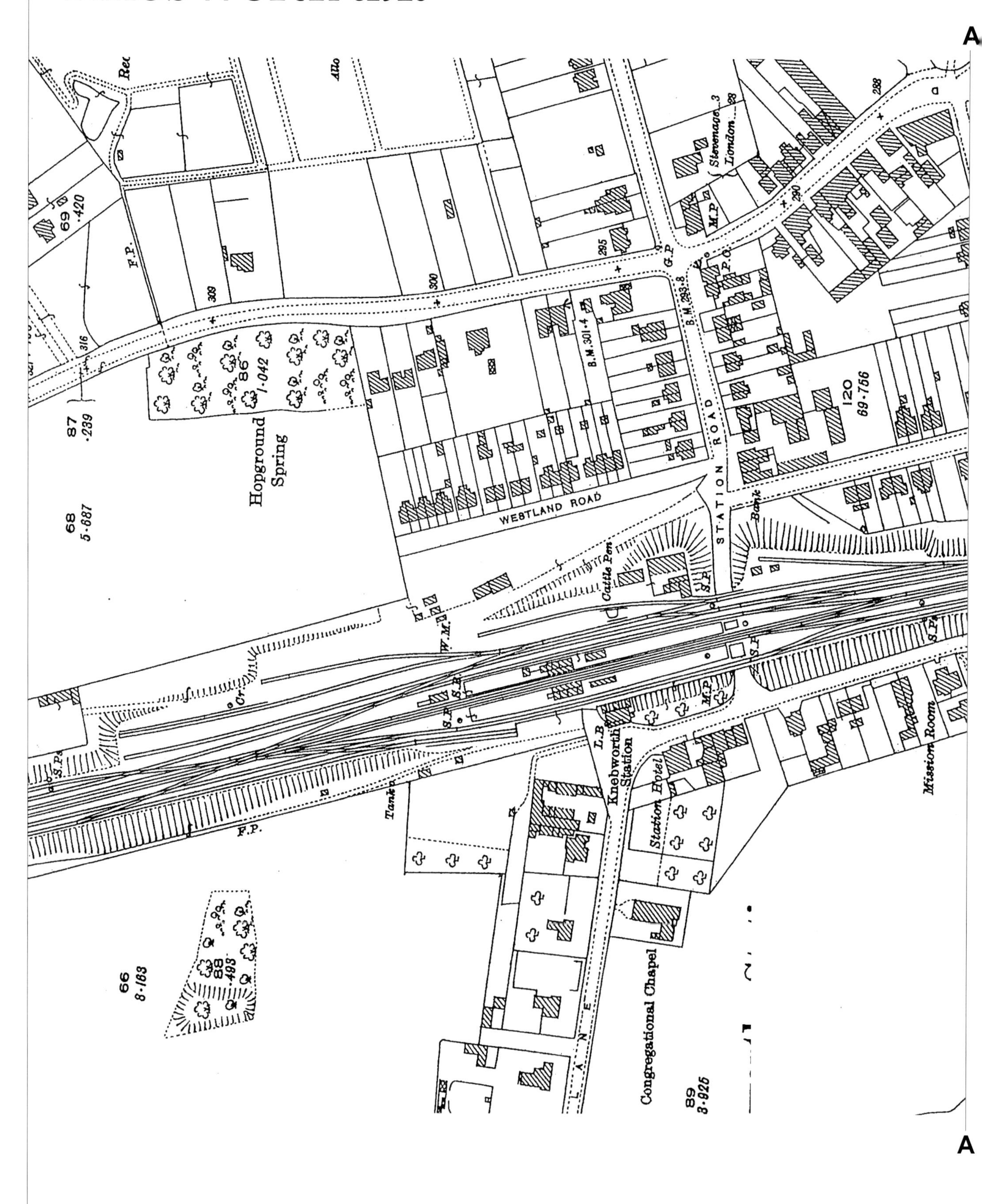

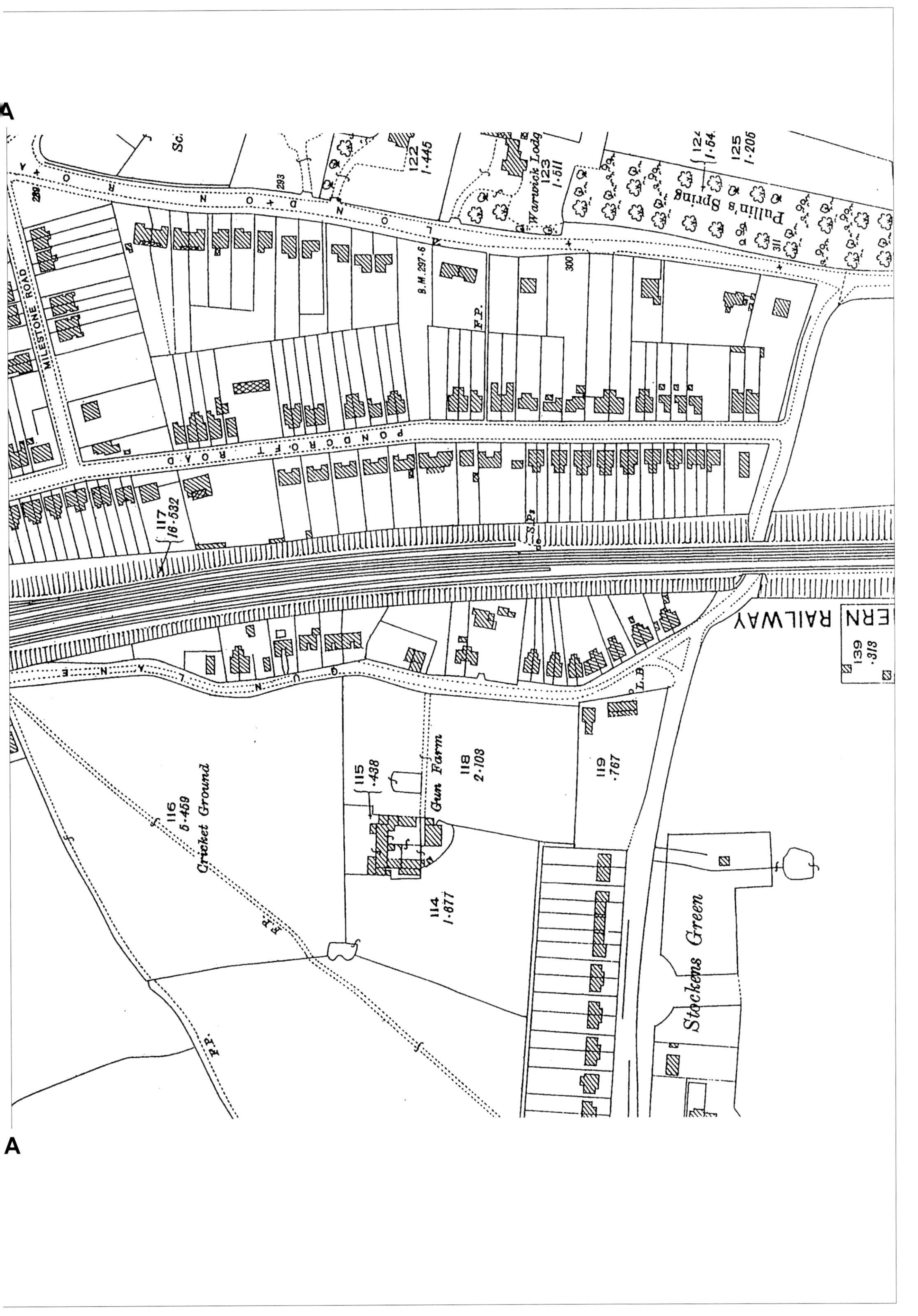
A
MILESTONE ROAD
POND CROFT ROAD
Warwick Lodge
123
1·511
122
1·445
125
1·206
Pullin's Spring
B.M. 297·6
F.P.
117
16·532
RAILWAY
139
·313
116
5·459
Cricket Ground
115
·438
Gun Farm
118
2·103
119
·767
114
1·877
Stockens Green
A

The up Yorkshire Pullman on 19th June 1957 approaching Woolmer Green signalbox behind A1 No.60117 BOIS ROUSSEL.

not to be seen on the footplate unless one had a legitimate presence there; you could be spotted both from the station and in silhouette from the adjacent golf course! From here it is a short distance to the reunion with the New Line at Langley Junction, where water troughs were installed on the main lines in 1918.

Just beyond Knebworth station is a remarkable bridge that has attracted little attention over the years. Deards End Lane overbridge spans a deep chalk cutting, and for the location Cubitt designed a remarkable single arch bridge rather than the conventional multi-arched – viaduct – structure that would have been the alternative, such as that at New Southgate. It is a segmental rather than a semicircular arch with a span of 96ft, and a rise of 20ft 9in. The diameter of the arch is 132ft. The abutments are supported on hard chalk halfway up the cutting slopes. Its size would in any case make it a remarkable bridge but in order to reduce weight, the space above the five ring brick arch is cellular. The strength of the arch is supplemented by the rigidity of five longitudinal ribs on the back of the arch rising to road level, two of which are the external spandrel walls. The road surfacing is carried on 6in York stone slabs bedded on the longitudinal ribs. The same cellular construction was used in the wing walls and abutments. The bridge is quite clearly one of the Cubitt family designs, related to Welwyn Viaduct and many other larger GNR bridges. It is a magnificent bridge, one of the largest brick arch spans, seventh largest in the country as far as I can trace. Its construction was no doubt underway well before the cutting had been completely excavated, and the supporting timberwork and centring was no doubt a substantial temporary work. It spans a full width cutting, which suggests that it was built in the early 1870s when the line was quadrupled.

Continuing past Knebworth golf course, we come to Langley Junction, where the New Line rejoined the East Coast main line, where the first set of water troughs were laid. The troughs were laid towards the end of the 1914-18 war on the main lines only, coming into use in 1918. Roughly half a mile in length, the troughs had a ramped entry and exit, requiring the firemen to refrain from lowering the scoop too early, and to lift it before reaching the end, to avoid damaging it. This was particularly important for non-stop services, needing to lift as much water as possible. The water level and rate of supply was set for the service pattern, although the driver of a fast moving train, closing on the one ahead, could find to his embarrassment that the troughs not yet refilled.

The GNR's successor, the LNER, had a good record on water treatment which was reflected in good boiler lives. The water for the troughs was treated at the lineside treatment plant, and at Langley it was on the down side. For many years it had a series of spare tenders to carry the precipitated sludge to tip. One of these, as late as the 1960s, still had vestiges of the apple green livery and its pre-1946 number, for it was the tender off the NBR Reid Atlantic MIDLOTHIAN, earmarked by Gresley for preservation. Would that she had followed the other LNER treasures that were the basis of the National Collection into preservation.

The troughs were an excellent location for those with a lineside photographic pass, but all water troughs were extremely treacherous under foot whether at work or not. In wet or icy weather they were all but impossible. To fall over with a plethora of very hard objects about was not advisable. The best rule was to tread only on ballast and avoid smooth, slippery surfaces. Therefore one picked one's steps with care, but the resulting photographs could be wonderfully evocative, especially if the fireman had dropped the scoop early and was unable to raise it due to the force of water. Now and again the photographer got an involuntary shower as well. I remember a York Green Arrow on fast

Farther north, the inaugural up Morning Talisman in the cutting between Knebworth and Woolmer Green on 17th June 1957 hauled by a gleaming A1 No.60157 GREAT EASTERN.

Knebworth station in 1957, with the remarkable single-arch Deards End Lane overbridge in the distance. A B1 4-6-0 bears down on the station with a short up express. It is something of a puzzle, as it seems too short to be anything other than a 'parley', and these were the preserve, overwhelmingly, of the New England varieties of A2. Alternatively it might be a Cambridge Buffet Express, but again, B17s were preferred to the B1s.

A4 No.60017 SILVER FOX heads the down Flying Scotsman through Deards End Lane bridge north of Knebworth in 1959.

freight 714 down on the troughs, which had a hole in its tender filler cover, sending a strong jet of water in a beautiful trajectory on to the lineside, which unfortunately passed over the cess 5ft above ground level. Water troughs would freeze when the weather was colder, especially in the north, making a water stop obligatory with consequent delays. It was difficult and disagreeable to have to break the ice to keep them operational, and a more serious problem with a saturated environment – not just at troughs – was that the track became 'ironbound'. This was permanent wayspeak for frozen solid. Once a thaw set in the deficiencies of the track became all too obvious and a TSR was a possibility or even necessity. They had a general speed limit of 70mph which optimised the lifting of water, but also recognised the greater difficulty in maintaining the track. It was honoured by some in the breach rather than the rule!

The station at Stevenage was two island platforms just at the start of the downgrade, with signalboxes at each end controlling the crossovers. The new station is farther south, in the centre of the new town, again twin island platforms, while the old station has now been demolished. Stevenage North despatched down trains into an 'auto section', since Wymondley box had been replaced by IB signals in 1930. The down slow became the down goods beyond No.8 points, and passenger trains therefore had to be turned out on to the main at this point. Goods lines were worked on permissive block, which allowed the signalman to continue to send trains into the section ahead whether it was occupied or not. The driver of any following train had to be warned by a green flag or light from the box, that there was a train ahead, and be prepared to stop on sight, well clear.

The down side sidings at Wymondley were worked off a ground frame, for which the key was held in Stevenage North. The procedure was standard. In this case, the guard of a train calling at Wymondley collected the key from Stevenage North box, and on arrival he set the signals at danger

The up Flying Scotsman hauled by A4 No.60029 WOODCOCK approaches Knebworth in 1959.

The down Queen of Scots hauled by A1 No.60141 ABBOTSFORD picking up water at speed on Langley troughs on 9th September 1953.

A3 No.60044 MELTON with the 9.15 from York takes water at Langley troughs on 9th September 1953.

The up Yorkshire Pullman with A1 No.60141 ABBOTSFORD approaches Langley troughs on 9th September 1959.

A view looking north towards Stevenage, with the South box on the down side.

Stevenage
1920s
FISHER'S GREEN
HERN RAILWAY
Station
Goods Shed
Allotments
Furniture Factory
BURY MEAD (Recreation Ground)
Grammar School
The Grange
School
War Memorial
Tennis Ground
Nursery
Dell Spring
Clay Pit
Railway Inn
JUBILEE ROAD
SOUTHSEA ROAD
BOURNEMOUTH ROAD
LEAMINGTON ROAD
HUNTINGDON ROAD
NOTTINGHAM ROAD
ESSEX ROAD
FISHER'S GREEN ROAD
JULIAN'S ROAD
ORCHARD ROAD
WALKERN ROAD

behind his train, to protect it while shunting. Then he opened the sidings. If necessary the train could be locked inside, the signals cleared and the release given to the box, so that a following train could pass by. On completion the procedure was reversed, except that if another train was following, the signals remained at danger until that train had stopped. The key was returned from Hitchin by the first available train. The method of working an intermediate ground frame was fairly standard for the many isolated sidings operated in this fashion elsewhere in the system. Only the method of restoring the key varied, by walking back or carrying it forward for later return.

The long cutting north of the old station has a footbridge at the north end, which before electrification was known as the 'Skeleton Bridge', another of those fine photographic locations so thoughtfully provided by the GNR. After Wymondley, the main line starts the long and gentle descent to the banks of the Ouse. It is difficult for a Gresley man to pass the 30th milepost without recalling that quite fantastic run over 70 years ago when the concept of a high speed passenger train was born, the Silver Jubilee trial run with SILVER LINK. Having demonstrated an ability to accelerate uphill as well as downhill, it was here that the train first exceeded 100mph, and then went on to maintain what was, in 1935, an incredible speed for 25 miles without a break. Steam locomotive history in Britain had no equal to this demonstration of sustained high speed.

A general view of the old Stevenage station, looking north.

The old Stevenage station, looking south, with the north box on the left.

The down West Riding north of Stevenage, hauled by A4 No.60026 MILES BEEVOR (formerly KESTREL) in the late 1940s. The first four coaches were from the pre-war streamliners.

Nearly all freight locos spent most of their life in filthy condition, given necessary maintenance but tending towards low if not minimal in standard. In general they were simple, undemanding designs. For most of the post-war years the heavy freight traffic south of Peterborough was handled by WD 2-8-0s. The sight of a filthy WD, noisily announcing its presence, was a constant feature of the GN main line in the south. Here an up freight trundles – the WDs never seemed to be light of step – towards Stevenage on the up slow, hauled no doubt audibly by New England's No.90577. The fireman will be firing away, to judge from the smoke. The Stevenage North up distant is a fine somersault example – it is one of the signals that one needed to know about, one where the driver needed his fireman's assistance in confirming the indication. There is no date available but the four tracks are all bullhead, and with the somersault it must be around the early 1950s.

A 1959 view at the same location on 9th September 1959, with a K3 2-6-0 on a down fast freight. By that time few K3s came south of Peterborough, and New England had none. My guess is that it was the Colwick goods, which went north on Saturday afternoon.

Winchmore Hill in 1960. Some years after this the right-hand wing was demolished, because of subsidence it is said.

CHAPTER ELEVEN

The New Line

The New Line diverged at Wood Green, opening on April 1st 1871 as far as Enfield. The down line took off and swung north-east over a flyover towards Bounds Green and Bowes Park while the up connection ran in through the Bounds Green complex of carriage sidings to No.2 signalbox. Originally built as far as Enfield, in 1900 a Bill was presented for an extension from Enfield to rejoin the GN main line beyond Knebworth at Langley Junction. Even by that time, with numbers of slow unfitted freight trains, the two bottlenecks were becoming operationally difficult. In 1910 the New Line was extended to Cuffley, and with the onset of the First World War it was decided to press on northwards. In 1918 it was opened as single line through Hertford to Langley Junction for goods traffic only. By 1924 passenger services were extended northwards from Cuffley to Hertford North. GNR rail motors were used at one time from Hitchin to Hertford North, a coach with a small steam 0-4-0T as power unit, driving one bogie. Rail motor services were also introduced from Royston and Hitchin to the north, worked at times by Sentinel steam railcars. Like its rival companies the GNR had little luck with steam railcars, which were unreliable or lacked flexibility. In retrospect the GNR was very far-sighted in building a flyover at Wood Green: would that they had at Hitchin as well! 'The branch' (as it was called by railwaymen) was quite sharply graded, giving the impression that expenditure on engineering works was somewhat restrained. Despite early 20th century plans to have four tracks as far as Gordon Hill and to provide additional running lines, they were never implemented and it remained double track. The Hertford-Langley goods section survived even Beeching, and is now an integral part of the GN suburban network.

At Bowes Park there was a remarkable footbridge, originally not connected with the railway since there was another older version to the station itself. It was probably erected with the development of the Bowes Manor estates later, rather than during the construction of the line. It consisted of two plate girders roughly at least 60ft long with a wide footway between, carried on cross girders with jack arches between, landed on abutments at about 5ft above the tracks. The shape of the girders, in the vertical plane, was a segmental curve over the island platform and tracks, and a straight approach slope either side. So they had a clear span from abutment to abutment of about 60ft, and leapt comfortably over the loading gauge for both tracks. Of all the railway bridges that I have seen, or seen photographs of, there has been nothing remotely like Bowes Park footbridge. It was an expensive design and must have involved heavy crane work to erect it, and as the girders are far too big to have come by rail, they must have been built up on site. It has since been modified to gain access to

Grange Park, to a model used for the five boxes Grange Park to Cuffley, all with 25 lever frames. Integral toilets were an unusual luxury. The little door below the main one is the entrance to the locking room.

the station, and the older structure demolished.

From Bowes Park the line descended on a long straight to cross what is now the North Circular Road and a stream, on a high embankment before rising to Palmers Green, where there was a goods yard on the up side and sidings on the down. The line rose further to Winchmore Hill, and after a sharp dip before Enfield Chase, resumed its climb at 1 in 198. The goods yard for Winchmore Hill lay south of the station, on the up side. The old station at Enfield was used as a goods station, and this continued beyond the steam era before it finally closed. The daily trip from Ferme Park was headed by one of Hornsey's 0-6-0s, latterly one of the handsome little J6s: a tank locomotive would have coped but the greater water supply of the tender engine was important. The through line diverged at Grange Park Junction and climbed the long eight mile bank to the summit at Bayford.

The line had a gradient of 1 in 100 rising in the down direction to Bayford. Occasionally diverted freight and even passenger services used the branch, the loose coupled unbraked freights travelling the 1 in 100 with great trepidation. The road underbridges in the area were of steel construction with, in many cases, a distinctive ornamental parapet girder. At Enfield Chase the line was on a sharp rising left-hand curve, the wooden platforms sloped away from the tracks, and for up services in years past it was necessary for the guard to walk forward halfway along a quad-art set to a point at the back of the platform where the crew could see his green handlamp. As the N2 set off down 1 in 100, the guard needed to regain the now rapidly accelerating rear brake van quickly. One night he didn't, and was left stranded as his train disappeared into the night. There followed a lengthy wait at Grange Park until the weary guard had given chase on a borrowed bicycle!

Once clear of the great metropolis of Enfield the line becomes quite rural, laying as it does between rather than on principal main roads. The country between the A1 in the west and the A10 in the east has remained fairly rural, and one can understand that the GNR was reluctant to undertake heavy earthworks. Nevertheless, the line crossed Rendlesham Viaduct, 495ft long, with 14 arches of 30ft span and a maximum height of 70ft, south of Crews Hill, and then Sopers Farm Viaduct, 390ft, 11 arches and 30ft high farther north. Cuffley and Gordon Hill stations had the ability to terminate and originate services, and did so in the peaks. A short drop of ¾ mile before Cuffley intervened, but the summit was at the top of a climb to the country end of Ponsbourne Tunnel, just short of Bayford. Ponsbourne Tunnel was completed in 1918, and was the longest on the GNR by a long way, 2,684 yards, cut through clay overlaying chalk. Quite why it is such a great length is an interesting thought, as I would not have thought that the land mass above required such a lengthy tunnel. Again, one would need to know the terms of the original land negotiation to see what onus was placed on the GNR by the landowners of the day. In earlier days the presence of Ponsbourne Park may well have been significant. The stations on the New Line had in some cases a rather less substantial look about them, none more so than Bayford. Before modernisation it was as near Colonel Stephens as the GNR ever got.

In the 1970s in order to carry larger containers by rail, it was decided to enlarge three tunnels, one of which was Ponsbourne. The enlargement was only feasible, as in the case of the Irish donkey at the canal bridge, by lowering. Tunnel construction in hard or rocky ground was effected by building two walls and an arch where adequate footings existed, in other words a rather long bridge. In softer ground it was judged necessary to construct a tunnel profile, bringing the walls in at the base to be braced apart by an invert, an arch in reverse, under the tracks. Taking out the invert – even so as to replace it – was not a good idea, but if it was imperative, 'carefully' was the essential adverb. Short sections were opened with temporary bracing. A modern reinforced concrete invert at a lower level, robustly interlocked with the existing lining, was structurally superior – once one had got it in. This was successfully done in the 1950s in Buckhorn Weston Tunnel on the SR, but it was a disastrous, indeed tragic failure 20 years later at Penmanshiel. As I recall, Ponsbourne was done in two halves,

Crews Hill box in 1960; hereabouts shallow slopes were cut in the clay as a device against ground failure.

down and up tracks. Even then I believe there was an incident with the support for the higher road collapsing and an engineering train having to be recovered.

From Bayford there is a three mile descent into Hertford North, crossing first Horns Mill Viaduct and then Hertford Viaduct. The first is a short six span structure, and the second is longer, 20 arches with a steel skew girder bridge in the middle spanning the Hatfield- Hertford branch. The GNR had built the branch from Hatfield in 1868; it ran past the North station site to the Cowbridge station and linked with the GER at Hertford East. Hertford North was a two island station using mainly the down island, but its role has changed from terminus to through station after the end of steam. Hertford has grown out of all proportion, and its traffic is far larger now. The optimum site for the new Hertford North station was where the two routes ran parallel, not far from the sharp curve at the old Cowbridge station, but apart from a connection to allow Hatfield trains into the North station, there was never any interest shown in linking up with the GER branch at the East station. Relations between the GNR and GER were said to be poor.

Then the New Line continued northwards through Molewood Tunnel (347 yards) climbing towards Langley Junction almost continuously at 1 in 198 where it converged with the main line. Intermediate stations at Stapleford and Watton-at-Stone had two platform faces, while the signalling was fairly basic. Another station was intended at Datchworth. The two tracks separate before Langley where there is a burrowing junction with the slow lines, but not the main lines. Therefore in the steam era, trains diverted via the New Line were unable to take water from the troughs in either direction. This was not a problem for locomotives with large tenders, but otherwise a water stop at Hitchin was essential. As already mentioned, the line had a rural air about it, especially north of Enfield, and it was strange to think that a few miles to the west, things were quite different. It was used by slow freights, but its capacity, with a half-hour all stations service, was very limited. As referred to earlier it was looked on as being the second pair of tracks that were lacking at Greenwood and Welwyn, but in truth one could not put very much extra over the line with any hope of punctual running.

Bayford, Stapleford and Watton-at-Stone stations had goods yards but no proper signal boxes. Points were worked instead from a pair of ground frames at each station. They were adapted as block posts to reduce the length of section when switched in; this is the unmemorable Bayford 'block hut' in 1960.

On 19th November 1958, a down freight off the new Line was taking water at Hitchin, and in thick fog a following freight on the main line overran and collided with it. The Ardsley goods was coming up on the main line behind V2 No.60885 at that time, and ran into the considerable pile of wrecked wagons. The accident assumed farcical dimensions as the derailed V2 cannoned into L1 No.67785, coming off Hitchin shed and driven by Driver Bill Atkins, knocking it over.

CHAPTER TWELVE
Hitchin

Hitchin was approached from the south by almost two miles falling at 1 in 200, and this was where expresses gathered speed for the fast section to the north. At Hitchin South there was a group of sidings used by the District Engineer on the up side where at one time prefabricated track was assembled before the larger facility at Chesterton Junction, Cambridge, took over production. The number of sidings was increased with engineering activity. Usually an older GNR 0-6-0 pilot engine lurked here, making up engineers trains. Of the four tracks here three were passenger lines, the fourth being the down goods. In the 1950s the down goods changed to passenger for the evening peak, with the authority conveyed down from Stevenage, and reverted back later. There was a water column by the signalbox for trains that were on the down slow at Langley, either off the New Line or simply turned in at Woolmer Green. At Hitchin South was another single span arch overbridge in the style of Deards End Lane at Knebworth. Benslow Lane overbridge carried a narrow lane but was used as a footpath, and was the most wonderful photographic location. It was a slightly smaller structure than Deards End Lane bridge, pitched lower, and as it fouled the electrification loading gauge on the slow lines, sadly it was replaced by a footbridge.

Just before Hitchin South signalbox was a set of mailbag pick-up apparatus, when there was a General Post Office, and it used railways. Often the inspiration for jokes and cartoons, this equipment served its purpose very well until the end of the steam era. There was no laid down track speed restriction, but 60-70mph was deemed to be adequate for TPO services. With the advent of significantly higher speeds, the robustness of the system was inadequate, and a flying mailbag became a projectile that destroyed the receiving nets. In an experiment elsewhere, picking up at 100mph proved impossible. Apart from the damage to the contents, some bags missed and were torn open, and one bag that missed the net was driven so completely into a common crossing vee as to require removal from the track and dismantling of the crossing. With the increase in train speeds, pick-up apparatus fell out of use and is now very much a thing of the past.

Hitchin was the junction for Cambridge, and our inspection trip would probably have stopped here, the train recessed in the down sidings, and the area inspected on foot. The junction for Cambridge was on the up side north of the station, and that for Bedford was on the down side. The layout of the station can be seen from the maps, and by the 1922 Grouping the track layout had almost completely evolved. The station comprised two platform faces on the slow lines with bays or docks at three ends and the engine shed at the fourth, the south end of the up platform. The GNR station layout was controlled by three signalboxes, Hitchin South, Hitchin Yard and Cambridge Junction, each of which controlled a short section of the main line. The control of the three boxes was complicated. Because they were close together, no adequate braking distances existed and the three had to act in union. The regulating box was Hitchin Yard. Hitchin South had to clear down stopping services with Hitchin Yard before accepting from Stevenage North and clearing signals. For down expresses, not only did Yard have to clear first but also Cambridge Junction, before South could accept.

In the up direction the procedure was reversed. Up stopping services had to be cleared with Yard before Cambridge Junction could accept from the main line, Cambridge or Bedford. Stopping down services for Bedford were despatched from Yard directly to the Midland signalbox on the Bedford branch; main line stopping

Benslow bridge at Hitchin in the early 1950s. The ever-present WD waits at Hitchin South on the down goods. The two signals by the bridge are the up main and slow homes for Hitchin South, and again these are signals that the fireman needed to check for the driver, who was unsighted.

Hitchin c 1920

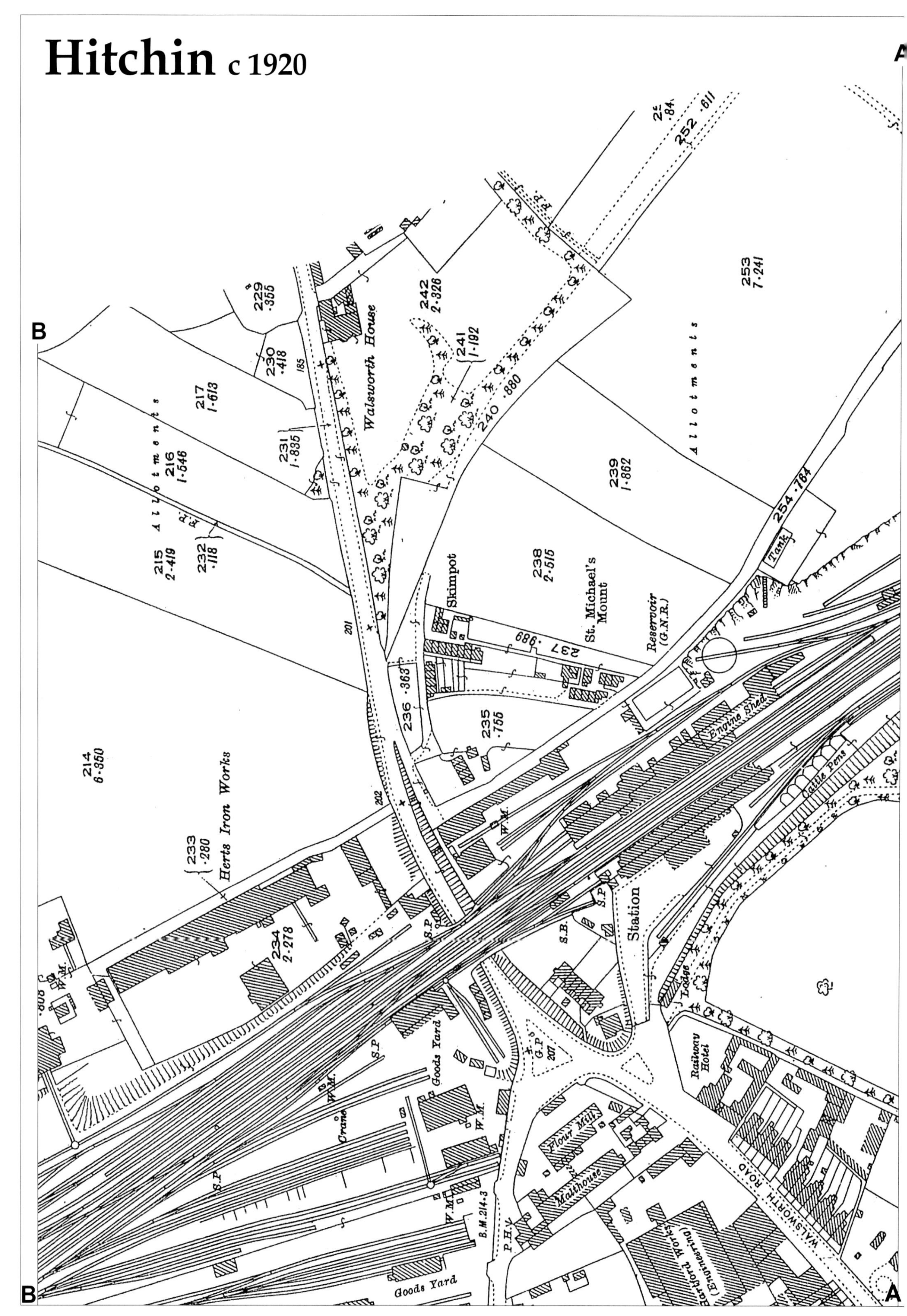

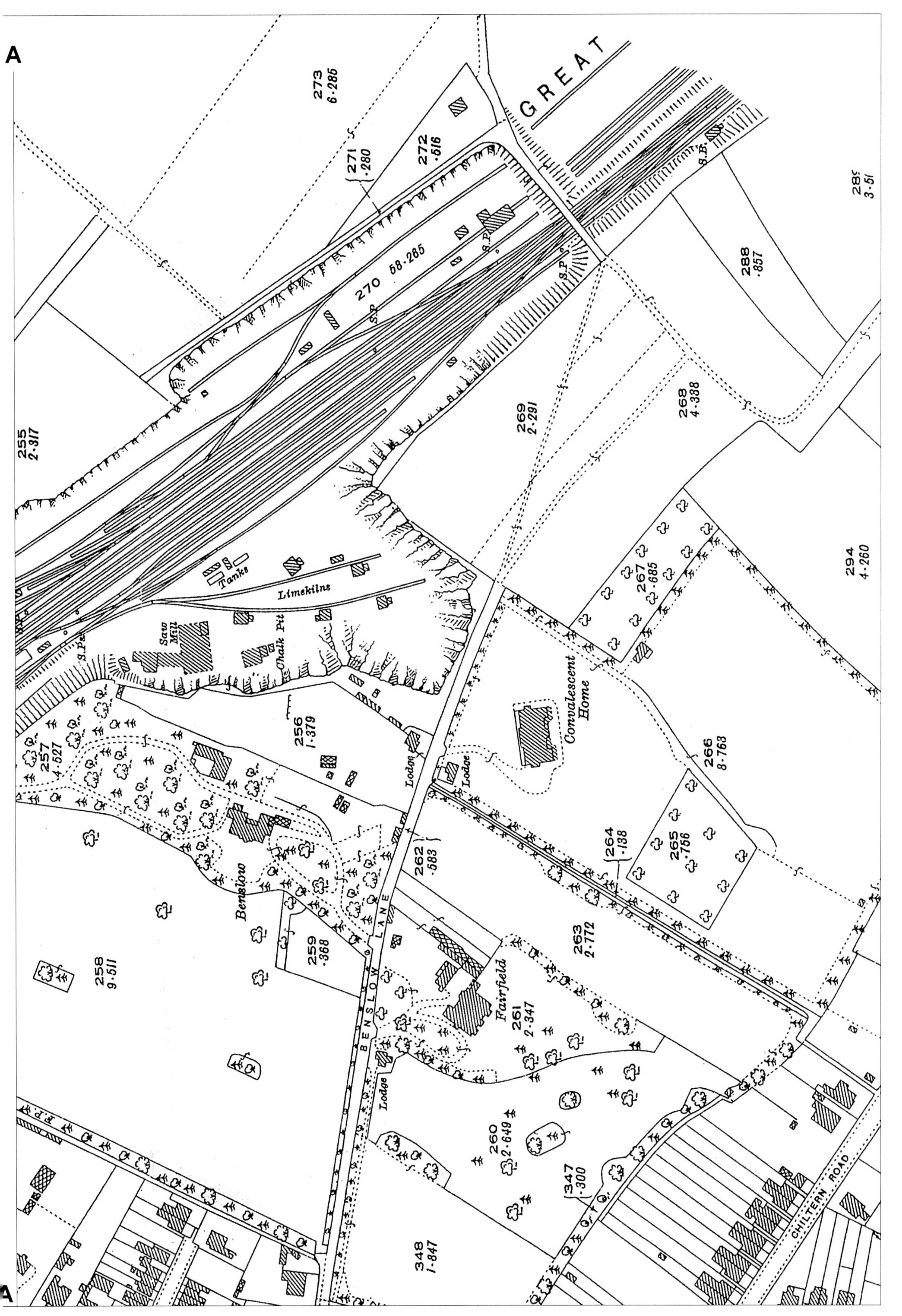
A
GREAT
273
6·285
271
·280
272
·516
270 58·265
S.B.
S.P.
288
·857
255
2·317
269
2·291
268
4·338
267
·685
294
4·260
Tanks
Limekilns
Saw Mill
Chalk Pit
Convalescent Home
266
8·763
256
1·379
257
4·527
Lodge
Lodge
262
·583
264
·138
265
·756
Benslow
263
2·772
259
·368
258
9·511
Fairfield
261
2·347
BENSLOW LANE
Lodge
260
2·649
347
·300
348
1·847
CHILTERN ROAD
A

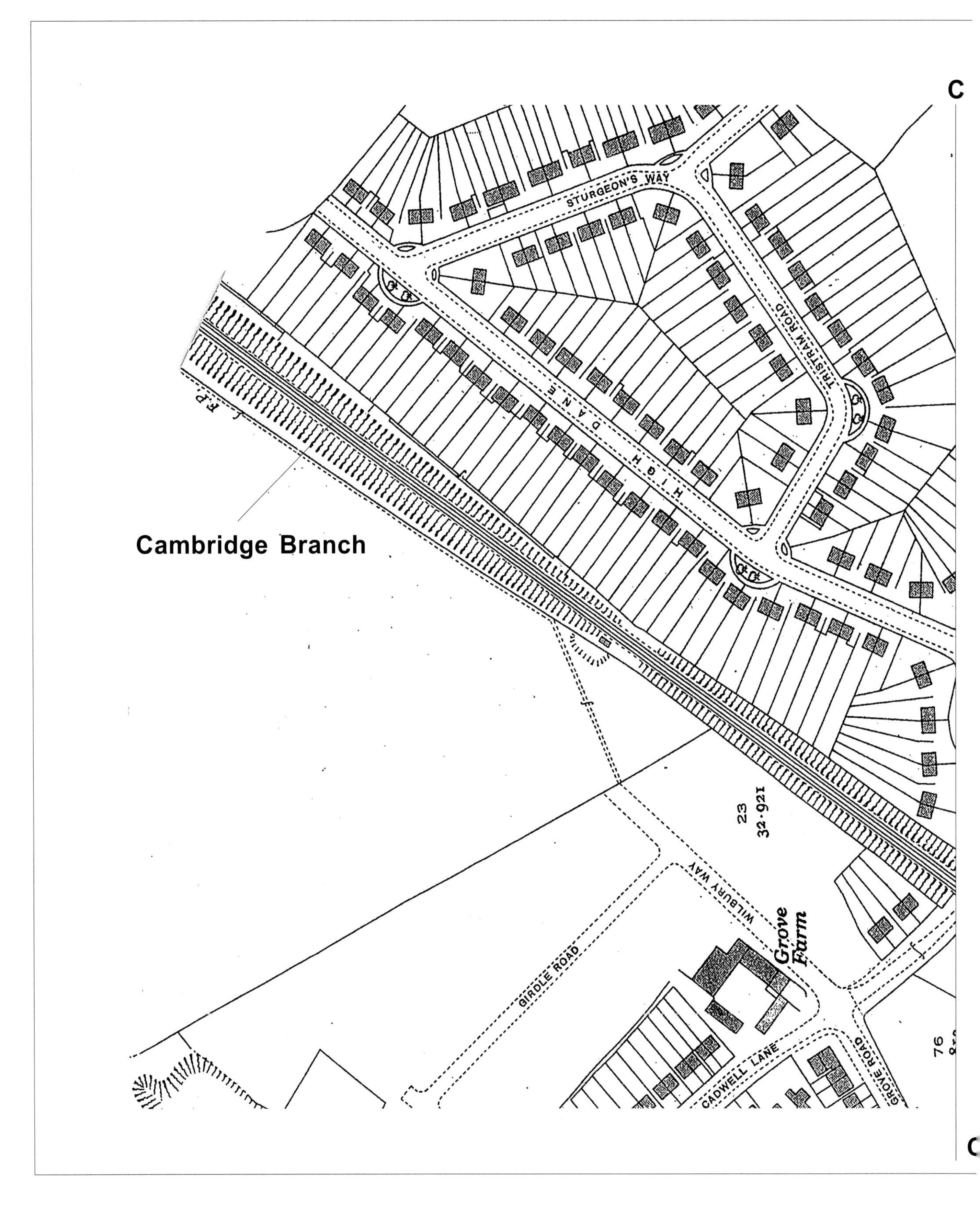

services were sent to Cambridge Junction. Trains for the Cambridge line were offered from Yard to Cambridge Junction and on to Letchworth, but the road was not set and signals cleared until Yard decided that a margin existed on the main lines. However when the logistics of operating the station is considered in relation to the complexity of the signalling, with the outer suburban and Cambridge expresses, movements to and from the depot and the branch, and a steady stream of slow freights in both directions, it is remarkable that signal checks were not more frequent.

The engine shed was always interesting. Its allocation included power for the outer suburban services, which was a growing passenger market. The locomotives ranged from Ivatt Atlantics, 4-4-0s and larger wheeled 0-6-0s of the late GNR through LNER days to the Thompson B1 4-6-0s and L1 2-6-4Ts of the post-war period. The Atlantics spent their autumn years on outer suburban and Cambridge services with J15s and N2s on the slower services. Short distance passenger trips to Hertford, Baldock, etc were worked pre-war by steam

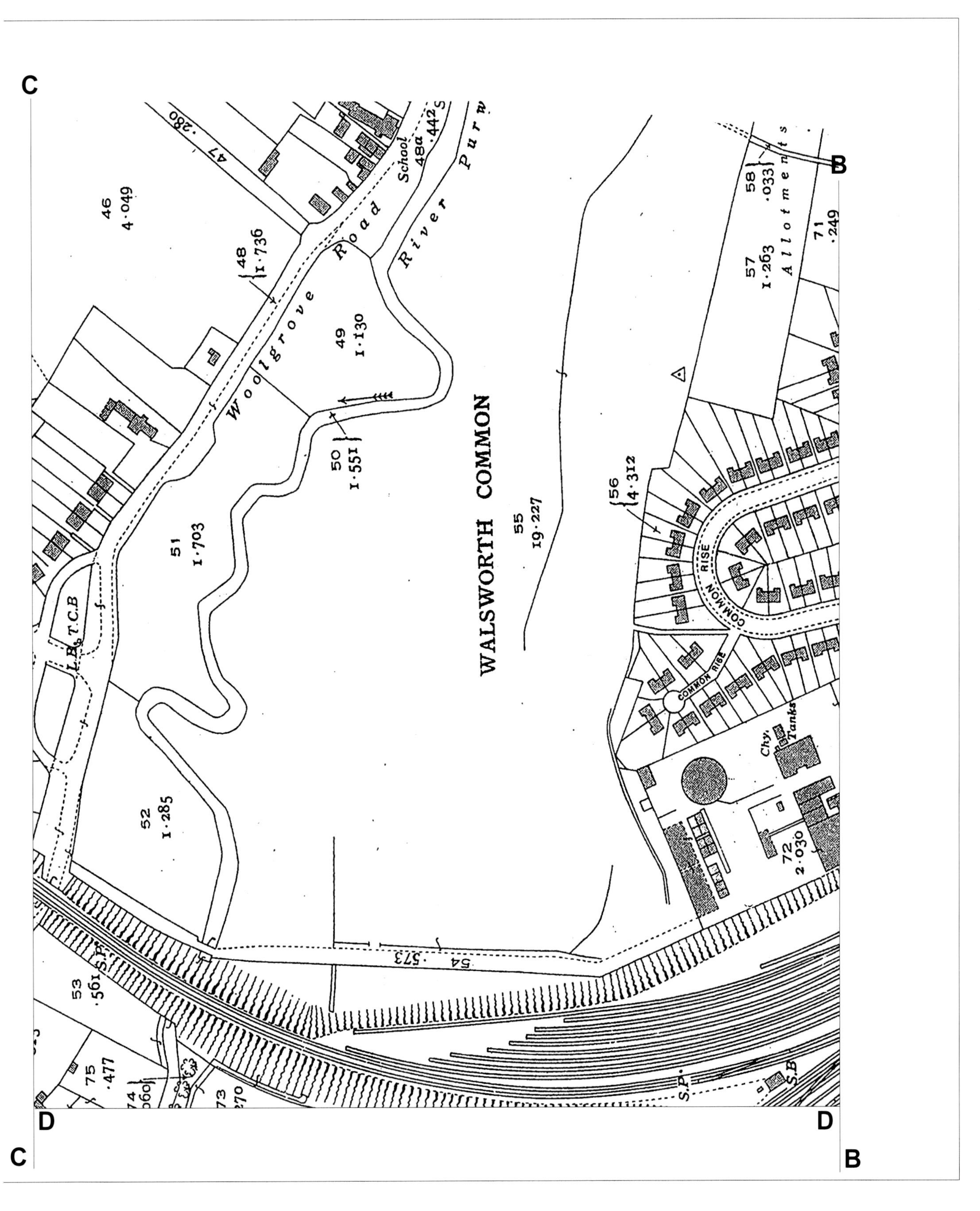

railcars, and for a period a class Y1 Sentinel 0-4-0, No.8175, was based at Hitchin. It was the last resting place for many Atlantics and several other classes. The pilot duties, like those at many other stations, were carried out by the halt and the lame, together with GNR 0-6-0 tank and tender classes. In later years three GER 'Buckjumper' 0-6-0Ts arrived, along with two at Hatfield. To power the local freight trips to Hertford, Cambridge, and down the main line, Hitchin had a selection of venerable 0-6-0s of classes J1, J3 and J6. There was still a certain amount of freight for the farming industry in the numerous goods yards down country. Often in later days a failed Pacific or V2 lay cooling its heels in the yard, and there would be an ancient visitor from New England or Cambridge. On one occasion I peered into the depths of the small two road shed to see a Hull Dairycoates J39 fresh from Doncaster!

The GNR 0-6-0, in a sense, echoed Joseph Cubitt: Gresley, Ivatt and their predecessors produced a handsome locomotive of a similar classical simplicity to the architecture of the GNR system. The

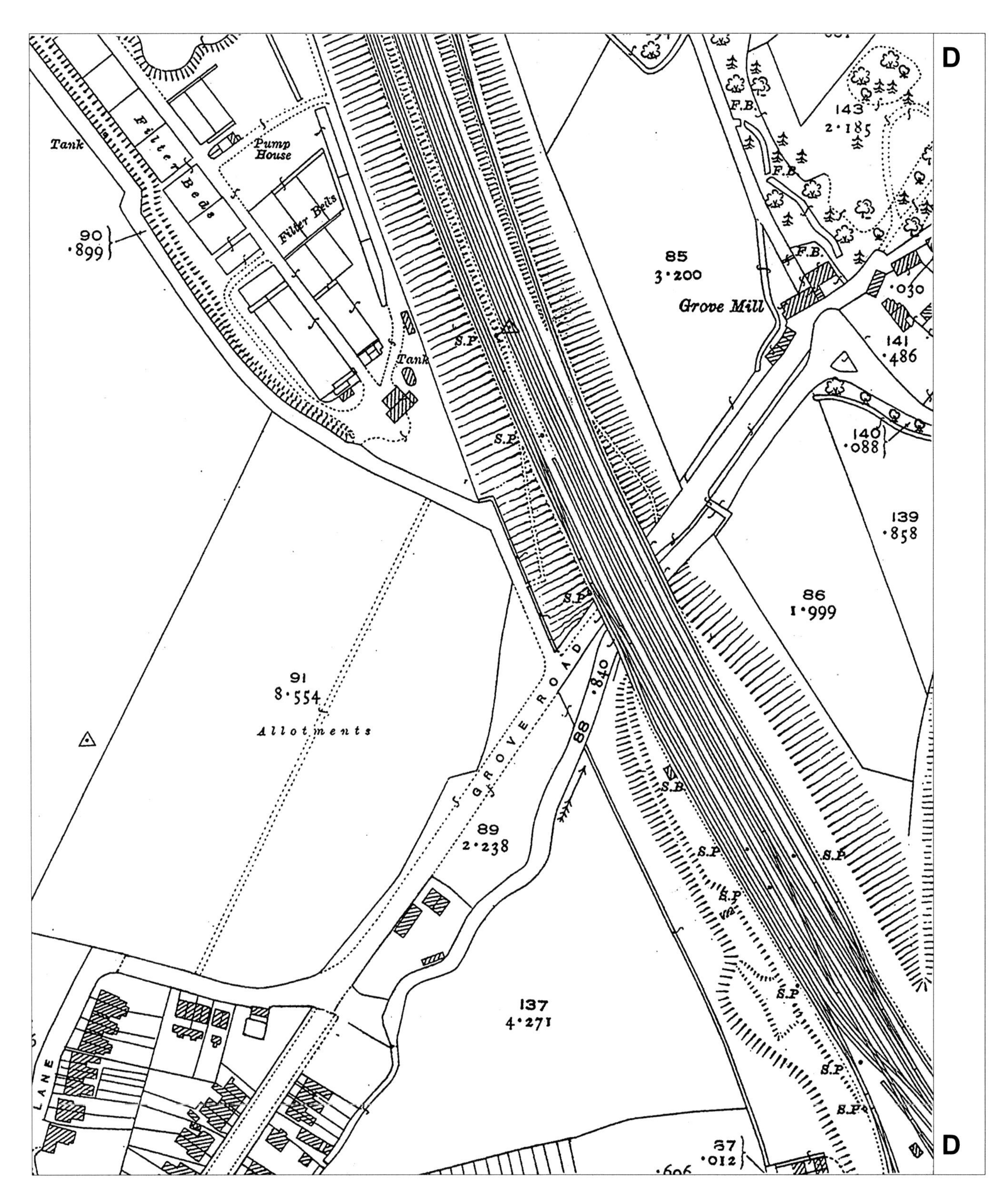

J1, J3 J4s and J5 0-6-0s, with slide valves, looked rather more ancient, but the later versions with piston valves, the J2s and J6s were fine looking machines. The J1s and J2s had 5ft 8ins wheels intended to cope with fast freight, and they had a good turn of speed. They were used successfully prewar on outer suburban work, but with advancing years they retired to goods trips.

Post-war, on Fridays one of Hitchin's three J1s worked into maroon territory down the Bedford branch with the Henlow RAF camp leave train. In later years every so often a number of the L1s would be stopped, succumbing to some passing infection – no doubt associated with hammering that their connecting rods suffered at speed. Then we had a glimpse of the old GNR, with Hitchin's two remaining N2s, Nos.69515 and 69557, and the better of their 0-6-0s cleaned and pressed into service on outer suburban duties. The N2s, if used, normally ran short goods trips, but pressed up to L1 speeds on the up main, swaying and rolling chimney first, they were an alarming sight. The J6s seemed to cope well, having a reasonable turn of speed. The last of Henry Ivatt's J1s, No.65013, was turned out in lined passenger livery, and she had her swan song on the 20.21 Kings Cross-Cambridge semi-fast on October 13th 1954, before being withdrawn shortly after. The message that there was something special on 2052 down came down the line, and I saw the remarkable sight from New Southgate signalbox. It was a startling initiative, although whether the crew were of the same view on a cold night might have been debatable. Her replacement on the Henlow train was E4 2-4-0 No.62785 and when, as the last of the class, she was preserved,

A general view of the north end of Hitchin in February 1927, from Yard box. The Bedford branch bay existed then, while the up sidings were well used. A train is starting on the up goods by Cambridge Junction box. The underbridge visible is Walworth Road.

another elderly GER engine, a 'little black goods' (as they were known on the GE) J15 0-6-0, No.65479, took her place.

Hitchin had no GE engines for the Cambridge services, and used Atlantics and 4-4-0s, some of the latter being allocated there. As the large Ivatt Atlantics were displaced by Pacifics in LNER days, they took a greater part in the Cambridge services. Services beyond were limited to Newmarket race specials, sometimes Pacific hauled. They were modified to include a number of faster 'Cambridge Buffet Express' services, quickly reduced by the student population to 'Beer Trains', but basically adhering to the historical pattern. It was not until electrification from Kings Cross was extended to Kings Lynn that services from the GN main line went beyond Cambridge.

Cambridge shared in the workings, which brought GE 4-4-0s and occasionally 4-6-0s to the GN. Later, B17 4-6-0s were introduced, but it was not until the 1950s that the former GE classes were fully displaced as more B17s were transferred from the GC section. On four or five turns the Cambridge engines worked through to Kings Cross. Curiously, the B17 was a rare sight between Hitchin and Doncaster, although in later years a sizeable fleet gravitated to March shed, and they were not unknown at Peterborough. Their lively riding at speed was not an obstacle to fast running on the GC section in the 1930s, but on the main line it would have been regarded with less enthusiasm. The later B1s were a two cylinder version of the B17, very competent, free steaming and capable of being worked very hard, but they were not the most comfortable of locomotives either, especially when the mileage was over 40-50,000. They were easily masters of their modest suburban workload.

The other post-war arrivals, the L1s, did not enjoy universal admiration, and were known as 'Concrete Mixers' or worse. As previously mentioned they were handsome, powerful, free steaming locomotives, but less than robust and short of adhesion and braking power. At low speeds on a dry rail they were impressive, but the outer suburban services required speeds up to 60-70mph. The 5ft 2ins coupled wheels seemed to be too small, and 5ft 8ins would have been better. With the small coupled wheels, the clatter from the motion was at best noisy and at speed, deafening. At speed the L1, like the N2s, seemed to roll, especially bunker first, although I believe the ride was better with the bogie leading. On the straight from Cemetery to New Southgate at night, the distant sight of flying red-hot ash over a mile away gave the prognosis, confirmed shortly after by the growing crescendo of noise; as the train drew nearer the sound of clattering motion was almost unbearable. Occasionally some of the local men pushed their L1s faster, and the sight and sound at 80mph was not for the faint-hearted! Driver Atkins of Hitchin for example, was well-known to the local signalmen, indeed notorious might be a better description, and he must have had nerves of steel. The impression of an L1 at speed could only be described as extremely vivid. In the 1950s the L1s were not coping well with freight trips on the Cambridge branch largely due to braking inadequacy and as a result two Fowler 2-6-4Ts with better braking were transferred to Hitchin. They were quite often appropriated for the outer suburban services, and they seemed fairly quiet and speedy machines. The experiment was not perpetuated unfortunately.

One of the duties at Hitchin was to come to the aid of flagging main line engines, often, but not always a single chimney Gresley engine. The restriction on underline capacity at Digswell Viaduct and the Ouse Bridge required RA9 locomotives to be piloted by a smaller and lighter locomotive – as if Hitchin had much else! The J1s and J3s were often down country on shunting and local freight, so were on hand if the need arose. As a result some eccentric combinations were noted over the years. In the post-war years we were used to Retford's small stud of B1s coming to the aid of such as the Tees-Tyne Pullman, and they were known as 'Retford Pacifics'. Hitchin's 'Pacifics' were much smaller and older! In the late 1940s for example there were reports of an ailing GREAT NORTHERN having been helped to Kings Cross by a J3 0-6-0, No.64153 if I remember correctly: would that someone had photographed this wonderfully eccentric combination! One delightful occasion remains in my mind. At some time around

One of the handsome Ivatt J1 0-6-0s, indeed the last survivor, No.65013 at Hitchin shed on 7th March 1953. She was one of the 'Hitchin Pacifics', very occasionally called to the aid of a main line engine, as underline weight restrictions prohibited the use of anything much bigger. Stephen Gradidge.

early 1954 in snowy weather, one of the morning semi-fasts from Grantham, either the 7.30 or the Mark Lane Flyer, was south of Huntingdon running normally, when the brakes on GANNET came on. The fault was with the ATC, the prototype AWS equipment, and various attempts to isolate the equipment or release the brakes were unsuccessful. The A4 was not for moving, a fresh engine was called for, and one of Hitchin's J1s was conscripted to replace GANNET. The train was heavy, and I would imagine that a B1 would have taken over from Hitchin, but not before two or three passing Top Shed crews had enjoyed the sight of Joe Howard and Ivor Brooks, two of the more substantial figures in the top link, standing in the spartan GN cab of the J1, pull-out regulator, lever reverse, and minimal comfort, in distinctly wintry weather.

The political battles between the London and North Western (LNWR), Midland (MR), Manchester, Sheffield and Lincoln (MSL, later the Great Central) and the GNR are chronicled elsewhere, but the offer by the GNR to carry the MR traffic did not result in a great benefit to either party. The Bedford branch was opened by the MR in 1858, as its means of reaching London, but it was already clear that the volume of traffic would test the GNR. Remember that this was before quadrupling of the main line. Very soon it had become excessive. I am no historian, but it seems clear to me that the intention already was to carry on to St.Pancras. The bridge structures that I had examined were light and quite unsuitable for regularly carrying anything heavier than a LMSR 2F 0-6-0, and Old Warden Tunnel, although wide enough for two tracks, was always single tracked.

It was worked by small MR locomotives such as the attractive little Johnson 0-4-4Ts, later replaced by Fowler and Stanier's indifferent 2-6-2Ts, and later still the Ivatt 'Mickey Mouse' 2-6-2Ts, one of which, No.41272, was the 7,000th engine built at Crewe. In the last year or two, two car diesel railcars and the heavier Fairburn 2-6-4Ts were used, although there was no evidence that the latter had been authorised by the CCE. The pilot for the down sidings at the north end, usually in later days one of the GER 0-6-0Ts, shunted both GNR and adjacent MR sidings. The MR had its own engine shed, now a civil engineering plant depot, at the back of the sidings. Later class 03 diesel mechanical 0-6-0s replaced the GER tanks. In late 1958 a four-wheel diesel railbus took over, but it was unreliable and on jointed track rode poorly. When the main line from Bedford North to St.Pancras was opened in 1868, the Bedford branch went to sleep, it seems. No attempt was made to make the best of the situation, and right up to 1960 the Midland presence was quite distinct. The possibility of linking the branch onward to Northampton was not explored until late in the day, although it seemed to me to be more of an attempt to serve both branches with one railbus. The connections at Hitchin in the late 1950s looked very much as though the 1858 layout had been relaid like-for-like, with no attempt at simplification in the intervening century! Ironically, a scheme to eliminate Hitchin Midland box by transferring control to Cambridge Junction was under way, when in January 1962 the branch was closed by the BTC. Twenty years later the branch would have become a valuable part of the outer suburban network. For decades BR continued to be operated as though the 1947 Nationalisation Act had never happened, and Chinese walls as a rule prevented the system from being fully exploited. The branch survives after a fashion in the film 'Those Magnificent Men in Their Flying Machines'. The preserved Jones Goods 4-6-0 was used for the film, travelling from Scotland and resting at Bedford shed between shooting, some 500 miles from its native heath. North London was galvanised at the time with the incredible news, and a thousand cameras bore down on Bedford!

Trains off the Bedford branch were sent from the Midland box to Cambridge Junction and on to the Yard as previously explained, using the up platform. They crossed to the down side at Hitchin South, and returned from the down platform. If one was careful, it was possible to photograph the up branch train between the connection where it joined the up main, and the turn-in off the up main to the platform. Knowing that, one could photograph a Johnson 0-4-4T and two coaches on the up main of the GNR! A freight trip with a 2F 0-6-0 looked even better.

I have dwelt at length on Hitchin, partly because it was a fascinating place that I remember fondly. It had an interesting history, and in the steam era, apart from the bigger designs, locomotives did not travel far, for a variety of reasons. In travelling a short distance one might encounter a number of different classes that I have referred to, usually old and interesting, that one would never see locally. And of course, the operation of the station, with its signalling, and the work of the pilots was another source of fascination.

Hitchin has always been a place where one could see trains at speed. Real speed In the steam era, there was not the sustained high speed of today, and high speed sections were far fewer. This, in the early postwar years, was a novelty for one from farther south. The speeds were actually not so high in steam days, but the spectacle of a steam locomotive, especially a single blast one, being driven fast was thrilling beyond measure. The A3s and V2s were the most spectacular, full of sound and fury, while the A4s were faster but quieter, and the A1s sailed by without any apparent effort. I remember. I remember, from one of my first visits there, the down White Rose, complete with the famous five car Gresley articulated restaurant car set, hurtling through the station at an apparently enormous speed hauled by a filthy New England V2. The down trains were travelling fast, and some were even faster – though not always the ones that one might expect. An Ivatt Atlantic at speed on, say, the down Queen of Scots Pullman must have been quite a sight. When the Gresley Pacifics were fitted with double Kylchaps, their greater speed capacity was clearly evident at Hitchin. In an hour or two spent at Hitchin, a succession of A3s and A4s on down expresses would have come tearing through the station and leaning to the curve down to Cadwell, the next signalbox to the north. Then, on the up main there was the experience of watching expresses travelling fairly fast but working very hard. They would appear on the curve round from Cadwell, and the pounding exhaust could be heard, faintly at first, growing louder, the whistle approaching the station, and then roaring past, under Benslow bridge and on uphill to Stevenage. Peter Handford, sound recordist *extraordinaire*, recorded a couple of evocative tracks at Hitchin, memories of days that were. The subsequent development of express power seen at Hitchin, with the Deltics, then HSTs both diesel and electric, has made the speeds of the steam days quite pedestrian. The roar of a Deltic on the up road at speed was almost an acceptable substitute for the Gresley Pacifics. An express passing through at 125mph still has an awesome quality, even without the sound of the exhaust and the sight of flying wheels and motion.

So, having examined operations and equipment, and met the senior staff, we return to the saloon. The Klondyke whistles for the road, and we set off slowly towards to north. The section north of Hitchin was as fast as any in the down direction, and no doubt the subject of high speed track maintenance would have been discussed on the journey. The maintenance of track for high speed was a matter of constant inspection and prompt action, but it could not be described as intellectually challenging. After the 1939-45 war it became still more difficult with poor pay and conditions and seemingly perpetual staff shortages. It was labour-intensive, and in view of the numbers involved, it had considerable significance financially. It involved keeping the track alignment to its design position as closely as possible, and keeping the rail levels to their prescribed relative level. This was usually referred to as 'line and top'. The greatest risk came from

Just south of Benslow bridge the up side yard was used for permanent way work and the preparation of engineering materials trains. J6 No.64186 is at work making up weekend trains on 27th March 1953. In the foreground is a 'stillage', on which 60ft prefabricated track panels were assembled. Stephen Gradidge.

the track settling differentially over a short distance, with changing cross levels ('twist') under load. The short wheelbase vehicle could not always cope with varying track levels at running speeds. Sometimes its suspension could not accommodate the amount of movement required sufficiently. The most likely sites for excessive twist were at the railjoints, and their elimination later with welded track was a great step forward. Railjoints, by virtue of their design, were points of vertical and horizontal weakness. They were subject to greater downward deflection under load, often differential, which not only allowed twist but reduced the rail end fatigue life as well. Add to that the presence of two bolt holes at each end of a 60ft rail that were very effective stress raisers, and one can understand why joints were thoroughly undesirable. In 1971 a series of tests were carried out to ascertain the impact on a typically poorly maintained rail joint. At 131mph, the rail end impact was *68 tons per axle*, and few of us could be confident that such a rail joint did not exist in our area!

Twice a year it was necessary to regulate the expansion joints on jointed track, before and after warm weather. Jointed track suffered from sympathetic rail movement – in short the rails tended to follow the traffic, as a result of wheels striking the running-on end of the rail. Where the expansion gap had increased from 0.375ins, the joints needed correction. Under a local possession, a length of track would be released from its fastenings, one end unbolted, and hauled back manually. This was known as 'pulling back' and a length of new rail was introduced to make up the accumulated deficit. Where it had closed up, as the rails were regulated, every so often a rail was cut short by one bolthole and another drilled. The rail ends were cleaned, examined and greased in the process. Rail failures or cracks were very unusual, since speeds were much lower, axle loads were less, and train frequencies considerably less. Although it was not a GNR, LNER or BR problem before electrification, afterwards one also had to be aware that, to the CME's electric traction engineers, a rail was also a return conductor.

Often on plain line the suspension allowed 'hunting' (oscillating laterally) with increased speed, but the presence of railjoints broke up those oscillations. Unfortunately, the introduction of CWR in the late 1950s coincided with the arrival of diesel traction, and short wheelbase wagons were now travelling at roughly 50-100% above the normal speed of previous days. With the greater rigidity of CWR, the number of wagons hunting progressively or becoming generally unstable at speed increased, and as BR were intent on removing signalboxes, guards and second men who might otherwise have seen rogue wagons, lengthy derailments became the norm. The lateral force generated by hunting at progressively greater speeds was sufficient to make the wheels ride up on to the railhead, and a derailment ensued. Although it was not a GNR, LNER or BR problem before electrification, afterwards one also had to be aware that, to the CME's electric traction engineers, one of the rails was principally a return conductor.

***Above*. Hitchin and its shed were tucked in a recess quarried out of the chalk. Dumped out of use as suburban services were rapidly changing to diesel traction, L1 No.67757 and N2 No.69586 await the move north in 1960. Peter Coster.**

A new English Electric Cl.40 diesel, No.D206, with a down Leeds express in summer 1958. The depot has the usual mixture, with a New England V2 and J15 No.65479 beyond, with WDs and an L1, while one of Hitchin's two non-condensing N2s approaches on the down slow. Peter Coster.

The junction north of Hitchin with the Bedford branch. An up Newcastle express hauled by A3 No.60078 NIGHT HAWK recovers speed after being checked by Cambridge Junction for a crossing move to Cambridge. The Bedford goods waits for the road behind Bedford's 3F No.43428 on the up branch road. Hitchin Midland signalbox is in the distance while on the down slow, a light WD sets off to the north tender first. Gateshead, post-war at least, found cleaning difficult for a variety of reasons, but by December 1959 the arrival of numbers of new diesels had resulted in even less attention for steam traction, as witness the dreadful state of NIGHT HAWK. Peter Coster.

CHAPTER THIRTEEN

Hitchin-Huntingdon

The main line track was always of excellent quality, and in steam days the permanent speed limit (PSR) had increased to 90mph. The layouts on the main lines consisted largely of single leads that rode well, and the tandems, slips and diamonds that gave access into wayside sidings in GNR days were steadily removed. The pace of removal accelerated in the late 1950s with the introduction of continuous welded rail (CWR). An S&C (switches and crossings) layout apart from comprising thousands of components that perpetually loosened under traffic, invariably had a congestion of timbers which were difficult to keep packed tightly with ballast. A somewhat pedantic point, but sleepers were 10ins x 5ins in cross-section, while switches and crossing layouts were carried on timbers which were 12ins x 6ins and of varying length. With rising staff shortages post-war, S&C maintenance deteriorated, and on the footplate the long crossover at such as Biggleswade was best anticipated, to avoid a sore head!

Mechanical maintenance started to replace manual maintenance with tampers in the mid-1950s, and with more powerful and faster machines in the 1960s, lining machines were introduced. More modern machines combined tamping and lining, and plain line maintenance is almost entirely by machine. In the 1970s, tampers that could work round S&C were introduced. The use of CWR required considerably greater quantities of ballast for stability, and the means of unloading and placing was mechanised and improved with Ballast Regulators and Consolidators. The old MR engine shed on the down side at Hitchin has become a Civil Engineering Depot, where the current civil engineering fleet of machines can often be seen. The CCE department required a large wagon fleet for permanent way work but it was usually the poor relation where adequate wagon capacity was concerned, although as the network was privatised new engineering wagons entered service. For many years engineering work depended on the availability of spare revenue earning wagons, although demand only started to escalate in the mid-1950s.

Over the years, with the closure of the depot and introduction of multiple unit operation on all but the expresses, the layout was simplified and relaid in modern materials. The crossovers were lengthened for higher speeds, and of course continuous welded rail (CWR), first introduced in the late 1950s, was extended to all running lines progressively. Cambridge Junction, which to footplate crews in steam days was always known as Sabotage Junction, was one of the early conversions to swing nose crossings for high speed when the whole layout was simplified and relaid, and rode better as a result. While relaying, it was important to remember to lock the crossing as well as the points out of use but unfortunately forgot the swing nose.

Hitchin lay on a long right-hand curve, and after the 33rd milepost there was a long four mile straight descent to Arlesey. This was always an exciting experience on the faster steam services as the speed increased rapidly. The first box after Hitchin was Cadwell, only 1.4 miles north of Cambridge Junction. At Cadwell the down slow became the down goods, while the up slow became the up goods, with connections to allow passenger trains to be turned out on to the main lines. It was necessary for the signalman to be quick at such closely spaced boxes as Cadwell, since it only took top link express drivers a minute from the box in the rear, in this case Cambridge Junction. Normally in the London area the short section version of absolute block was used: the signalbox in the rear offered a train, which if the section was clear, was accepted. It was offered to the box in advance immediately, and on receipt of acceptance, the signals were cleared. If the box in advance was too close to allow a correct braking distance, the box in advance could not accept until the box further in advance had accepted. As a result the bell signal went forward much faster than the train and every so often a regulating box held the bell signal to avoid blocking the line too far ahead.

The crucial difference was that normal absolute block required that the signalbox,

Another view of NIGHT HAWK as she pulls away, past Cambridge Junction. It always amused me that the number had to be cleaned, presumably for the crew to see which filthy locomotive was their rostered mount. Peter Coster.

The junction with the Bedford branch with the branch freight waiting behind 3F No.43428 in December 1959. A Drewry 204HP shunter attaches to a down freight, and the main lines are now clear. Hitchin Midland box is in the left-hand distance.

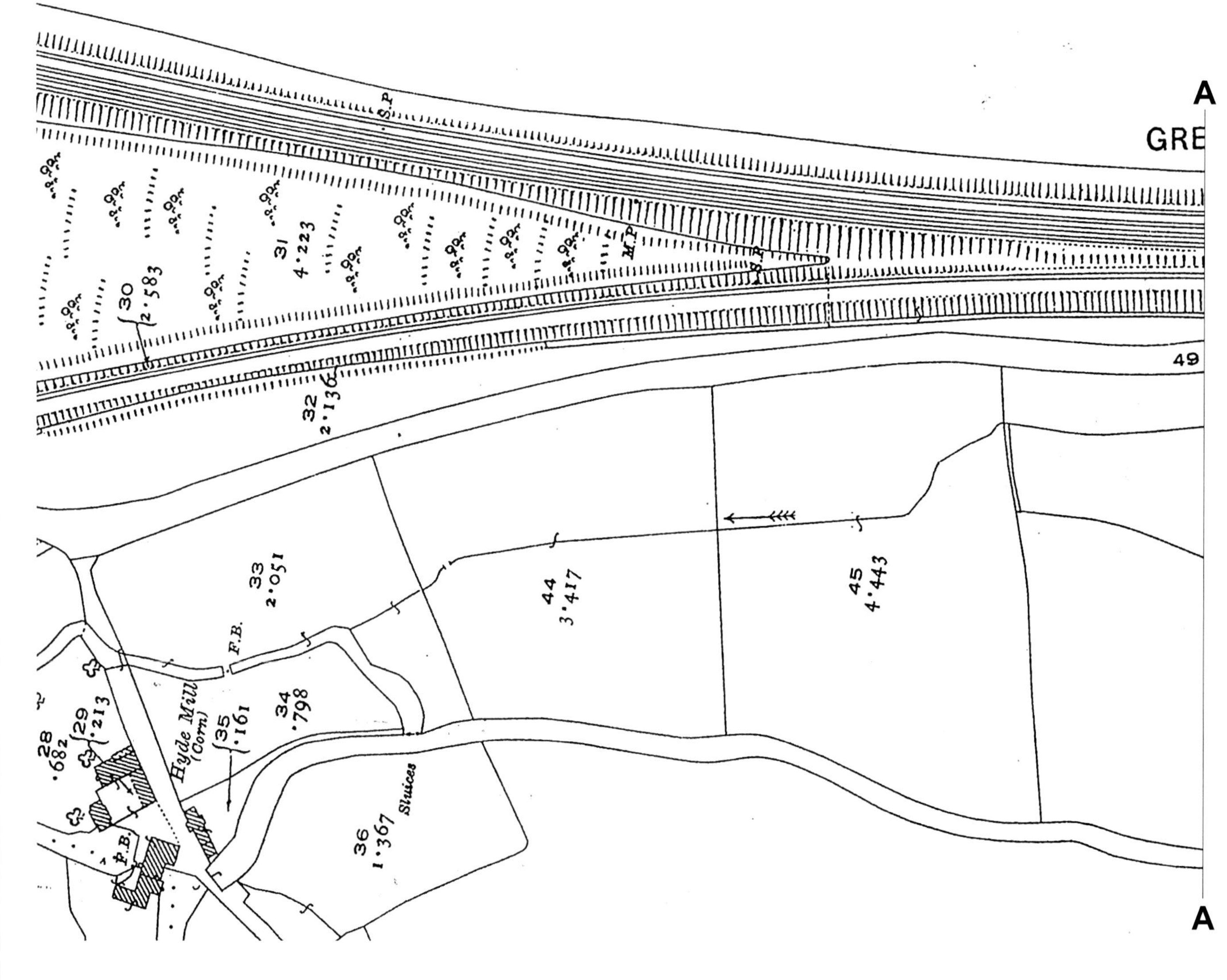

Cadwell c1917

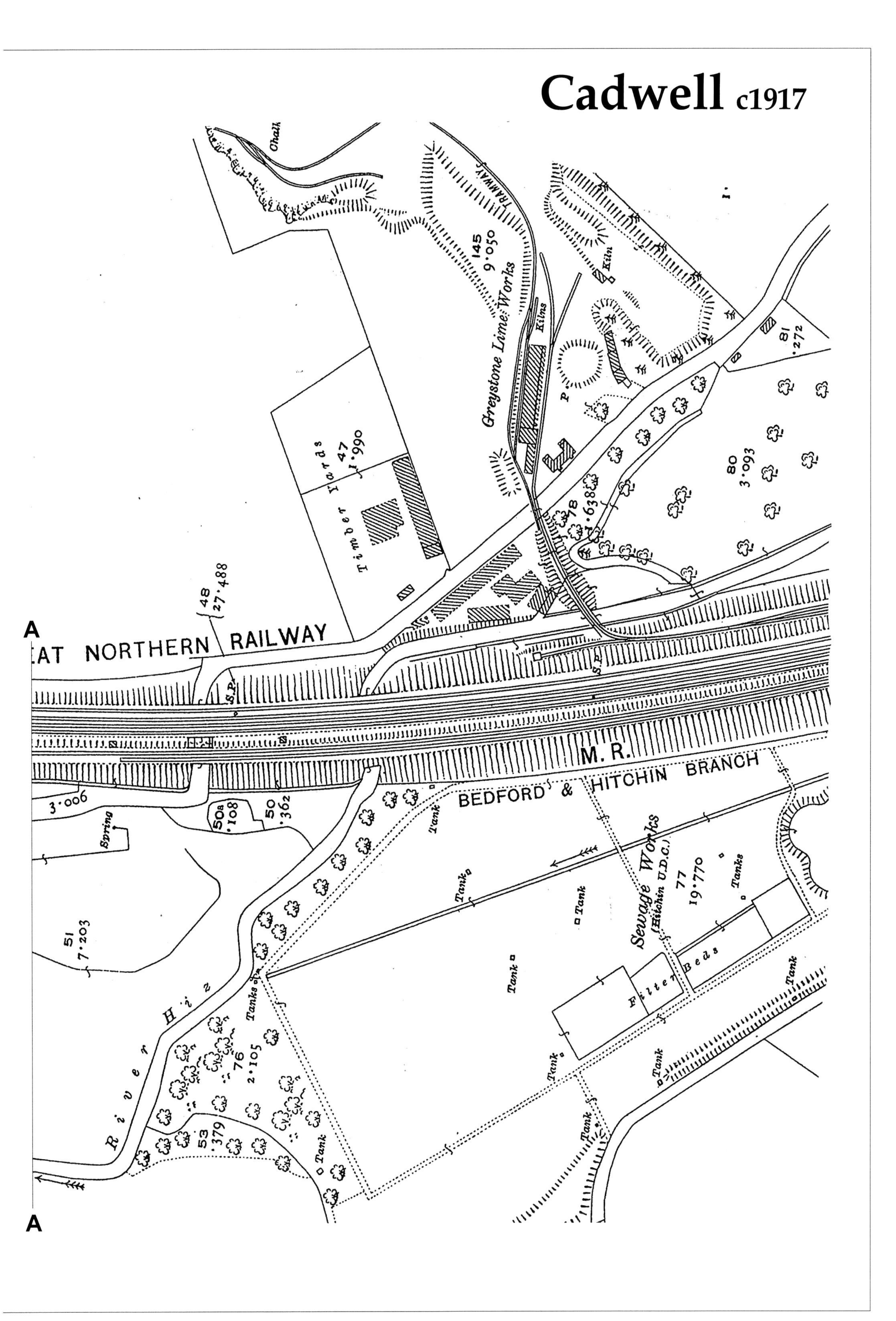

A very unusual meeting at Hitchin in December 1959. An O4 was seen south of Peterborough two or three times in a decade, and No.63626, from Frodingham I recall, was borrowed for a run to Hornsey and back. As she pulls away from taking water, she passes the Bedford freight with No.43428, still waiting patiently for the road. Peter Coster.

The first part of the Scots Goods, 262 down, goes flying north behind York's A1 No.60153 FLAMBOYANT. The full spread of lines north of Hitchin is visible, with the Bedford branch coming in on the right, and the Cambridge line to the left. Tall signal posts give a splendid vantage point, but the vibration from an A1 and 300 tons of train passing at speed left a vivid impression of their stability! Peter Coster.

A4 No.60033 SEAGULL was one of the triumvirate of double chimney A4s at Kings Cross, with MALLARD and LORD FARINGDON. Here she is hauling the down 14.00 Tees-Thames express in summer 1959, and I clearly remember that she was travelling very fast indeed. Peter Coster.

Gresley's A3 was one of the most handsome of steam locomotives from any angle. Here a gleaming No.60063 ISINGLASS passes Cadwell in March 1961 with the 9.50 Leeds-Kings Cross. Peter Coster.

Top Shed's V2 No.60903 was reduced to more lowly duties with this freight in the late 1950s. She was one of the V2s equipped with a double Kylchap almost at the end of her life. Peter Coster.

The 9.50 Leeds-Kings Cross at Cadwell behind A4 No.60025 FALCON during spring 1959, with a new double Kylchap and her roller-bearing tender. The A4 was going fast and working hard, but there was little exhaust visible. Peter Coster.

having accepted from the box in the rear, did *not* send the bell signal forward and maintained signals at danger. Only when the box in the rear sent the 'train on line' signal did one offer the train forward. It required the box in advance to accept quickly so that the signals could be cleared. It meant that in theory a top link driver travelling fast through the shorter block sections was looking at distants coming off as he approached. Sometimes it was not just in theory. When the prototype Deltic was transferred from the LM Region, full power running achieved such speeds as to beat the signalling uphill since, even with the early warning, the train was likely to pass the distant before it was cleared.

In fact, after a short pause, the train was sent on. Also, 'on line' was given early, again to give more adequate warning, but it negated the purpose of the bell signal, which was to signify 'train complete'. This helped by clearing signals early, and with the occasional level crossing it gave the signalman time to get his gates closed and clear signals. Nonetheless, it was uncomfortable keeping the signals at danger knowing that good friends, known to hold pretty warm views on signalmen, were minutes away, at high speed. One watched the Pacific come flying round the bend from Hitchin, and hoped that the distant was cleared before the driver had seen it. It was an object lesson in seeing how the railway *worked*, the signalman using his judgment, the driver searching keenly for the next signal, using his skills to give enough room to stop comfortably and safely if necessary.

The long straight was always marvellous, the speed rising, or in the up direction the crew were working hard to keep up speed until past the troughs. An evening by the main line or in a signalbox was always engrossing, first of all with a cavalcade of the evening expresses, and then with a succession of fast freights, almost entirely hauled by Green Arrows. By this point the freights were travelling at speed, and a 40 to 60 wagon train at 60-75mph was an impressive sight. Nowadays the diesel and electric motive power fly at greatly increased speeds through the familiar country, albeit much more overgrown and populated. Part of the way down, where the Arlesey road passes underneath, there was an up siding, ground frame controlled. Here the key was kept at the next signalbox, at Three Counties station. The four tracks extended to the south end of Arlesey station and resumed north of the level crossing, then again were brought down to two through Sandy station. The down slow became down goods at Cadwell, and only became down slow again from Sandy to St.Neots. Otherwise it was a goods line, but the facility to suspend permissive block and change to passenger operation was used more and more in the steam era. Likewise the up slow reverted to goods only from Huntingdon to Paxton, between St.Neots and Offord, from Everton to Sandy, from Biggleswade South to Arlesey and south of Cadwell.

In fact Three Counties could only manage two counties instead of three, for the name came from the Mental Hospital a mile to the east, served at one time by a tramway, and presumably intended to serve three counties. Originally the station was named Arlesey, but the name was transferred to Arlesey Siding just over a mile further north. Three Counties looks fairly desolate now, but it can be seen from the map that in GNR days it was a busy place. It had a large brickworks on the down side south of the station, and a limeworks on the up. Just over a mile north lay what became Arlesey & Henlow, a two track station with a gated level crossing over the A507, a large goods yard on the up side north of the station. Like Three Counties, it had sidings between the lines south of the station, presumably for empty wagons worked across from the yard. At both ends of the station, as can be seen from the map, there was another compact S&C layout, which at full speed left more bruises on the unwary footplate occupant. Arlesey must have shared with Sandy the distinction of being the fastest location on the East Coast down main line as was Essendine on the up main. The A507 level crossing was replaced by a bridge after the steam era, and as part of the modernisation, the bottleneck was removed and the two platforms were renewed on each slow line only.

It had a notoriety of another sort for some. Over the years there have been many

It was unusual, with a number of larger wheeled locomotives available, to see a WD 2-8-0 on a class E long distance freight. No.90151 is turned out at Cadwell on to the up main in order to overtake a slower freight taking water at Cambridge Junction. Knowing a number of drivers, this move was only made having ensured that a considerable margin existed before the next up main express was due! Peter Coster.

Three Counties 1918

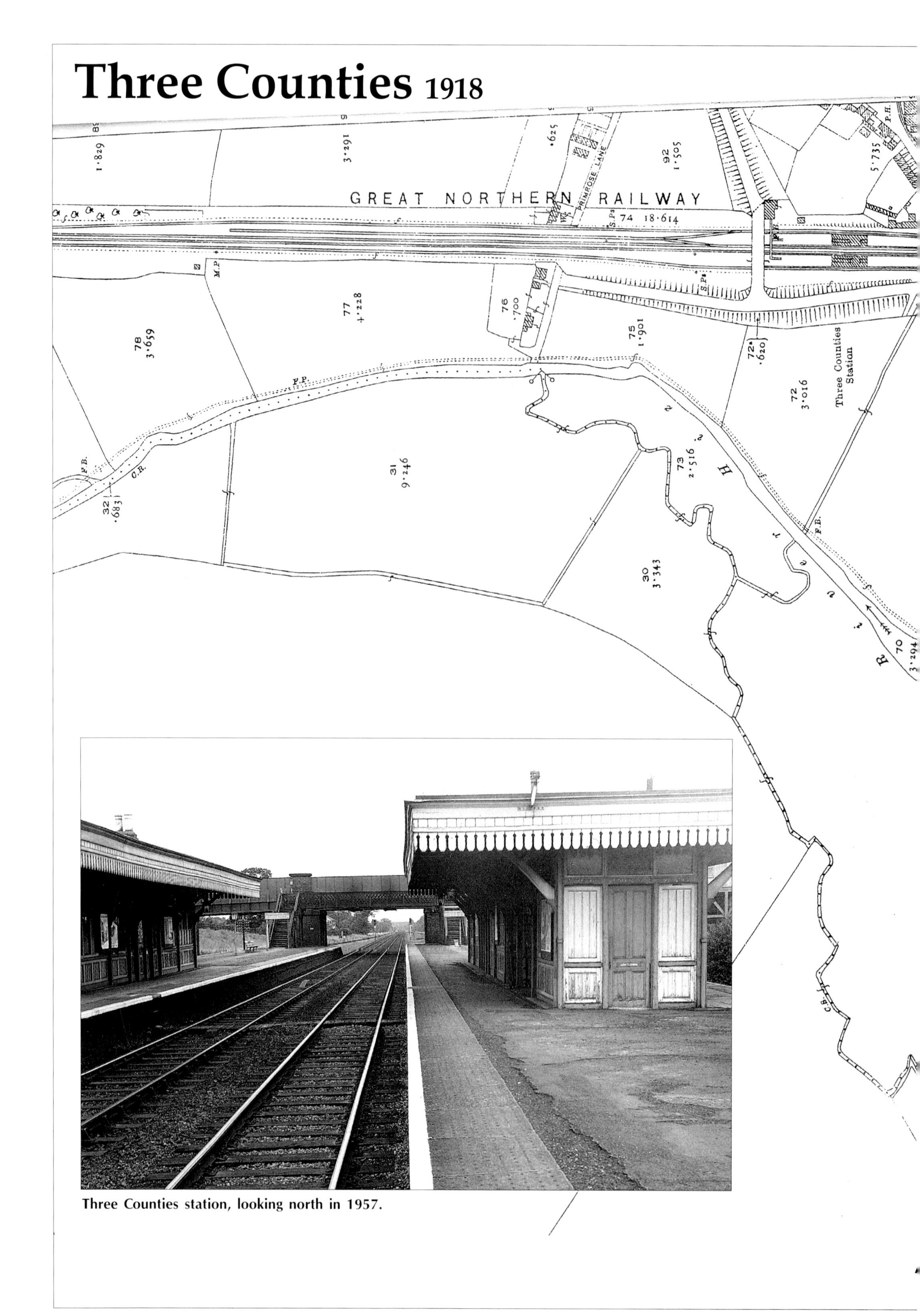

Three Counties station, looking north in 1957.

A

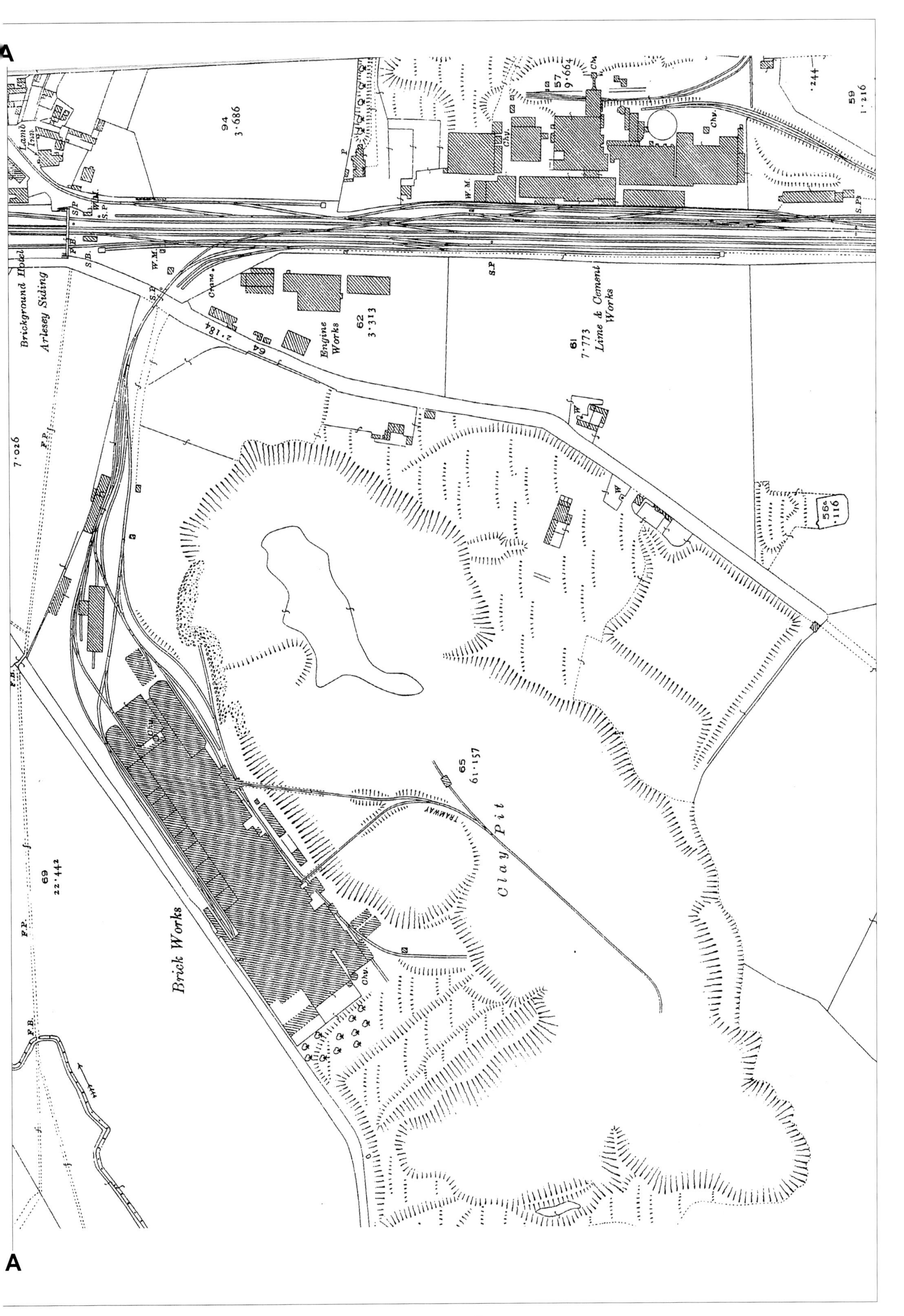

Lamb Inn
94
3·686
57
9·664
59
1·216
·244
Brickground Hotel
Arlesey Siding
S.B.
W.M.
Crane
64
2·184
62
3·313
Engine Works
61
7·773
Lime & Cement Works
7·026
56a
·116
65
61·157
Tramway
Clay Pit
69
22·442
Brick Works
Chy.
F.B.
F.P.

A

Three Counties in 1957, looking south. A very exhaust-permeable footbridge indeed... The small concrete pillar name board on the left is of a type introduced at Finsbury Park (see examples illustrated there earlier in Part One) some time before in the 1950s.

Arlesey and Henlow station in 1960, looking south. The alignment of the main line is superb, as it needs to be at one of the fastest, if not the fastest location on the East Coast main line. The soft ground on the right is where three A3s at least came to a halt, overrunning the home signal in the distance.

Arlesey looking north in 1957. The A507 level crossing that constrained the layout for years was later replaced by an overbridge. That 'failed' in recent years and has been replaced in turn by a motorway-style bridge, dominating a very modern station with four tracks instead of two between the platforms. A K3 2-6-0 waits on the up goods in the distance. Where the wagons are standing is, inevitably, now a car park.

derailments, indeed if those occurring in marshalling yards were added, few weeks would have passed without an incident. Early in the 1950s the 20.00 Leeds Goods to East Goods (1343 up), and the 19.15 return from Kings Cross Goods (1224 down) were worked by Copley Hill shed, which received three Green Arrows (V2s) for the duty. Ardsley, the senior shed, worked the 22.30 from Leeds Goods to East Goods (1357 up) and the 21.05 return from Kings Cross Goods (1266 down). I may be wronging them, but the Ardsley men did not seem so conversant with the signalling of the GN as they should have been. A late running 1357 up was diverted on to the up goods loop at Barnet to allow a passenger service to overtake on the up slow. Unfortunately, as mentioned earlier the driver took the signal for the up slow and not the up goods, and V2 No.60861 sailed through the sand drag and came to a halt in a bramble patch by a footbridge at the north end of Oakleigh Park. On Saturdays 1266 down ran earlier, and the driver seems to have taken the down main signal, wrongly again, for the train was on the down goods, and BLAIR ATHOL slid through the sand drag and came to a stand in the quagmire behind Arlesey down platform, on the banks of the River Hiz. The A3 took some getting out! However, the accident did not prevent at least two repetitions, also with A3s, CENTENARY and ISINGLASS if I recall correctly.

There was a spectacular collision at Hitchin in the small hours fortunately not involving a passenger train, when one 9F hauled down freight, which had stopped to take water, was run into by another 9F hauled train. As wagons flew everywhere, what should run into the wreckage but Copley Hill's V2 No.60865 on 1357 up, and with sufficient force to cannon into Driver Atkins and his L1 on the up slow, having just come off shed, and knock her over, off the track. It must have been terrifying at the time. A later collision at Sandy with 1357 up resulted in the withdrawal, sadly, of the first A1, H.A. IVATT.

In the GNR days most freight moved at a necessarily low speed, in order to be able to stop safely. Only the brakes on the engine, tender and brake van were available to stop the train clear of any adverse signals. The few faster freight services introduced were timed to run at higher speeds but were piped to the locomotive to provide much greater braking force. Greater numbers of larger locomotives in LNER days brought greater speeds on the faster freights, but the improvement or replacement of the huge number of old unfitted wagons remaining in service required an impossibly high level of investment. As a result the GN main line was condemned to suffer from numbers of slow moving freight trains, usually coal but sometimes iron ore and stone, until almost the end of steam. The speeds of these trains had changed little from the GNR through to BR.

The descent from Hitchin crossed an area draining with minor streams such as the Hiz into the Great Ouse. Just beyond Arlesey the River Ivel was crossed, and the railway rose for under a mile to Langford Bridge, where there were sidings on the down side. Then the downward progress was resumed through Biggleswade to beyond Sandy. Biggleswade had two boxes, South and North, with a large goods yard on the down side, and consisted of two island platforms with the usual standard buildings. The goods facilities expanded after the layout shown in the 1926 Survey. The GN station buildings were timber as usual supported with wrought iron

Arlesley

1926

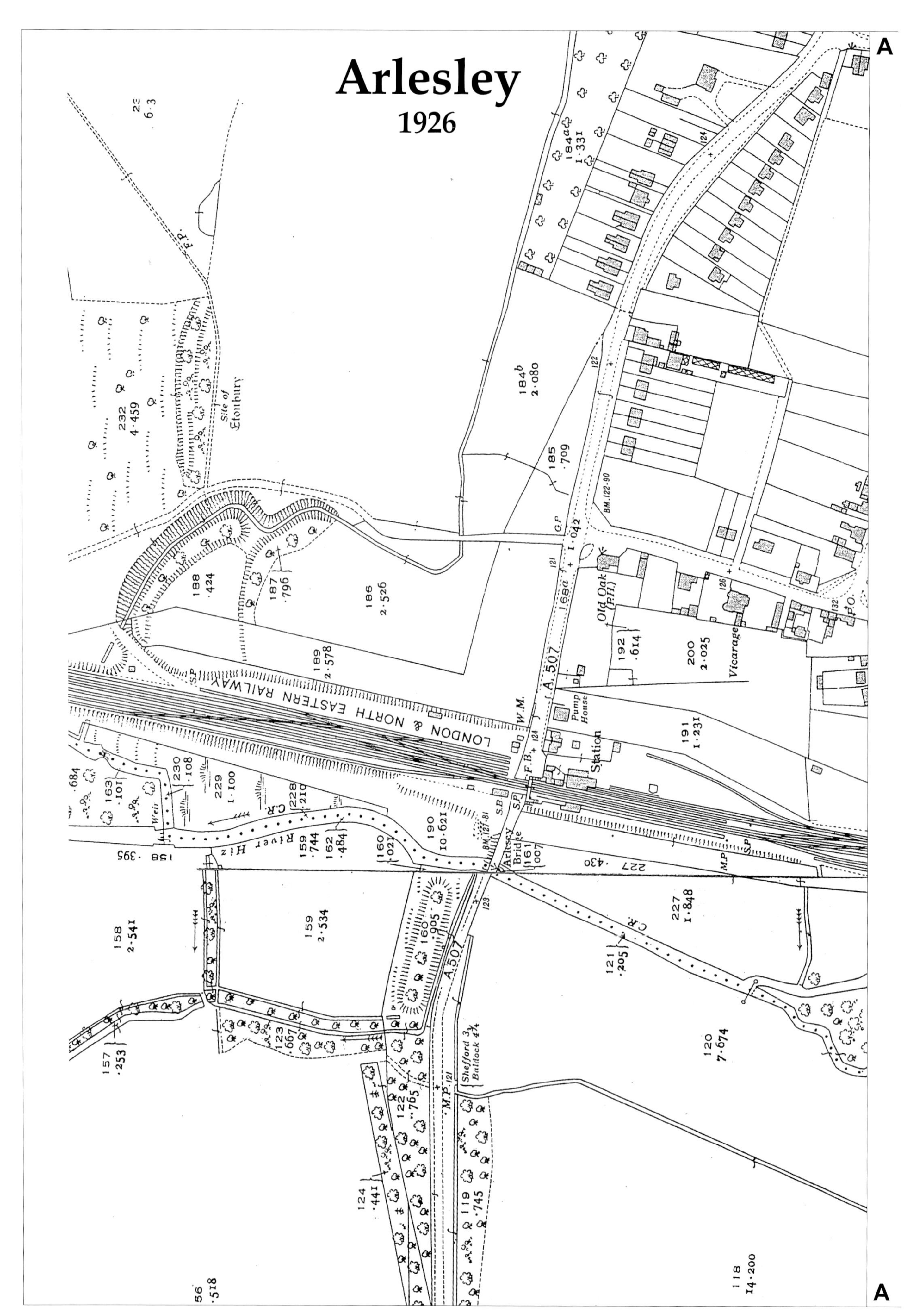

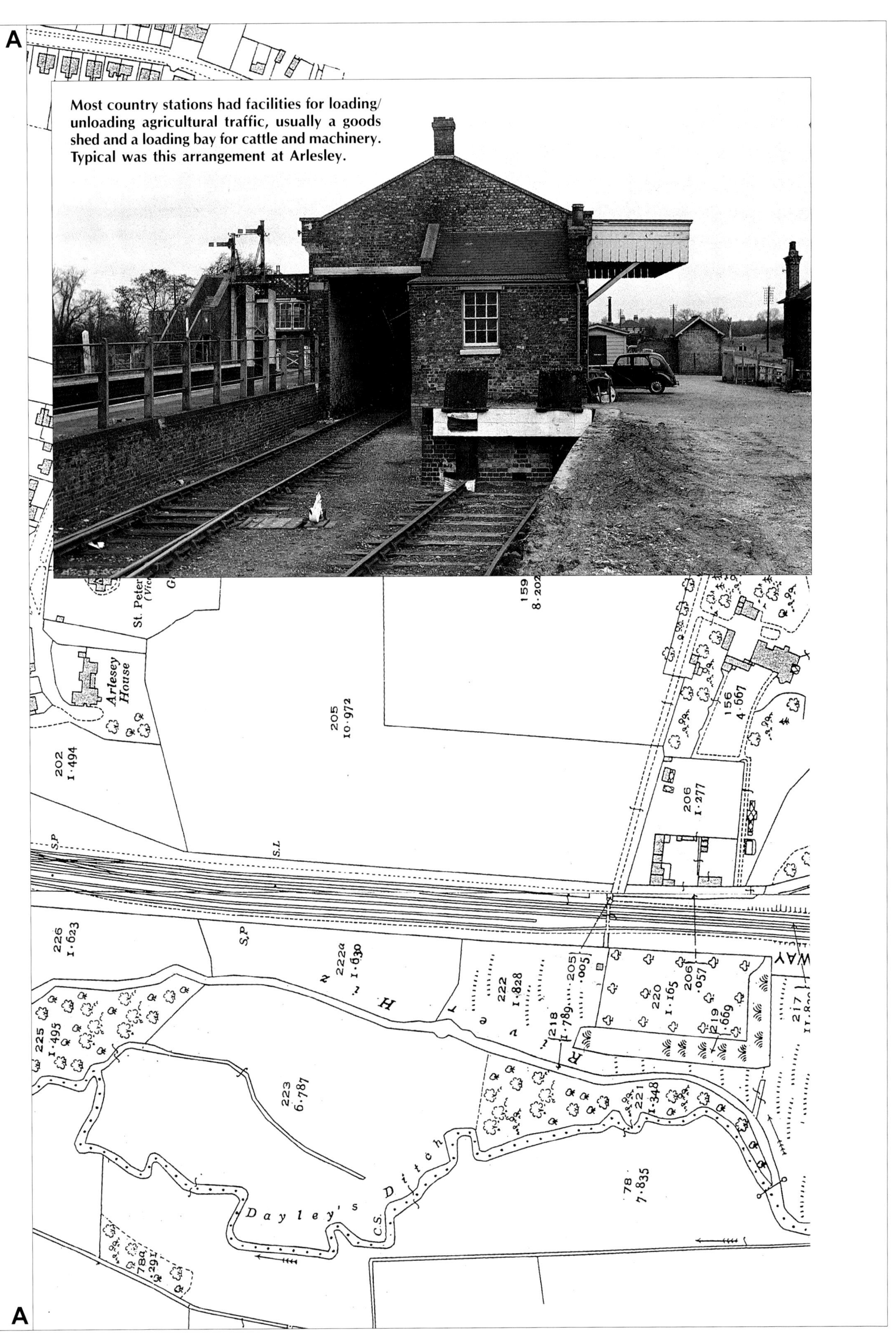

Most country stations had facilities for loading/unloading agricultural traffic, usually a goods shed and a loading bay for cattle and machinery. Typical was this arrangement at Arlesey.

Post-war, the LNER nominated a special locomotive for the haulage of Royal trains to Sandringham. The locomotive selected was a rebuilt 'Sandringham' B2, No. 61671 MANCHESTER CITY, and alas for half the residents in that fair city, it was renamed ROYAL SOVEREIGN. Turned out in LNER lined apple green, later rebranded under BR ownership but retaining apple green, she was a glorious sight. The B2s were handsome engines, even though they had ersatz tenders from anywhere and, I was told, cracked their frames too often. When eventually she succumbed to Swindonian khaki she was still well cleaned, and on a railway used to trailing axles rather than 4-6-0s, a remarkably strong starter. Here I suspect that despite the headcode, she was posed with a train of ECS purporting to be the Royal Train, a fine sight. If it was indeed 'The Grove', the Royal train's telegraph codename, I doubt whether a photographer would have been allowed this close. The period would be 1950-56.

Biggleswade station in 1957 having just had a repaint by the look of it. It is salutary to recall that men worked in dark clothing without high visibility jackets for well over a century, and many met their end because of the want of it. Working in platforms was dangerous since safety was not simply a step or two away, and it was certainly asking for trouble to stand in the other road. At such a location as this with fast-moving expresses with steam locomotives that were often fairly quiet at speed, even greater care was necessary.

structural frames, built in timber sections, mounted on brick plinths. Biggleswade was quite a large community, on the A1 Great North Road, and has, like the other stations down to Peterborough, changed out of all recognition in nearly a century or so.

It is worth recalling that in the steam era, the passenger service north of Hitchin barely existed. It was based on the operation of 'parleys', the basic service requirement as defined by Parliament. There were at one time, for example, seven in the down direction, all from Kings Cross to Peterborough or beyond. In addition there were two in the afternoon from Hitchin, the former to Peterborough and the latter to Sandy. The parleys were hauled by 4-4-0s and both classes of Atlantic, or sometimes even a J1 or J6 0-6-0. At one time in the 1930s ex-GC D9 4-4-0s were also used. The Hitchin departures were worked by the same classes, but sometimes an N2 would go to Sandy. The district was still rural, but the development of a user-friendly service would have been worthwhile. Unless the railway provides a reasonable service in the first place, communities will not develop – it was ever thus. Later the services were worked mainly by Pacifics, occasionally by V2 2-6-2s, and some with B1 4-6-0s or L1 2-6-4Ts.

The line continued straight on over Biggleswade Common and then curved gently left to pass under Sandy Warren, a large sandy hill to the east of the main line. The 1862 LNWR Cambridge-Bedford branch came in on the up side to run parallel with the GN main line through the station. As can be seen from the 1926 Survey, the station had two platform faces with an island in the middle. The GNR passed between the down platform and the island, and the LNWR passed between the island and the up side with its own station. South of the station there was another large goods yard on the down side and in the convergence between the two railways there were sidings. There were facilities for transferring traffic which were signalled fully in the 1939-45 war years to expedite traffic movement. The LNWR line was double track from Cambridge through the station and single beyond, as it rose to swing westwards across the GN main line. The branch was largely single to Bedford although its capacity was increased in the 1939-45 war. I always understood that the GNR, in allowing the construction of the line, would only countenance a single track over the intersection bridge.

The bridge itself was a multi-span wrought iron girder bridge, and in the late 1950s the superstructure was completely renewed with welded steel girders. As the line was closed in 1968 one might groan at the waste of money, rightly. However, this was a common problem, especially in the Beeching era, and it is worth explaining why it happened. The problem for the engineers, where lines had an uncertain future, was that a major renewal such as this, at that time, put the future of a line at risk. There was then a debate over the action to be taken, with all of the pros and cons, to keep the line running at minimal cost, but eventually the debate moved into the general area and closure reared its head. During which time the need for renewal became more urgent.

A charming but frustrating characteristic of our nation is that while people fight tooth and nail to retain their railways, they prefer to use their cars instead of the trains. In an attempt to economise, the remaining

Biggleswade c1920

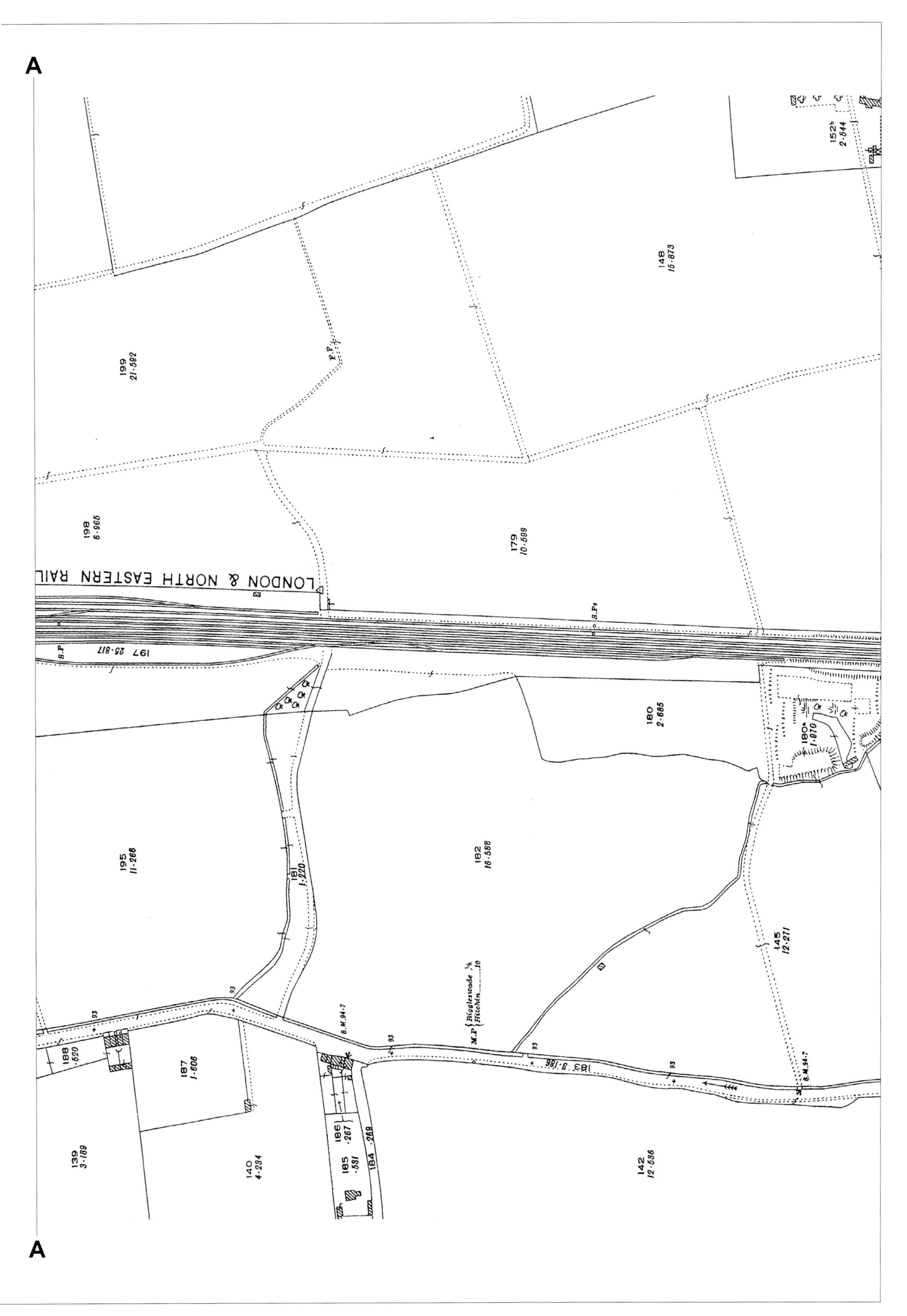
A
LONDON & NORTH EASTERN RAIL
199
21·582
198
6·965
148
15·873
152b
2·544
179
10·589
197 25·817
S.P
F.P
180
2·685
180A
1·870
182
16·588
195
11·266
181
1·220
145
12·271
M.P {Biggleswade ½ Hitchin 10
B.M. 94·7
93
188
·520
187
1·606
183 3·186
186
·267
185
·531
184 ·269
139
3·189
140
4·234
142
12·586
A

The down island platform and down goods at Biggleswade with goods shed, loading platform and the loading gauge. The yard expanded over the years and dealt with quite a lot of freight for a country station.

A general view of Sandy in 1957 looking north, showing the unusual arrangement with the GN main line on the left and the LNWR Bedford-Cambridge line on the right, sharing the same station.

The LNWR half of the station at Sandy. The up platform had an attractive glazed LNWR canopy gabled at right angles to the tracks. Closed for some 40 years, today it would be a useful link in the increasingly busy Bedfordshire area.

service was usually derisory, sometimes deliberately so. No real railwayman wanted to close a line of any importance: that was to give up. And so the stately minuet between the railway and the opposition continued until the CCE's patience was exhausted, when safety of the line could no longer be guaranteed, and the renewal went ahead and a new welded steel intersection bridge was provided to carry the few diesel railcars each day. Ironically, the decision, usually to close, came not long afterwards. Nearly half a century later, the revival of much of the route is under discussion.

The modifications brought about by the 1939-45 war also included a west to north curve joining the GNR at Sandy North Junction. The Didcot-Oxford-Bletchley-Bedford-Cambridge route was always a solution in search of a problem, but in the war years it was not commercial considerations so much as the need for a variety of strategic options in moving essential traffic when routes could be blocked abruptly. By the 1950s the wartime west to north curve was disused, and it was recovered in 1966.

This was still a fast section of the route in both directions, the down expresses at speed as at Arlesey, while on the up road, drivers urged their locos up to as high as speed as possible for the long 16 mile rise to Stevenage. The finest burst of speed in the up direction was on May 23rd 1959 when, on the famous Golden Jubilee railtour of the Stephenson Locomotive Society, Bill Hoole pressed SIR NIGEL GRESLEY up to 100mph north of Sandy. Beyond Sandy North the next signalbox was Everton, which had a level crossing. North of Sandy is the boundary between the two power boxes at Kings Cross and Peterborough, and Everton was retained as a Gate Box, controlling its own level crossing and that of Tempsford by CCTV. Both crossings were converted to barrier operation. Before modernisation, such as Everton crossing had lengthy gates that caught the wind, making it necessary for the signalman in windy weather to seek the assistance of the permanent way department. The next station was at Tempsford, a simple two island platform station which had a small goods yard on the down side, and a level crossing half a mile north.

The GNR main line, like any other, was crossed by all sorts of bridges, both over and under, of brick, stone as either concrete or masonry, or metal. A variety of designs was used and still is when replacement becomes necessary. Metal normally took the form of girder construction as in the case of Bridge 12 at Holloway. Where the tracks are supported between two deep girders, it is a through type bridge. Where the girders are beneath the tracks, it is a deck type, and unsurprisingly, when the tracks are supported between those two extremes, it is a semi-through type. The dimensions of the structural elements such as girders are related to the span, particularly the depth, and where the span is considerable, both the depth and weight can also be considerable. A means of containing increased weight for long spans was the lattice girder, which was used for example at Crescent Junction and in crossing the Nene and Trent. Metal bridges were initially of either wrought or cast iron, but the latter is weak in tension, and after a catastrophic failure of the Dee Bridge at Chester in 1847, the use of cast iron began to be questioned. Its use was confined subsequently to arches or fascia girders (non load-bearing ornamental/parapet girders). Steel began to supersede wrought iron notably with the Forth Bridge, but the change took a long while, and even in the early 20th century wrought iron continued in use. No doubt price had something to do with it as well.

Concrete apart, brick and stone were only

SANDY
Sandy
CAMBRIDGE ROAD
Fire Engine House
Queen's Head (P.H.)
Rectory
The Pinnacle (Recreation Ground)
Cæsar's Camp
Camp
Swading
Swading Hill
Quarry Hills
St. John's Cave
Lodge
Bell Inn
Station
Station Row
Woolfield
Mort. Chap.
CEMETERY
Goods Shed
Cattle Pen
Roman Remains found
Tower Hill
Chesterfield
Lock Corner
Weir

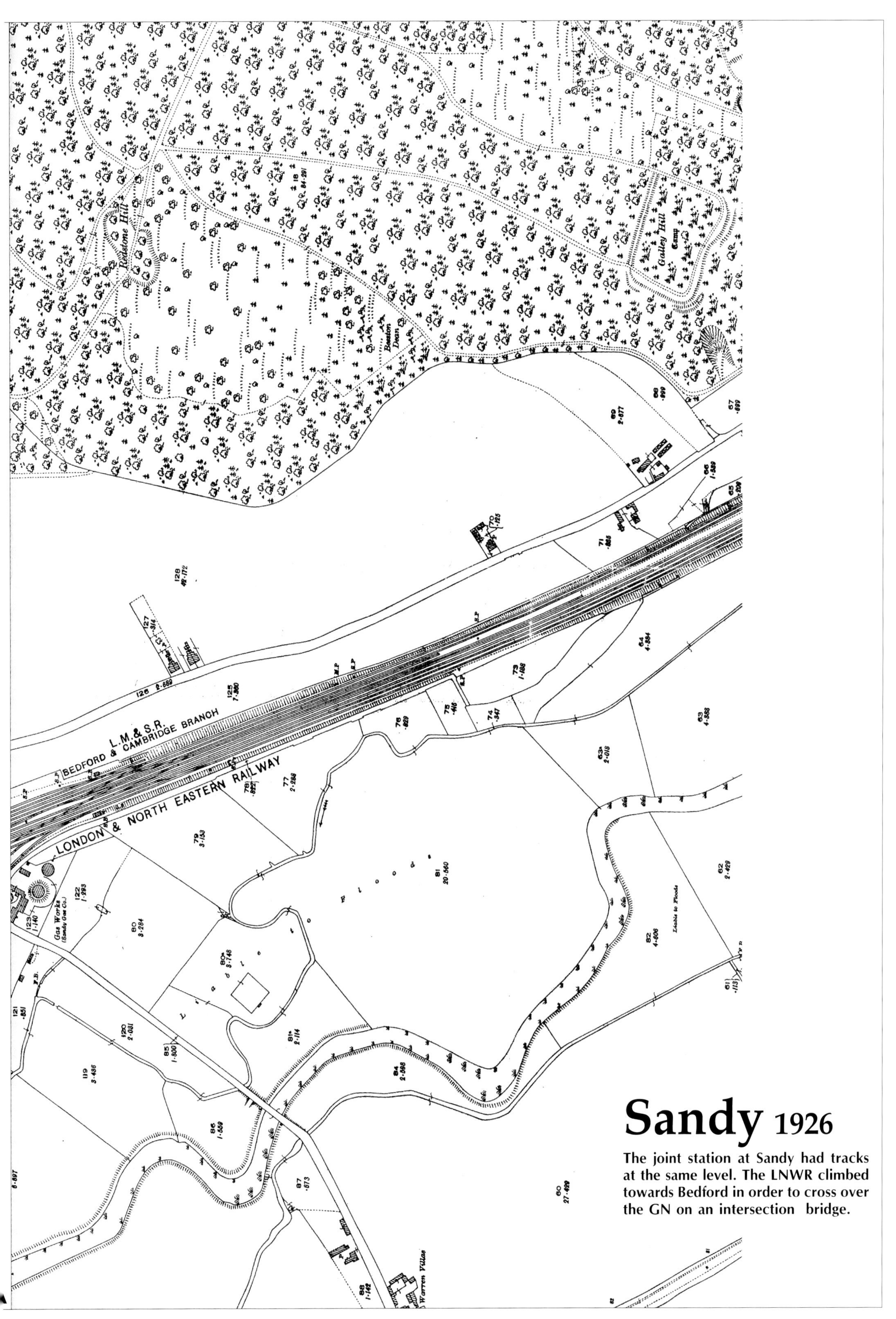

Sandy 1926

The joint station at Sandy had tracks at the same level. The LNWR climbed towards Bedford in order to cross over the GN on an intersection bridge.

With a down express signalled, this is a view of Sandy when it was one of the GN's notorious bottlenecks. Signal checks were not common due to the watchfulness of the signalmen, but I do recall the Non-stop grinding to a halt from 98mph as a light WD 2-8-0 ambled through the bottleneck ahead of us. Space forbids the inclusion of the driver's comments.

A3 No.60044 MELTON leans to the curve through Sandy with an up express in 1962. One can see where the overbridge was extended when the LNWR line was constructed a decade after the GNR.

A V2 heads an up relief express at Sandy in the early 1960s.

An up express headed by 60033 SEAGULL passes under the rebuilt flyover at Sandy.

A Cambridge train pulls out of sandy behind a D16 4-4-0. The LNW canopy can just be seen behind No.1 Box.

A service from Cambridge to the LM runs in behind a BR 75000 2-6-0. Note the oddly shaped lower part of the box.

A Cambridge bound goods coasts down from the flyover behind J17 0-6-0 65580 in June 1954.

Bletchley 4-6-0 75034 comes downhill into Sandy station with a Cambridge train in 1954.

A Cambridge train decends the ramp down to the station at Sandy behind one of the new BR 2-6-4Ts.

An up express at Sandy hauled by A3 No.60056 CENTENARY. The up expresses were usually travelling as fast on the Tempsford-Sandy section as anywhere south of Peterborough, gathering momentum for the gentle but long rise to Stevenage. The LNWR canopy can be seen here rather better, unusually with a number of passengers beneath. A detail – a run of signal wires down the main line six-foot was unusual, and together with the worn 60ft rails made walking around examining track unnecessarily hazardous.

The intersection overbridge – the 'flyover' – at Sandy was an interesting single track through bridge, almost certainly in wrought iron. For obvious reasons it was rarely studied at length by those passing by! It was a 'through' bridge since the track was supported between the main girders rather than by them directly. The girders were rather uncommon, for although they were of normal depth for a plate girder, they were of lattice construction. Lattice girders were usually of greater depth. The freight *apparently* eastbound for Cambridge on June 26th 1954 is hauled by an ex-GE J17 0-6-0. I say apparently, since it should be impossible to clear signals for a westbound service on a single line, in the opposite direction. Since the J17 is not banking a westbound service and probably not shunting it may be simply that Sandy Junction box on the LNWR line is switched out and the signals cleared. R.E. Vincent, www.transporttreasury.co.uk

A quiet moment at Sandy.

used in arch bridges. The arch bridge was and is a wonderfully simple structure. Arches are circular (segmental or semi-circular), elliptical, or in very few cases, parabolic, and the span of the vast majority is approximately 30-35ft. The arch structure was developed empirically by skilled craftsmen rather than by design and was in use ceturies before as a load bearing device in buildings as well as bridges. When a gap is bridged, the structure, to function, has to resist imposed bending. The arch resists bending by developing a direct thrust in the arch ring, enabling the use of material that withstands compression but not tension. That is why the arch ring is particularly important, built of top quality engineering brick, and the most important aspect of any bridge examination. As we travel north, we pass one, three and even five arch bridges, largely of brick since there was no source of good structural stone anywhere on the main GNR network. Where embankments are wider and deeper, the gap to be spanned is wider and the number of arches is greater.

The railway companies had to build a number of bridges over and above those carrying roads or other railways, either linking properties or restoring access to property, severed by the construction of the railway. Such bridges were called accommodation or occupation overbridges, and railways had an enormous number of them. There were also small bridges for farm animals, called cattle creeps, and bridges for watercourses. For example, where a watercourse had been diverted to cross the line of the railway at right angles, the diversion works belong to the railway. Where the railways' Estate Departments became aware of the sale of property on one side of the line linked to the other side by a bridge – 'severance' – the need for a connecting bridge disappeared, and it was closed and demolished. One of the bridges near the 48½ milepost was such a case.

With the development of demolition techniques using explosives, arch bridge removal became much easier. Approaches varied, depending on the nature of the bridge. As much of the structure and as much spoil as possible that could be safely removed was carted away beforehand. Then the underside of the arch – the soffit – was drilled with a pattern of shotholes. A layer of scrap sleepers was laid clear of the tracks. Once the track was under possession, the layer was completed across the tracks, and the explosive cartridges were placed and wired together. With the site cleared, the bridge was fired, and the resulting heap of debris was cleared into spoil wagons by a traxcavator or back-acter. Control of the manufacture and use of explosives improved considerably, and apart from dust and smoke the bridge could normally be 'dropped' down on to the sleepers. Very occasionally the policy of selecting the cheapest reliable quotation led to spectacular consequences with the bridge blown up instead of down. There were times when it led also to disagreeable correspondence with local farmers, who had found to their dismay bridge debris in their fields, with an expensive forage harvester or combine, and so sent BR the bills!

The line had levelled out by now, but by the next signalbox at Barford, the line started to rise over the higher ground at St.Neots before descending to the banks of the Great Ouse. This 'W' shaped gradient profile was known as the St.Neots 'hump' and was clearly visible from the footplate. Barford was replaced with an IBS early in the 1930s. During the early 1940s Little Barford Power Station was constructed, with a number of holding sidings. Later this went over to merry-go-round (MGR) operation. Access for incoming coal trains was complicated by the lack of proper connections, but the power station was demolished more recently and replaced with a gas fired installation.

St.Neots was another two island platform station, with a large goods yard. The country stations had the necessary cranes and so on for dealing with farm equipment, cattle, sheep, feedstuffs and cereals that, on the railway, belong to another age. Even in more rural days St.Neots was one of the busier stations, despite being two hours from Kings Cross and the irregularity of the pedestrian service. Beyond St.Neots was another

Sandy North Junction, looking south towards the intersection bridge shown on page 71, in November 1943. The connection to the LMS route was laid in 1940 during the 1939-45 war for strategic purposes, and carried little traffic thereafter. The junction was protected with colour light signalling, but I think that the junction was normally switched out post-war. The second view is looking north with an up express in the distance, and the junction box on the right, which became effectively a ground frame.

Looking back north with the war-time connection on the left.

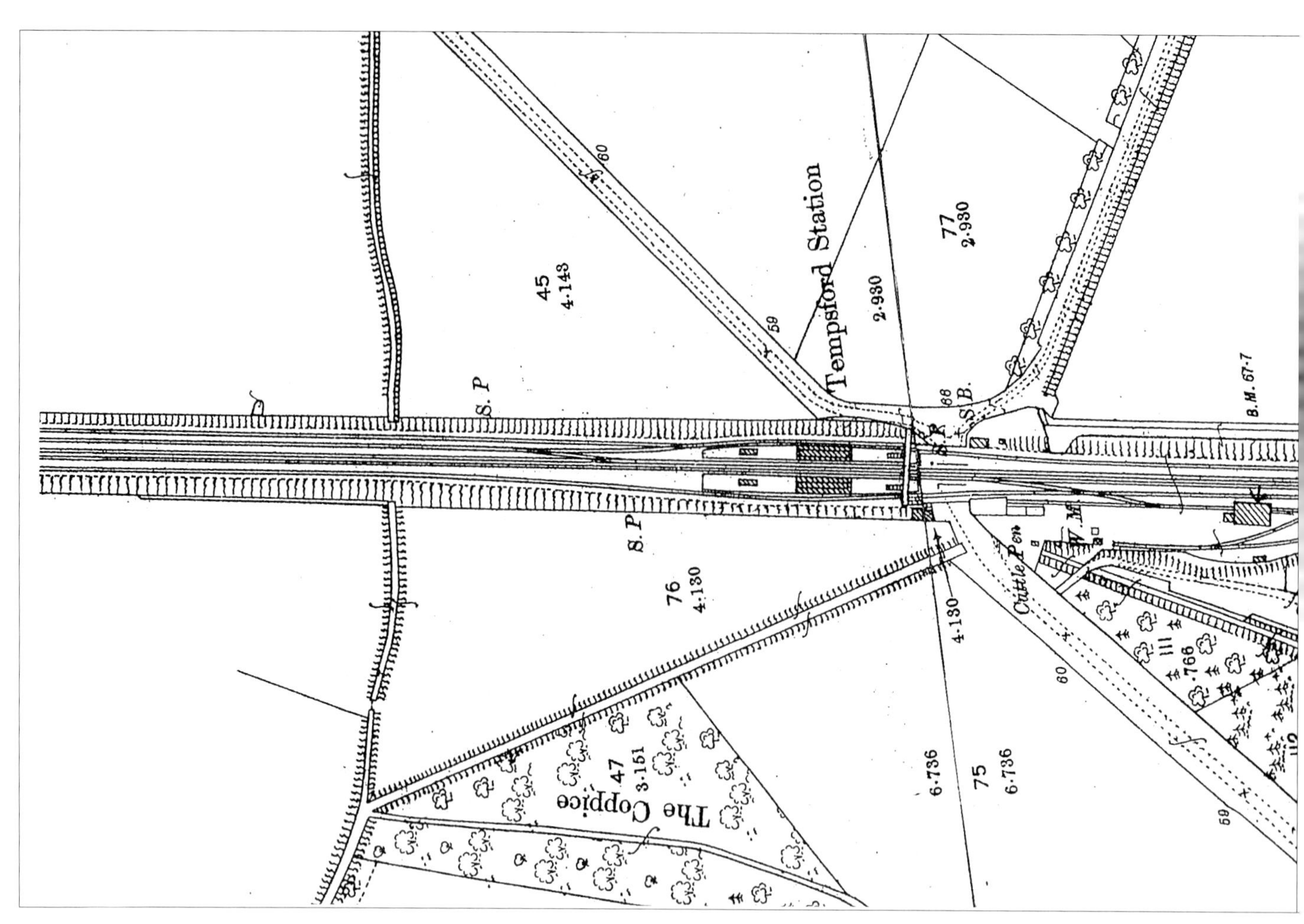

Everton level crossing lay at the foot of the long and gentle descent from Stevenage in fairly nondescript flat country. The 1957 view here is looking north, as I recall it, with an up train in the far distance.

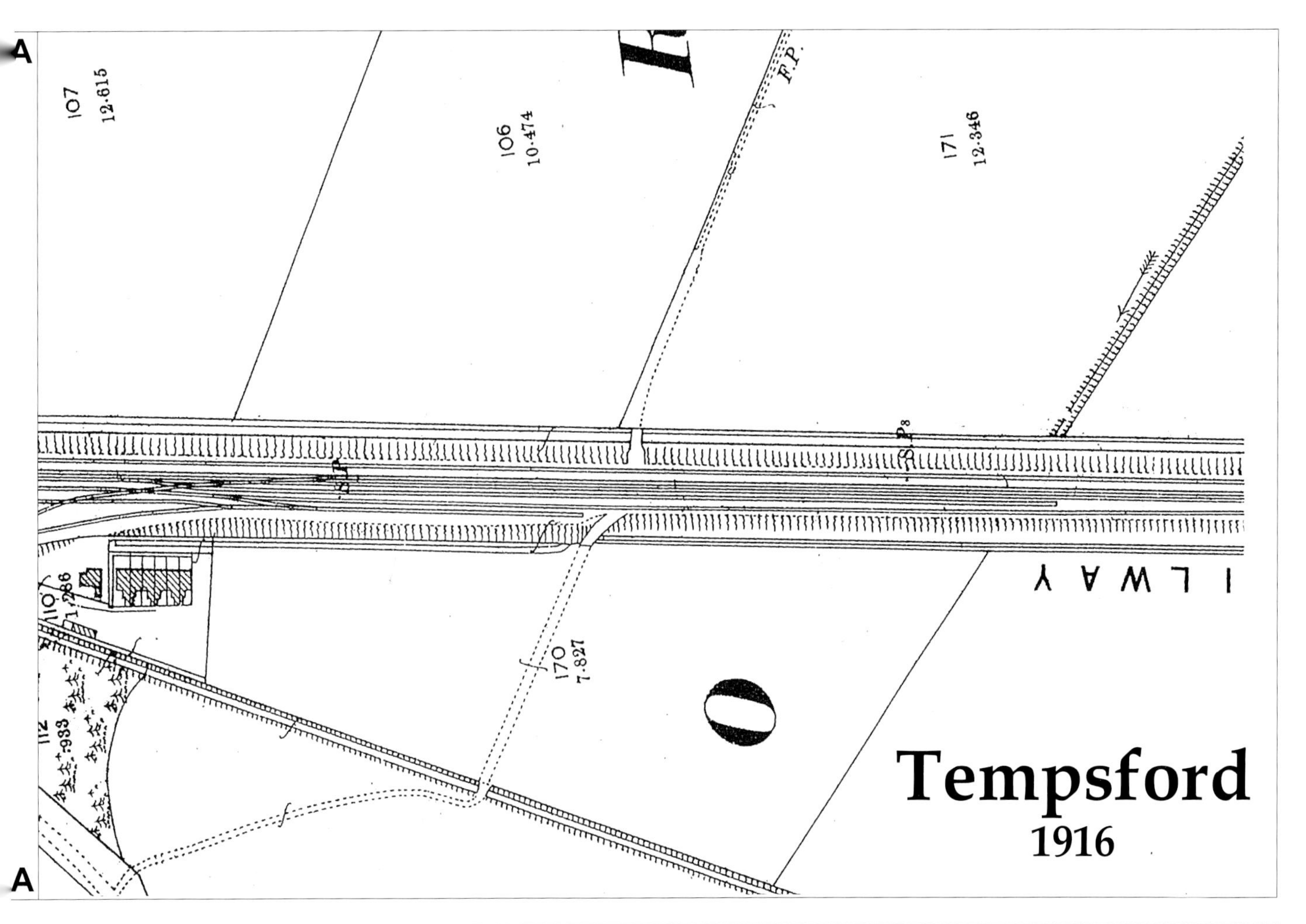

Tempsford station, looking south in 1960 with Everton footbridge in the distance. It is a typical country station with loading dock, goods shed and a small yard. The goods shed and the stationmasters house are unmistakeably standard GNR architecture. The sight of such good straight track is a treat for the permanent way engineer.

Above, below and top right. **Three views of Tempsford station in 1957. In the first general one, looking north, it is possible to see the four sets of gates, making effectively three level crossings although the gates operated together. In the second, the typical GN footbridge is well illustrated with the down slow crossing gates. The third view is of the line to the north towards Little Barford. There was a siding between the up main and slow lines for traffic waiting to be picked up by a southbound service.**

The view north from St.Neots showing the typical GN station buildings and a well-kept tidy station in 1960.

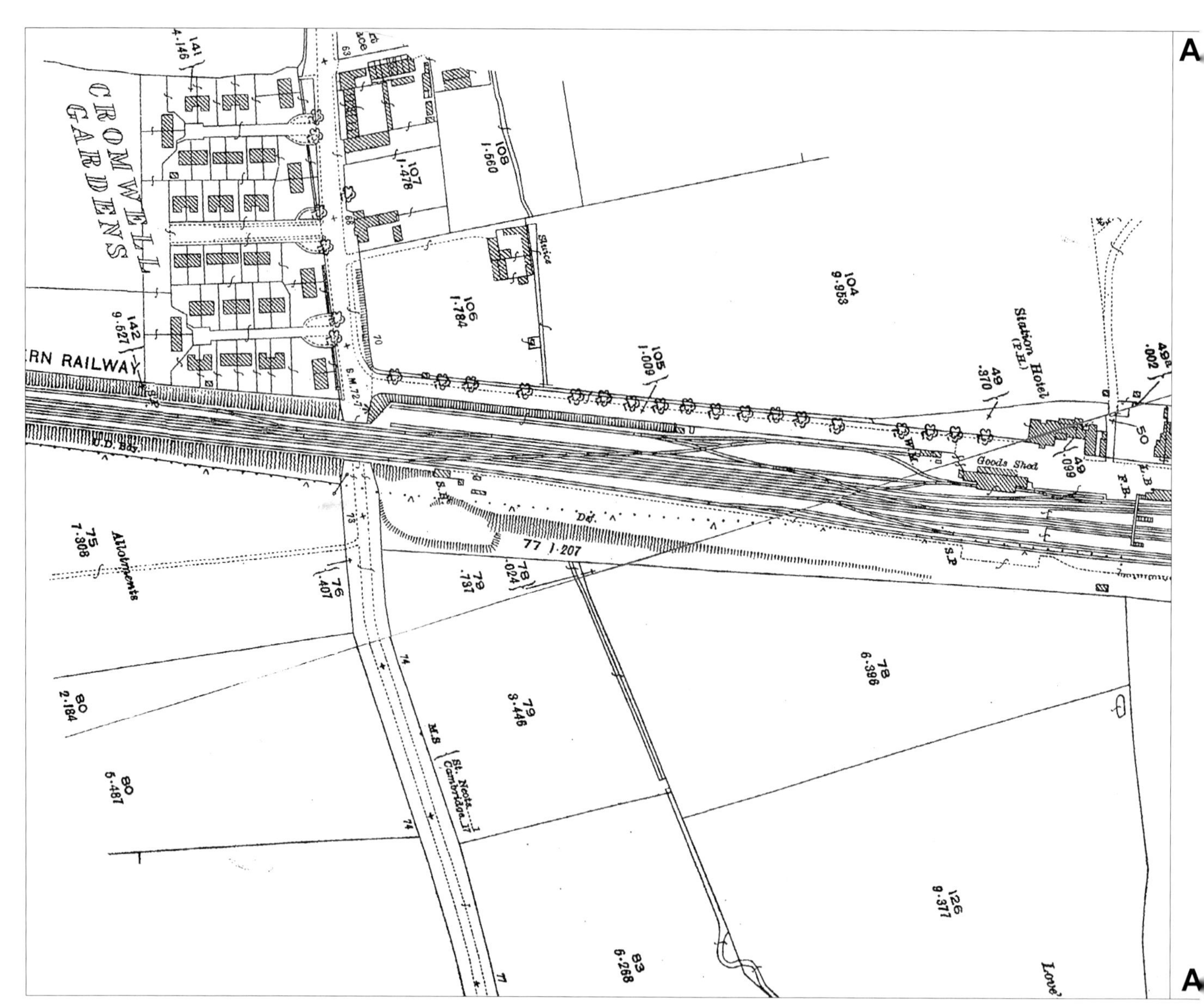

St.Neots station in 1960. The large warehouse indicates how much agricultural traffic was once carried on the railways from country stations.

St. Neots 1926

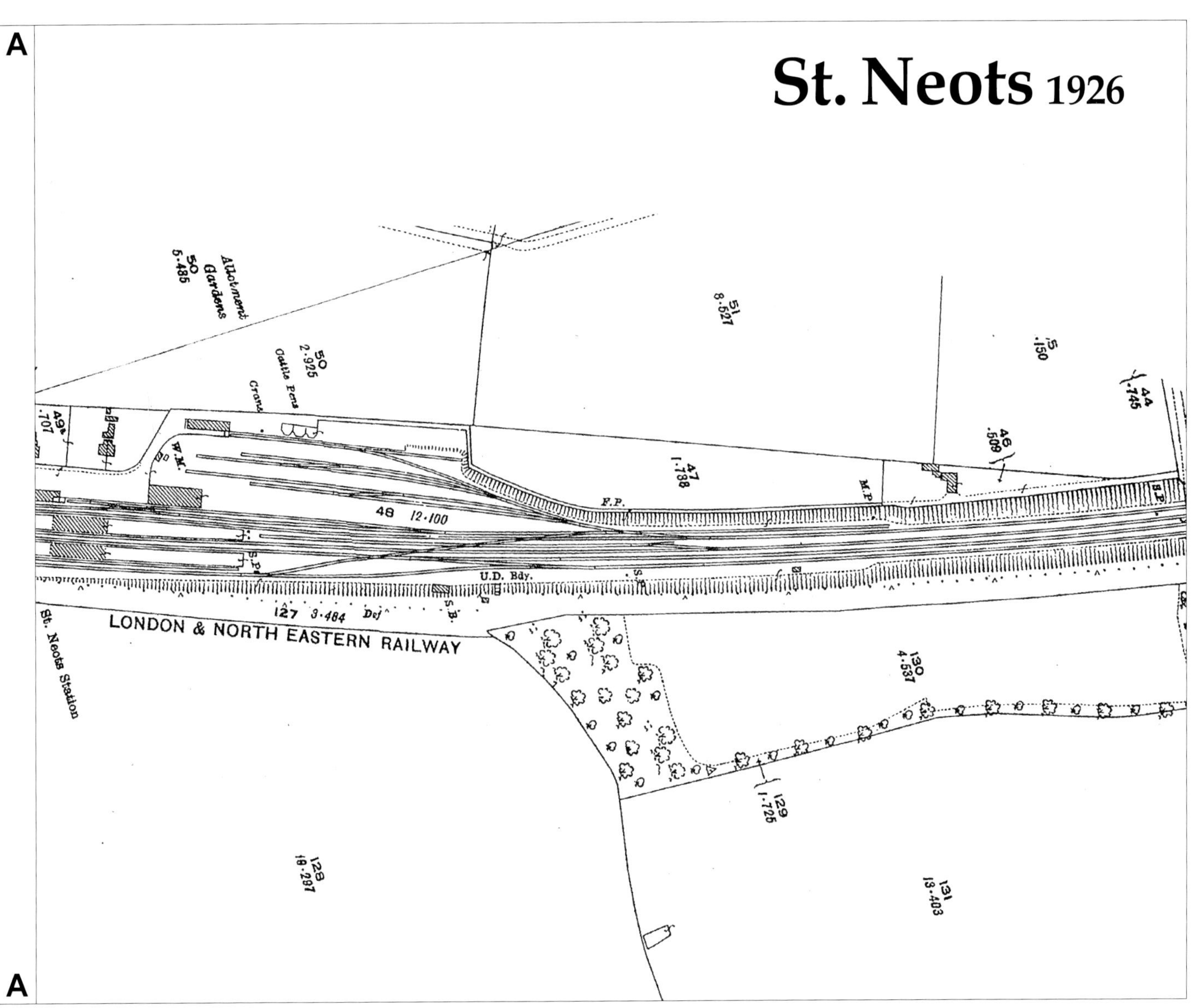

St Neots down platforms buildings in 1960. A good study of standard GN buildings and furniture. They were functional and lasted well.

A3 No.60062 MINORU with a down express at Paxton in 1961-63.

The main line at Paxton looking north with an A4 approaching on an up express. Here one can see the main line curving to the west towards the Ouse and Offord curves. From the vintage of the track fastenings and the presence of the pole route on the up side I would put the date in the early to mid-1950s.

The up Elizabethan hauled by A4 No.60031 GOLDEN PLOVER on 11th August 1958, on the Offord curves.

The up Norseman on 11th August 1958 headed by A3 No.60044 MELTON on Offord curve. The Ouse is to the left, and St.Peter's church, Offord D'Arcy is to the right.

The curves of the East Coast main line as it skirts the River Ouse between the two parish churches at Offord, south of Huntingdon. The view is southwards so the spire belongs to the second church in the parish.

Offord and Buckden station as seen from the south with the signalbox on the left.

Offord station looking north.

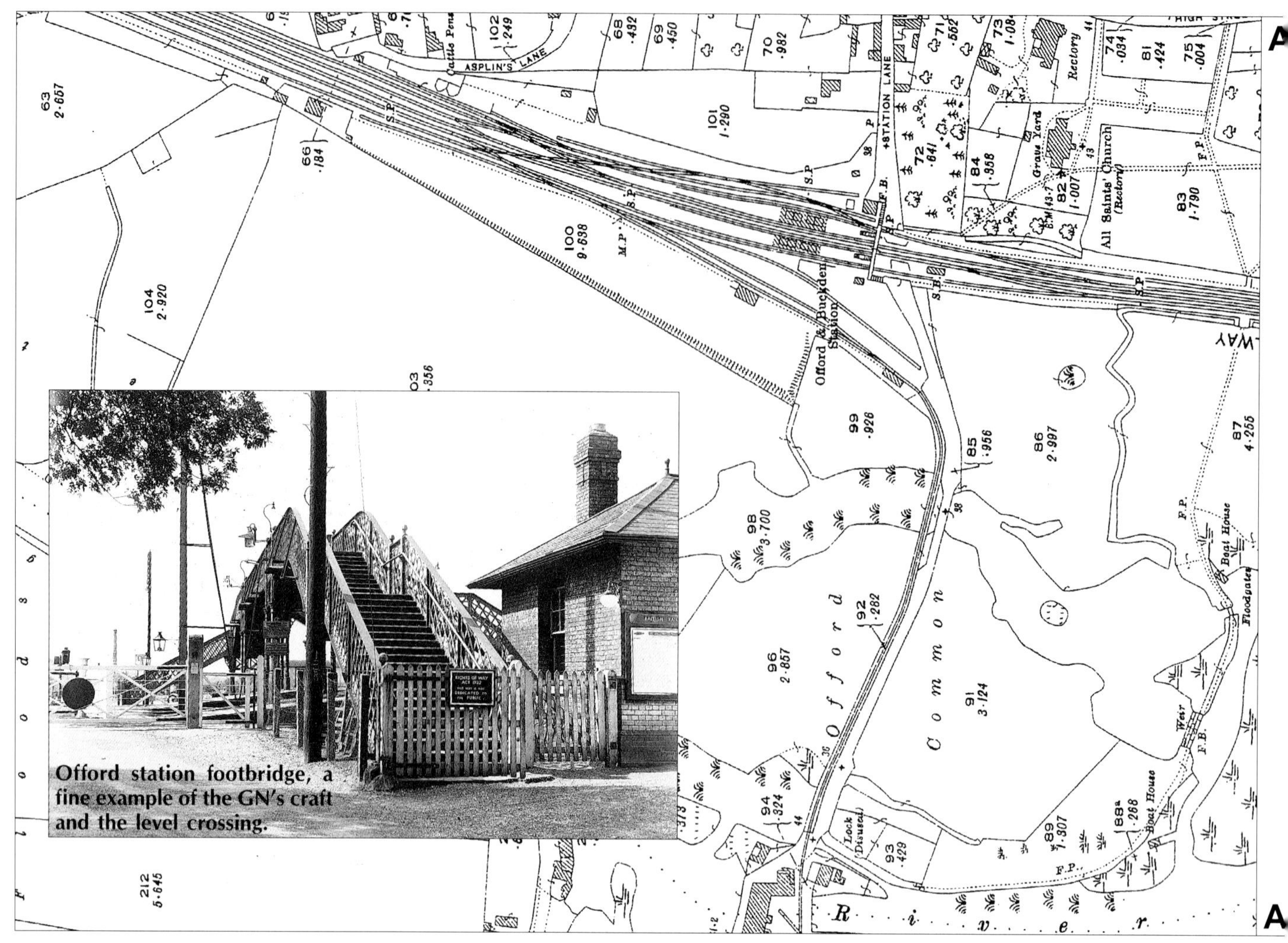

Offord station footbridge, a fine example of the GN's craft and the level crossing.

isolated box, Paxton, where the up goods reverted to up slow to St.Neots.

The next station was Offord & Buckden, on the east bank of the Great Ouse. Offord was a famous place on the GN main line, although at times infamous might have been a better description. There are two parts to Offord, Offord Cluny and Offord D'Arcy, each half with its own major buildings; church, manor house, etc, etc. D'Arcy was close to the river, Cluny was on the river bank. The fundamental problem at Offord was that the line taken by Cubitt from St.Neots went to the west of the villages of Gt.Paxton and Offord. As can be seen from the OS map, the Great Ouse swings across that line, forcing the GN main line into a narrow curved strip of land between the river and St.Peter's Church at Offord D'Arcy. A short distance beyond, as the 1926 Survey demonstrates, the river bank required some reinforcement in order to support the railway. As a result, the line had a right-hand curve reversing to left-hand and then back to right-hand. Over the years, the track was improved and the cant increased to the maximum value allowed, six inches. A PSR of 70mph was in force for the steam era but with the speed of the Deltics, it was an obstacle, and the curves were later realigned for full speed running.

Had Cubitt taken the line west, the problems would have been avoided but at the cost of extra bridgeworks crossing and recrossing the river. The OS map shows that the river had spread to two channels plus the millstream and I am surprised that there was no record of Thomas Brassey experiencing trouble during construction with soft ground in the area. Had he taken the line east of both villages, rejoining the present alignment at about the 57th milepost, the problems of curvature and bridgeworks would have been eliminated, but at the cost of more extensive earthworks through the higher land. Of course we are not taking into account the attitude of adjacent landowners, which was crucial. At Offord D'Arcy the manor house, St.Peter's Church and the princely rectory of those days were in an east-west line, the owners of which were highly unlikely to sell to the GNR.

Offord curves were a continual handicap to steam traction, especially to drivers trying to keep up speed with up expresses to charge St.Neots hump and the long haul to Stevenage beyond. The trial trip of the Silver Jubilee on September 27th 1935 nearly reached a premature end as the new A4 SILVER LINK flew through St.Neots at 104½ mph. Driver Arthur Taylor, deceived by the smooth riding of the A4, accelerated down past Paxton to 109 mph before Gresley came on to the footplate to tell him to 'ease your arm, young man!' It must have been not only a rude awakening for the driver, but a frightening experience, for he was all but 40 mph above the PSR and with little more than a mile to brake. On one occasion in the 1950s the Everett-Edgecumbe speed recorder was pressed into service to check speeds. This was a cumbersome device powered by car batteries and, knowing that it was the harbinger of bad news, it was not surprising that it should be damaged by loose lumps of coal 'falling' on it! The average speed on the curves for the down Queen of Scots Pullman over a week was 85mph, with 92mph on the Thursday. The miscreant was not driving an A4, but an A1. When the A1s were new, they rode well, as does TORNADO now, but later in their existence they could hunt badly at times on straight track, but on the curves the riding would have been excellent.

Offord station had a level crossing, and at one time a short siding went west to the substantial Buckden watermill, on the Ouse itself. The station had sidings on both sides and a yard, as befitted an important rural railhead. The more important stations handled considerable levels of agricultural traffic. Moving on north, where the GNR finally crossed the Ouse, there once was an Ouse signalbox. This was simply removed rather than replaced by an Intermediate Block. The Ouse was originally crossed by two 80ft spans, spanned by cast iron arch girders, but partly rebuilt in the 1930s with

Offord and Buckden 1920s

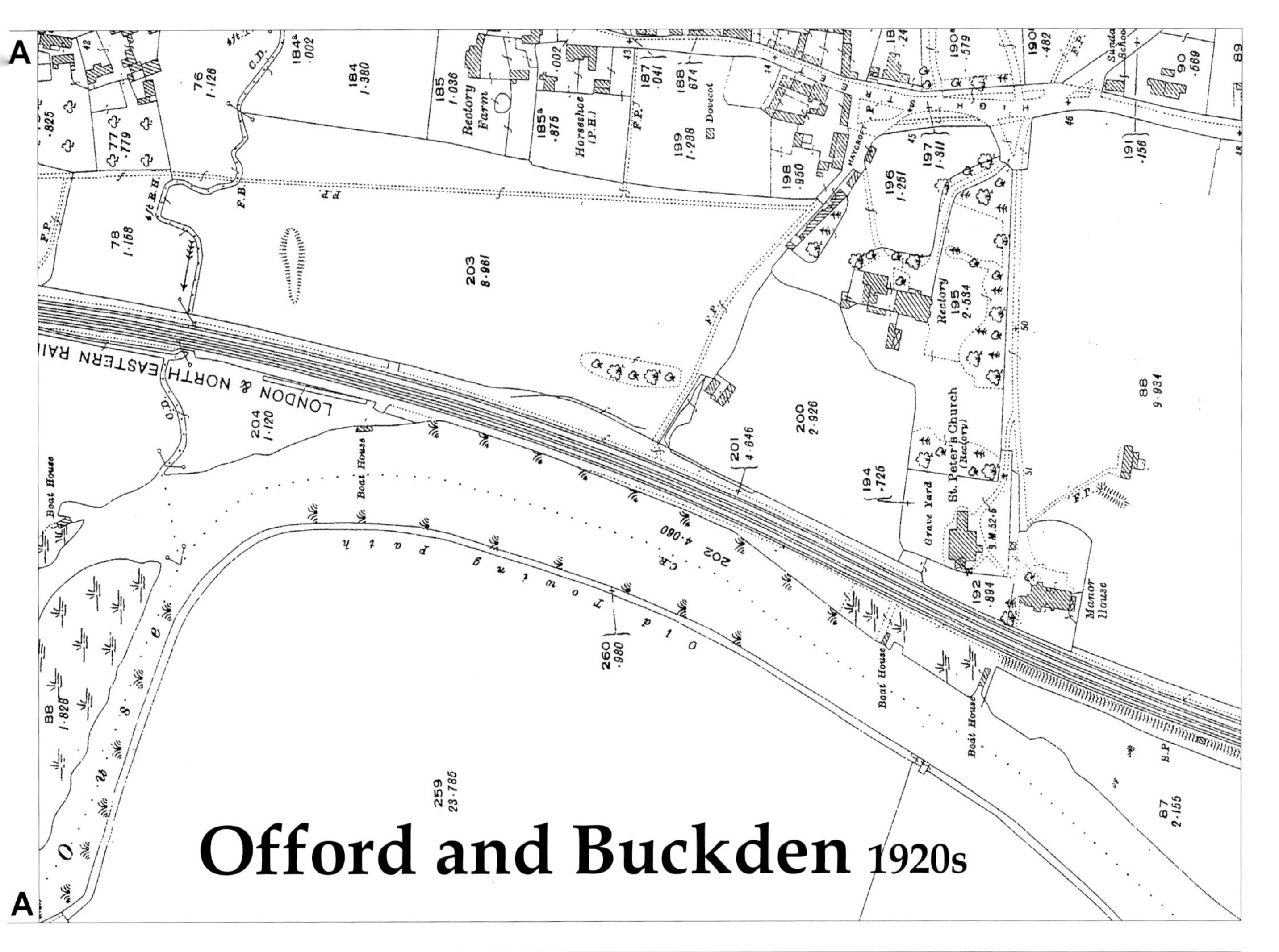

And quiet flows the Great Ouse, still. The down Queen of Scots Pullman heads north behind the usual Copley Hill A1 on 11th August 1958.

steel girders. The bridge had been subsequently widened. It was renewed again in 1958-59, a major project requiring the upgrading and change of use of the tracks to enable the bridge to be rebuilt in two parts. At the same time the up goods was extended from Leys to Huntingdon No.2. Temporary signalboxes were set up at the Ouse bridge and Wood Walton.

With the introduction of Pacifics, the bridge over the Ouse was one over which RA9 locomotives were not allowed in tandem. Normally this would have been unnecessary, but if one loco was disabled, then it became very necessary. As a result of the restriction the practice of using smaller pilot locos developed, since removing the failed locomotive was not always possible. The 1959 rebuilding, I assume, removed the weight restriction.

The next station is Huntingdon North, one of the principal stations on the route with a modest passenger business that has grown enormously in the past few decades. Huntingdon's railway history stuttered at first partly due to the poor relations with the Eastern Counties Railway, and partly due to the absence of any worthwhile traffic between St.Ives and Huntingdon. The railway actually reached St.Ives from Cambridge in 1846, then the east bank of the Ouse by 1847, all some three years before the GNR reached Huntingdon. By 1862 the east bank station, later Godmanchester station, had been connected to the GNR in 1851 and then severed. In 1866 a subsidiary of the Midland was completed from Kettering to Huntingdon, giving access to Cambridge. The Midland line passed under the main line south of the Ouse bridge, then rose to cross the Ouse parallel on the east side on its own span, continuing alongside as far as Huntingdon before turning sharply east to St.Ives and Cambridge.

This route was lightly engineered, in the same way as the Bedford branch, and the service was operated by lightweight locomotives, in later years GER E4 2-4-0s and J15 0-6-0s from Cambridge shed, while from the Kettering end the MR 2-4-0s ran their last miles, being replaced by modern Ivatt class 2MT 2-6-0s. One of the problems was the existence of timber bridgeworks over the Ouse, both as structures and substructures (supports), severely limiting line capacity. There were three to four through trains during the day, with extra services between Cambridge and Huntingdon. There was no service linking the GN directly with the route in either direction over the years. The East station had a small engine shed for one locomotive overnight. Despite the attraction to the photographers of such a rural service with its vintage traction, it was not well used and the line was closed in 1959.

Huntingdon North had three down lines, main, slow and goods, but it had only one up line. Three platform faces served the passenger lines. The main line was limited to 70mph (post-war at least) in the steam era. Again, it had a great deal of agricultural traffic, as one of the principal railheads for the rich fenland farming area. The principal road, the A14, passed by the station. The East station had three platform faces serving the down and up GNR/LNER branch to St.Ives, and the MR branch which converged to the east of the station. The 1926 OS map shows an abandoned excavation by the East engine shed that suggests that at one time it was an arm off the Ouse serving Huntingdon and Godmanchester. Huntingdon North had an extensive layout with a goods yard at the south end on the down side, and sidings on both sides of the line beyond the station. Huntingdon was quite busy with rural freight, and on the main line it was the practice to shunt the various goods yards from Hitchin and work the freight forward to concentrate loads for picking up at, for example, Sandy, Biggleswade, St.Neots or Huntingdon. Huntingdon had one engine from Cambridge shunting at both stations and stabled at the East station shed. Another reached the GN North station, working down from Hitchin. The Cambridge loco was a J15 in the 1950s, usually one with a tender cab for working tender first, usually No.65451 in my experience.

Huntingdon North station from the down platform looking north. The down main, in the foreground, has been prepared for measured shovel packing in order to correct the cross levels.

Huntingdon station from the down platform looking north.

The up platform taken from the same position.

Huntingdon 1932

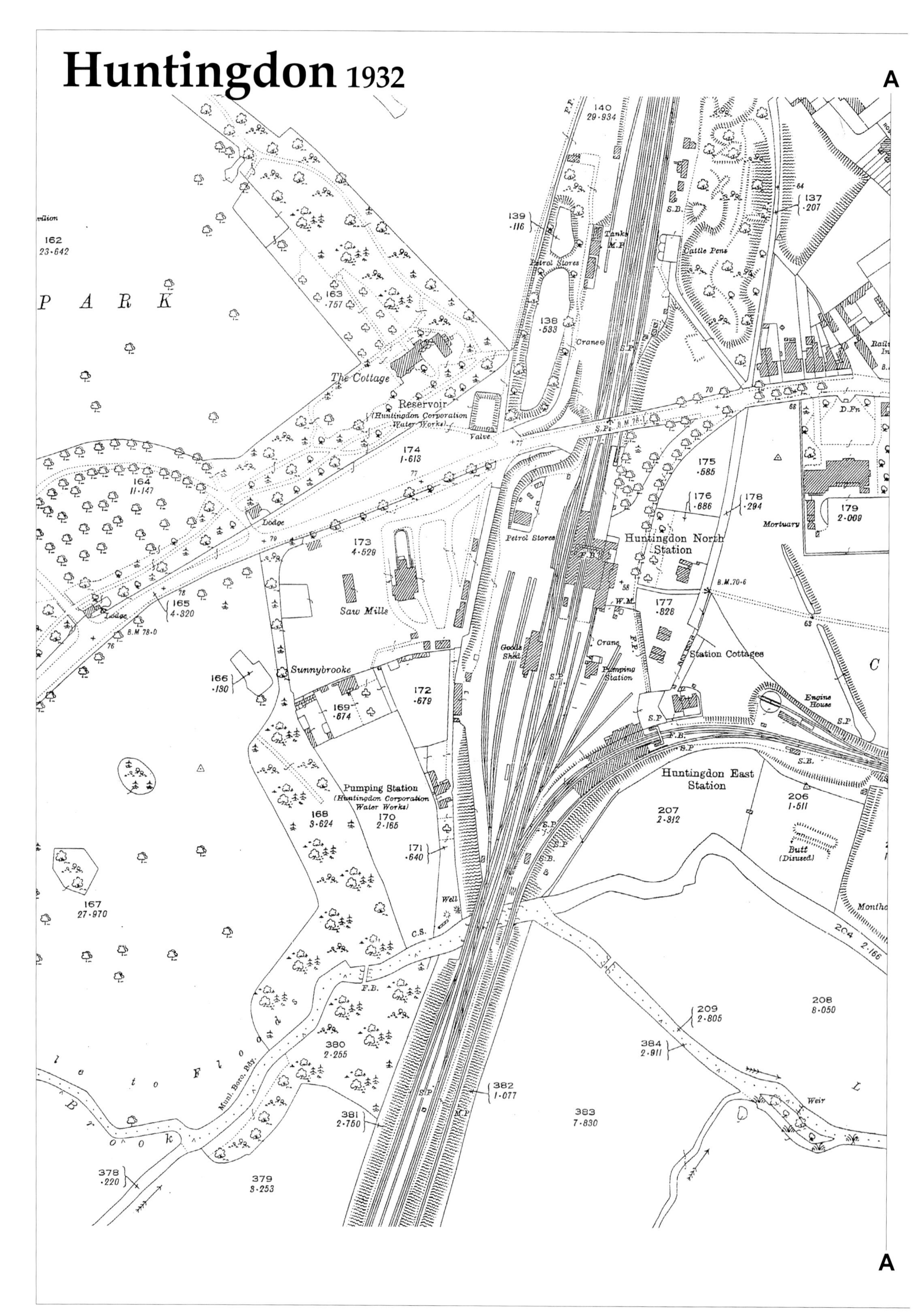

A

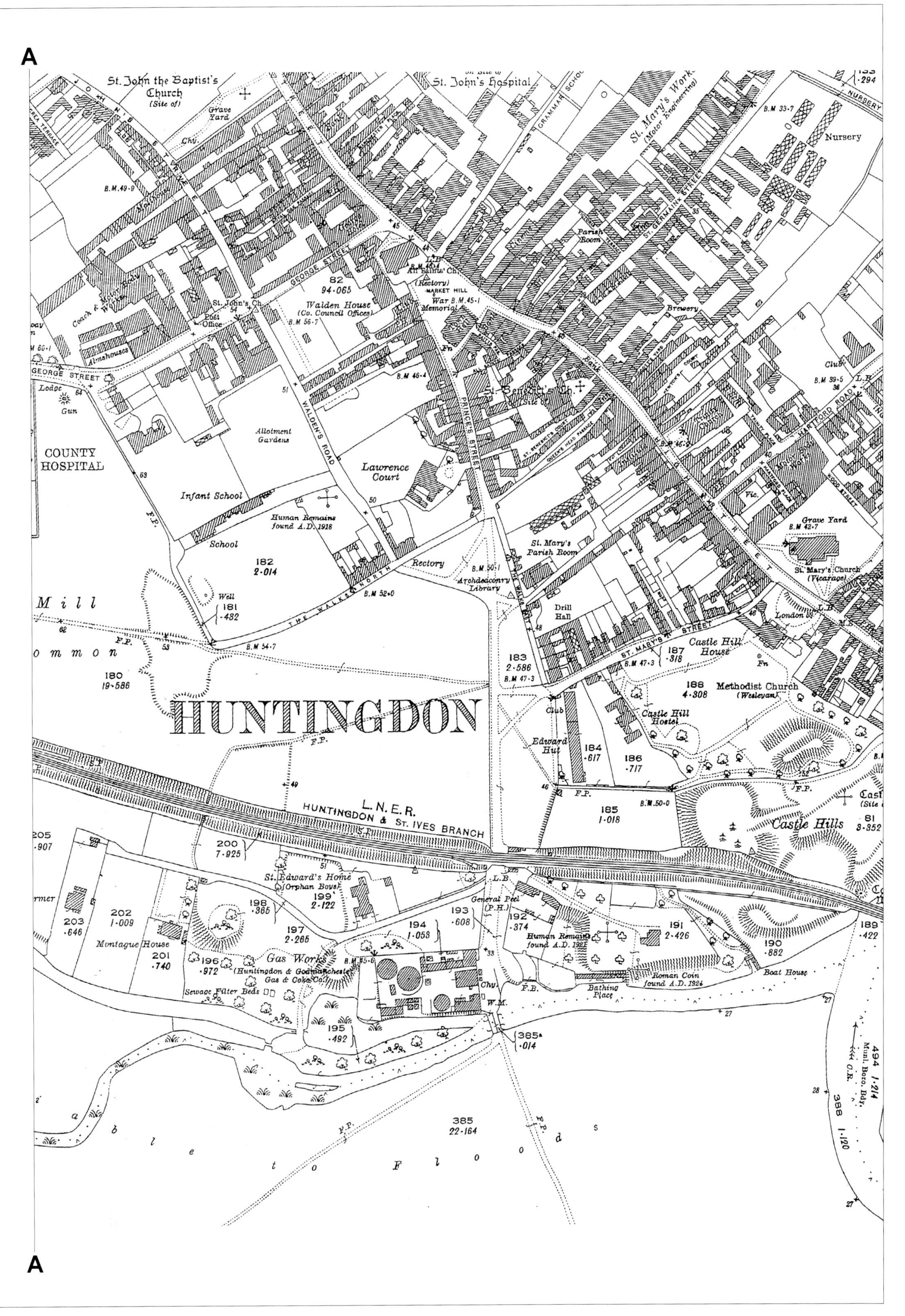
St. John the Baptist's Church (Site of)
Grave Yard
St. John's Hospital
Grammar School
St. Mary's Works (Motor Engineering)
Nursery
Parish Room
St. Germain Street
George Street
All Saints' Ch.
(Rectory)
Market Hill
War Memorial
Walden House (Co. Council Offices)
St. John's Ch.
Post Office
Coach & Motor Body Works
Almshouses
George Street
Lodge
Gun
COUNTY HOSPITAL
Brewery
Club
Hartford Road
St. Benedict's Ch. (Site of)
Allotment Gardens
Walden's Road
Prince's Street
Lawrence Court
Infant School
Human Remains found A.D. 1918
School
Rectory
Archdeaconry Library
The Walks North
St. Mary's Parish Room
Drill Hall
Grave Yard
St. Mary's Church (Vicarage)
Mill Common
Well
St. Mary's Street
Castle Hill House
Methodist Church (Wesleyan)
Castle Hill Hostel
HUNTINGDON
Club
Edward Hut
L.N.E.R.
HUNTINGDON & ST. IVES BRANCH
Castle Hills
St. Edward's Home (Orphan Boys)
General Peel (P.H.)
Human Remains found A.D. 1922
Montague House
Gas Works (Huntingdon & Godmanchester Gas & Coke Co.)
Sewage Filter Beds
Bathing Place
Roman Coin found A.D. 1924
Boat House
Mun. Boro. Bdy.
Fable of Floods

A

Huntingdon North. I am no historian but the left hand building has an original look about it. Perhaps the main entrance was a susequent addition.

The up platform at the northern end showing what was once the stationmasters house.

Huntingdon North, south end.

Looking north - I hope the photographer had a look out!

Abbots Ripton station in 1959 seen from the small goods yard on the down side at the south end. The up platform is in the distance, and the down is beyond the footbridge. The station was closed in 1958 and is being dismantled. The old signal box is on the up platform, whilst its replacement is on the down side.

CHAPTER FOURTEEN

Huntingdon-Peterborough

North of Huntingdon the land rises some 90ft, and for three miles the line climbed at 1 in 200 to the 62nd milepost at Leys, then levelling out to the station at Abbots Ripton. There were two intermediate signalboxes, at Stukeley and Leys, on the up side, but the latter was removed and control of the turnout transferred to the former using remote power operation. The descent for up expresses from Leys would have given steam locomotives valuable impetus for the long haul to Stevenage, but for PSRs at Huntingdon and Offord curves. Just before Abbots Ripton station the downgrade to the Fens at Connington commences. This was another fast section as far as Holme; indeed farther for some more colourful characters in steam days.

The station at Abbots Ripton was located at the end of a deep cutting, and had two staggered island platforms, with only the down main having a platform face. The passenger service was almost non-existent. The additional tracks were both goods lines, extending to Connington North on the down and Connington South on the up. Connington was on the southern edge of an arm of the Fens that extended westwards to the A1 road. Over the decades a large tip built up on the east side, and for many years there was an accumulation of spoil wagons and locomotives at Connington. The signalbox at Wood Walton was eliminated, and that at Connington South was rebuilt. It had an up yard and a small down yard, and tipping of spoil and waste was carried out on both sides. The down yard was considerably enlarged during the 1939-45 war to relieve New England at Peterborough and a new signalbox, Connington North, was constructed.

Abbots Ripton, like Welwyn, was the scene of a bad accident (in 1876) which had a subsequent impact on railway signalling. Briefly, railways were operated on the time interval system until 1872, when block signalling was brought into force – in theory. In practice it took a time to be adopted in full. Also at the time telegraph instruments were coming into use in the more important signalboxes. The GNR adopted the new block system, using the 'open block' philosophy as distinct from the 'closed block' used later. The signals stood clear until a train passed, after which they were set to danger until the 'train out of section' bell signal was received. Originally with the time interval system, the signals were cleared after a set period of time. The signals were then cleared despite no following train being expected. *So far as I understand it*, there was no system of offering the train forward and the box in advance accepting, as with the closed system. As the trains passed each box they were notified to the box in advance as 'on line', and 'out of section' to the rear. The only means of refusing was to send 'obstruction, danger', which was probably an entirely accurate description.

The old lower quadrant signals worked in a slotted post to give three positions – horizontal (danger), 45 degrees (caution) and vertical within the slotted post (clear), and the arms were not counterbalanced, so that in the much colder winters of those days, signals could easily become clogged and then frozen in position, usually clear. The situation was aggravated further by poor communications. The result was that while an up coal train was shunting clear at Abbots Ripton, the up Flying Scotsman collided with the coal train. The following up express stopped clear, but the wreck was hit by the 17.30 down Newcastle express, unable to stop in time. The principal result was the redesign of semaphore signals used by the GNR, the genesis of the famous somersault signal. A linkage rotated the arm at its centre, and moved the spectacle plate in front of the lamp, the

Abbots Ripton in 1959, from the up side.

Abbots Ripton 1926

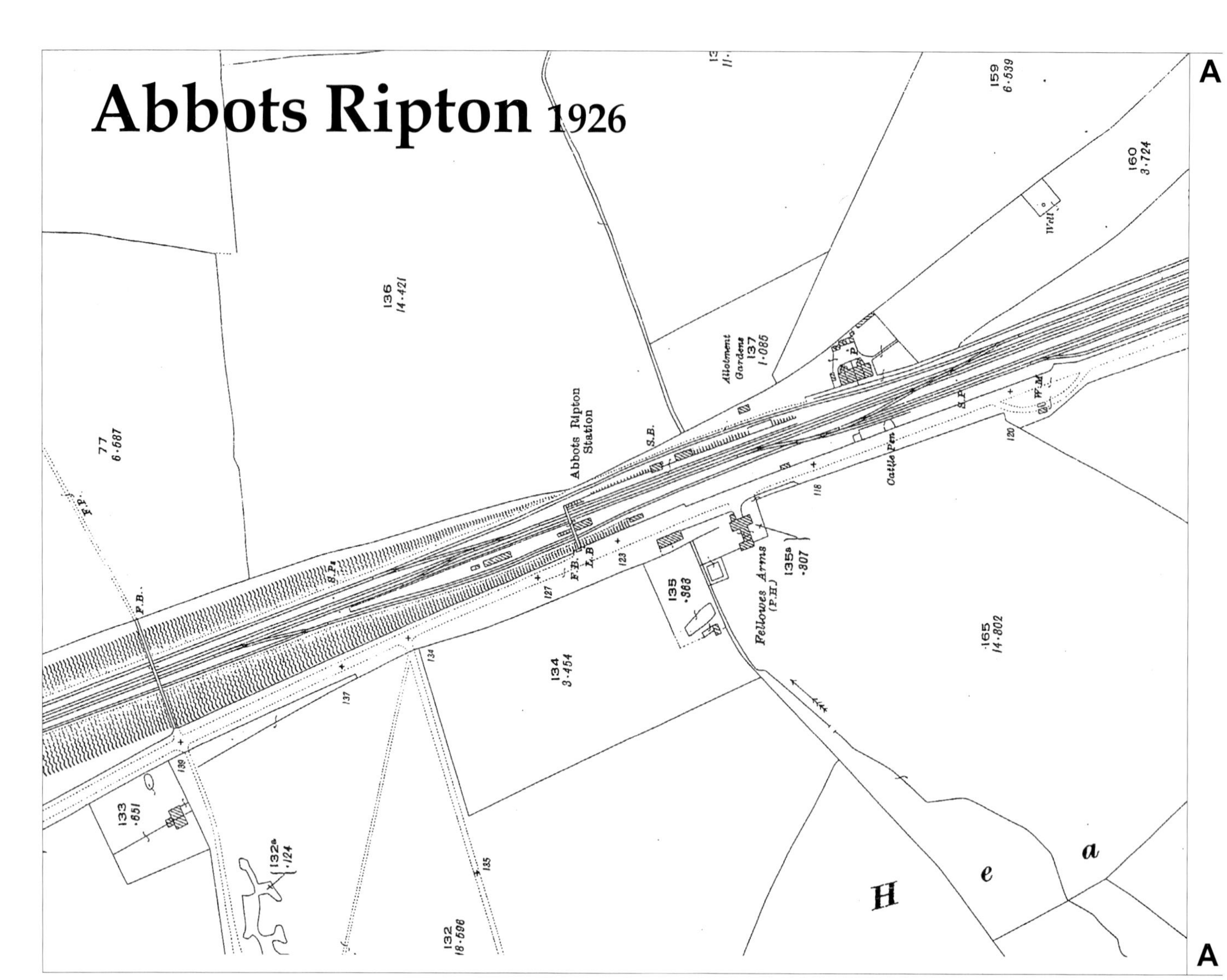

Abbots Ripton, from the footbridge to the north in 1959.

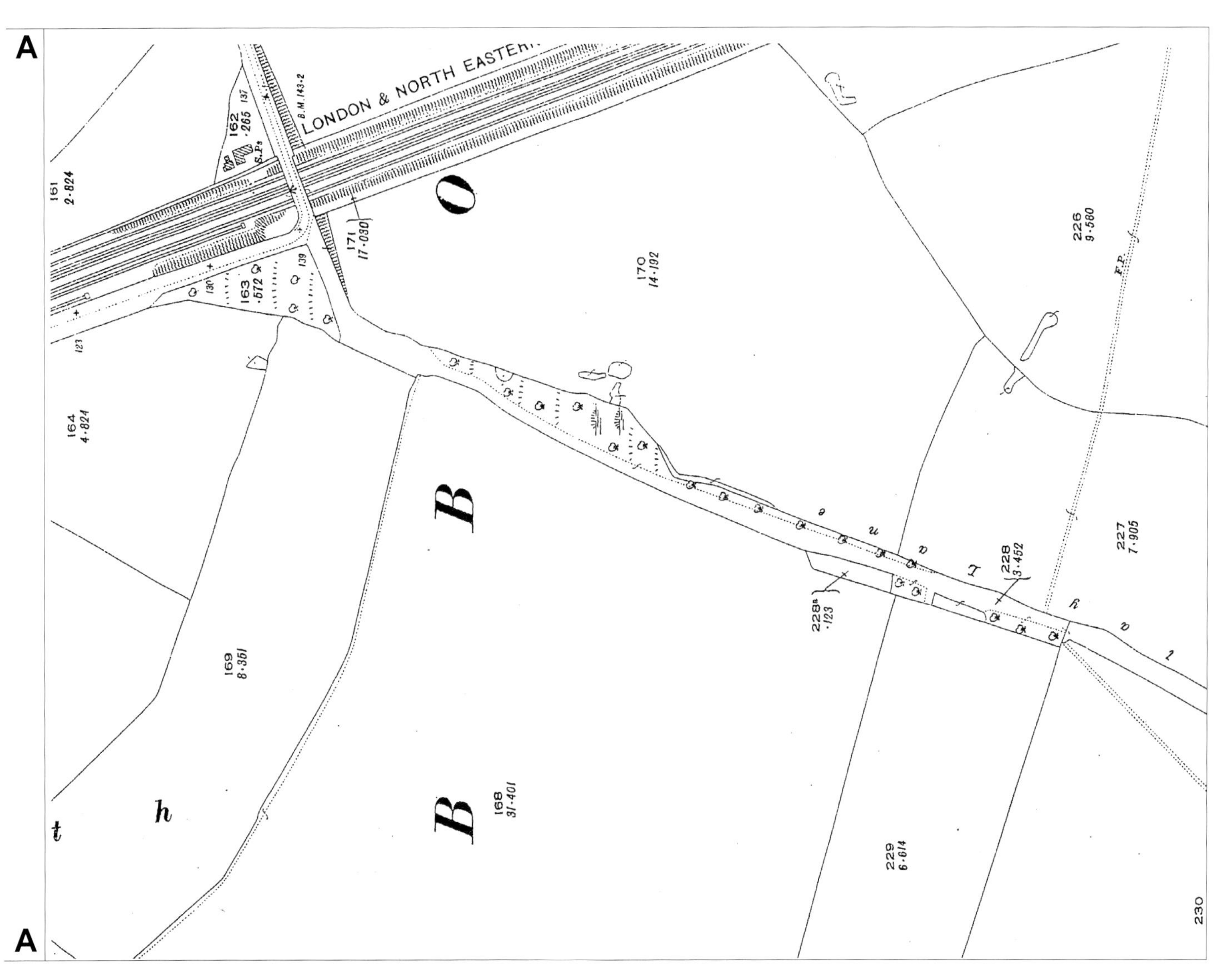

This is an earlier view, now from the station footbridge in 1948, looking north. An A4, working hard, breasts the top of the bank from Connington with a London express.

The replacement signal box at Abbots Ripton. It was an unusual design, constrained by the track layout. Interestingly there are no rodding runs where one might expect them, suggesting that the goods yard was out of use or on hand points by then.

whole assembly being counterbalanced. They worked perfectly well in service and it was regrettable that they should have been gradually superseded in BR days. Interestingly, the introduction of track circuit block with IBS, automatic sections and later, power box operation, reverted to open block for some areas with the green aspect displayed once the train had cleared two (three aspect) or three (four aspect) blocks.

Wood Walton was re-established as a temporary block post in the late 1950s in connection with several works, mainly the renewal of the Ouse Bridge at Huntingdon, but also the extension of the up goods to Huntingdon already referred to, together with some lengthy sections of formation renewal. The latter was an extremely important, if expensive treatment, necessitated by the failure or absence of working track drainage. Such sections tended to be founded on clay or alluvial deposits, which made them prone to deterioration from water not draining away quickly. Good track drainage was and is an essential for good maintenance, an imperative for high speed track. Perversely, it is the near-level fast sections that can suffer from poor drainage. The water affects the ground beneath, reducing the bearing capacity, which causes the track to sink. Life being what it is, the track never sinks uniformly or equally, and for decades if not a century or more, the railways had a device that was very effective in locating poor track. It was called the short wheelbase wagon. At speeds of 35mph or more, a rogue short wheelbase wagon would start to hunt violently as referred to earlier, and with the introduction of powerful diesel traction with a warm and insulated cab, the translation of the guard to the rear cab and the removal of railjoints, many a mile of track was destroyed as a result.

It was at Connington in the early 1960s that a signalman, for some reason bordering on lunacy, tried to pull and reverse points between the bogies of a coach on a passing passenger train, and precipitated a major derailment. Of course the interlocking would prevent any such possibility, but it was possible with mechanical signalling to insert a thin carving knife blade and lift the point locks, releasing the point lever. The discipline in mechanical signalboxes was quite severe, as anything that could distract the signalman or be used for illicit purposes was not allowed, and Signals Inspectors in the old days were quick to confiscate blades of this sort. From here at the North box through Holme to the 71½ milepost the line is level across the Fens, before starting to rise to anticipate the higher ground at Yaxley. This section had, and still has two tracks only. The lowland rivers that form the drainage system are slow flowing. A branch off New Dyke, part of that Fenland basin, came in from the east, south of Holme station, complete with towpath. From its alignment, running for roughly half a mile parallel to the GNR to a wharf south of the station, it seems very likely that its construction was connected with the coming of the railway. Transport in the Fens in the mid 19th century was easier on the water than on the roads of the time, and there was an exchange of agricultural traffic at Holme. Some of the materials for crossing the Fen probably were delivered by barge. The station at Holme had a level crossing, and the up bay platform was used by the branch train to Ramsey. The branch, opened in 1863, must have attracted considerable rural freight traffic, for the fenland is rich farming. The branch was worked by smaller 0-6-0s from New England; it closed soon after the 1939-45 war to passengers, but then survived for freight into the diesel era before complete

The down main platform at Abbots Ripton with the down goods behind, and a typical length of GN/LNER close boarded fencing with a battlemented top profile.

Earthworks are in progress and pre cast concrete drainage units line the up platform. The up side coping slabs have been removed prior to removal of the up platform itself.

Holme 1926

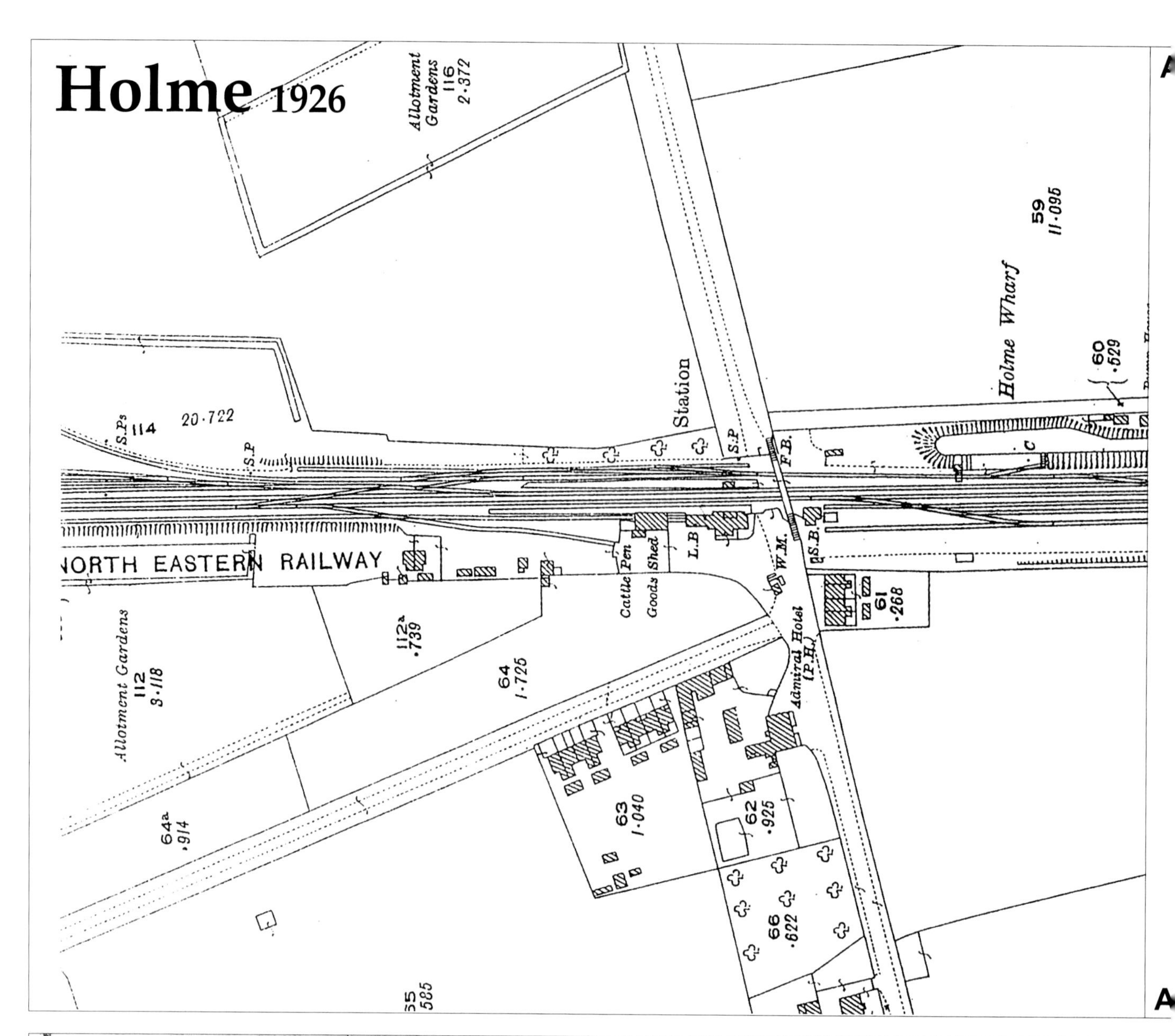

Holme station from the south. The Ramsey branch is in the foreground. The footbridge appears to be a simple lattice replacement for the earlier structure.

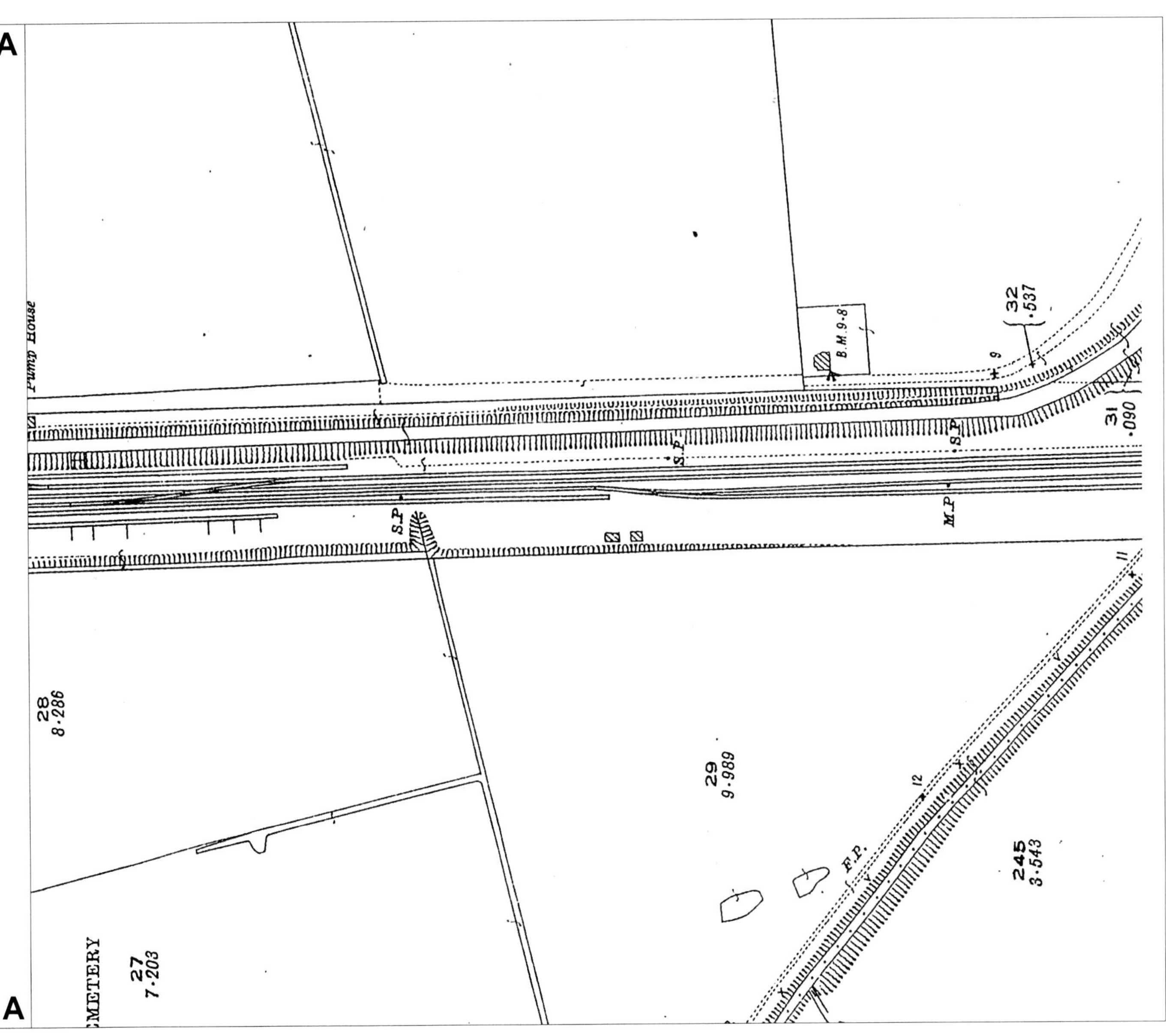

North of Yaxley at milepost 74¼, an aerial cable route connected the down side brickworks with the clay pits on the up side. A structure beneath protected the railway and its passing trains from spillage or worse; that is, until it was examined more closely in the 1960s and condemned as a result.

The brick industry used rope haulage to link their works with the claypits in decades long since passed. A continuous rope ran between pulley wheels at each end of the transit, with wagons attached at intervals loaded with brickmaking clay, providing a continuous supply to the kilns. A typical wagon is shown here. The system was usually in a state that defied the imagination as to how it actually functioned at all. The ubiquitous tipper lorry replaced such systems. Here the ropeway and its associated pathway appear to be crossing the main line, probably somewhere between Yaxley and Fletton, which is as near as I can place it.

A typical LNER replacement siganal box at Connington North, a brick structure with reinforced concrete roof and staircase. This box was built during the Second World War when rubbish dumps were established locally and sidings laid for for wagons to bring rubble from the London bombing.

Typical LNER standard upper quadrant signals at Connington. These replaced the famous GNR somersault signals from the 1930s onwards.

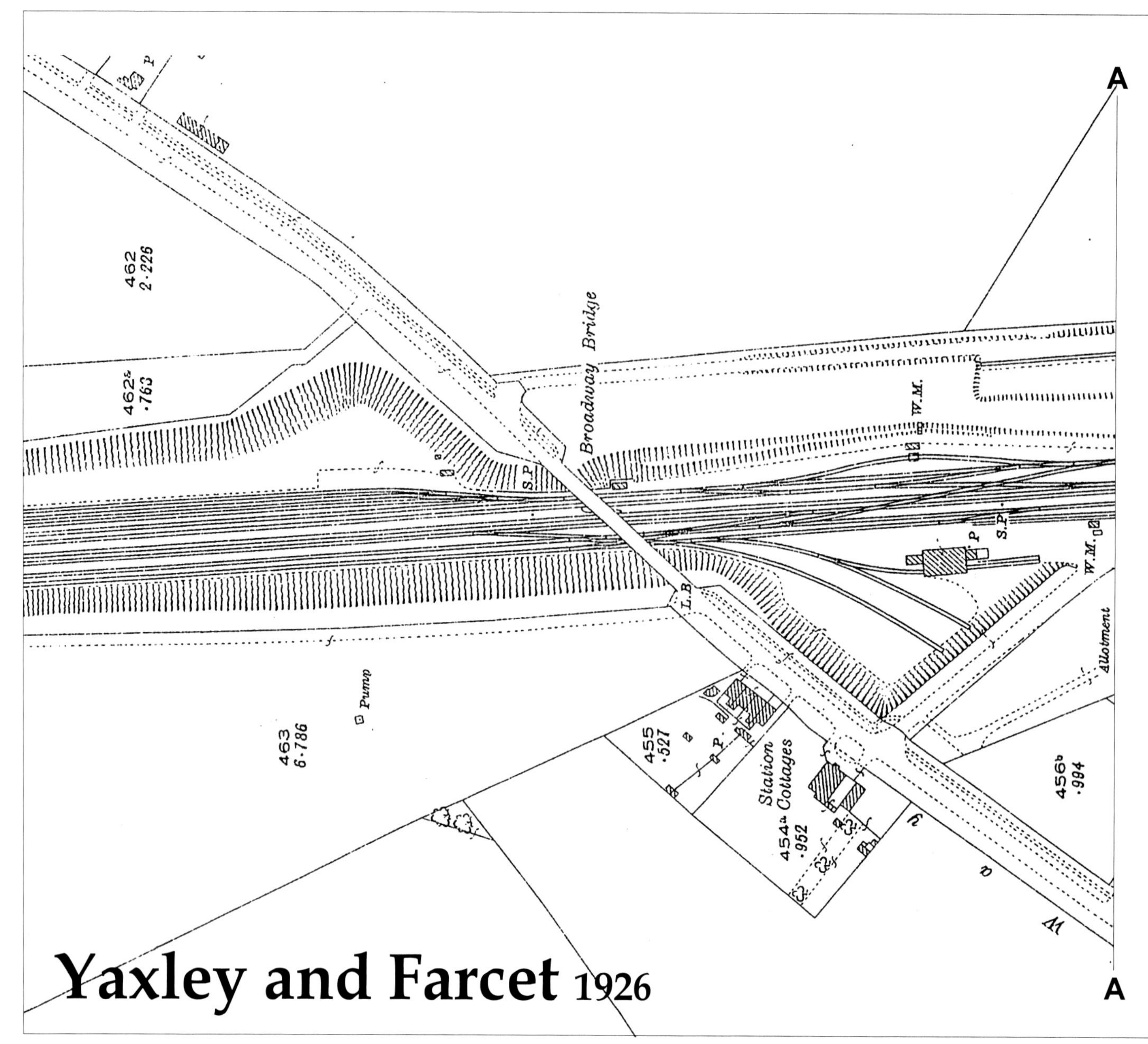

Yaxley and Farcet 1926

closure in 1973. The passenger service in later years was worked by GNR C12 4-4-2Ts from New England, or occasionally one of their J6 0-6-0s. Crossing the Fens cannot have been easy for Cubitt and Brassey. The latter had engaged the services of Stephen Ballard, an engineer with fenland experience. There are some 4-5 miles in which the ground was extremely soft and wet and the water table was virtually at ground level. In places the land was little better than a bog, very different from the well-tended and drained farmland one sees today. Load-bearing strata in the area such as gravel or hard silt were deep, at well over 100ft, impossibly so in the middle 1800s. The technique developed by Stephenson at Chat Moss, and probably borrowed from the army, was to cut a trench to the width of the railway, and fill it with a layer of brushwood. From descriptions of either site, it would seem that Stilton Fen was rather more difficult. Ballard's advice was to use what is known in the army as fascines, or faggots, which were similar but had heavier branches. He was an entrepreneur before his time, and since he realised that the demand for a large amount of faggot wood would inevitably cause the price to rise, he bought up as much as he could before the word got about!

In structural terms, it was an exercise in spreading the applied and dead load of the railway over a sufficiently wide area until the bearing capacity of the ground would support it. The bundles of branches, tightly secured, were laid across the trench, with another interlocking layer laid parallel, at right angles. Then a layer of peat, and a further layer of fascines. This continued until the road thus formed was capable of bearing weight, and soil and ash were then laid. As the road grew firmer, heavier layers of soil were used. All the while the layers would have been compressed and forced further and further into the ground by the weight of the soil above, driving out the ground water. The process was continued until a stable condition was reached in which the roadway was judged to be able to take the weight of the permanent way and trains. Bridges would have been built across the numerous waterways as the first few layers were placed. Perhaps Ballard's legacy was the number of silver birch trees lining the railway along this section in later years.

The section beyond Holme was always known as Stilton Fen or Whittlesea Mere, more often the former in more recent times. There was a signalbox known as Stilton Fen at one time, but it was replaced by a 1930s IBS scheme. It was a section where the normal '6ft' between the tracks was increased so as to spread the weight of trains over a larger area. It had a speed restriction of 65mph for many years with steam traction, not least because of the tendency of steam locomotives, carrying large volumes of water as they did, to lurch from one rail to the other, as well as exerting hammer blows. With the 'top' on such sections being much more variable, the lurching would have been worse. Again, the TSR was one observed in the breach rather than the rule. Bill Hoole told me that

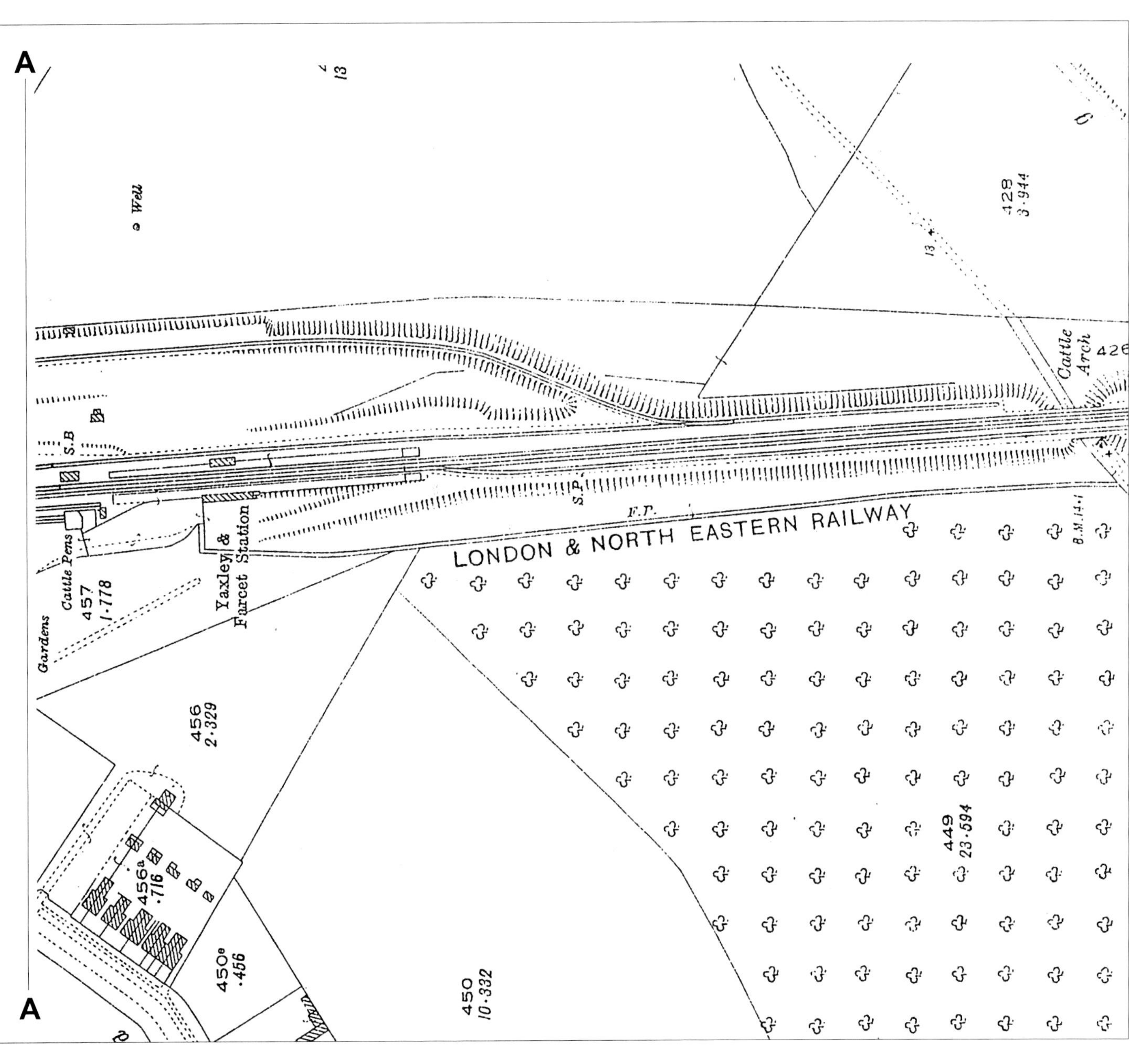

Yaxley and Farcet station, at the end of 1963 and shortly before demolition, it is presumed. View from the up side south end; the simple building was on the down platform, with the overbridge north of the station. It was closed in April 1959 and the up platform has already been removed as part of the track improvements. The down platform and walls have also been removed.

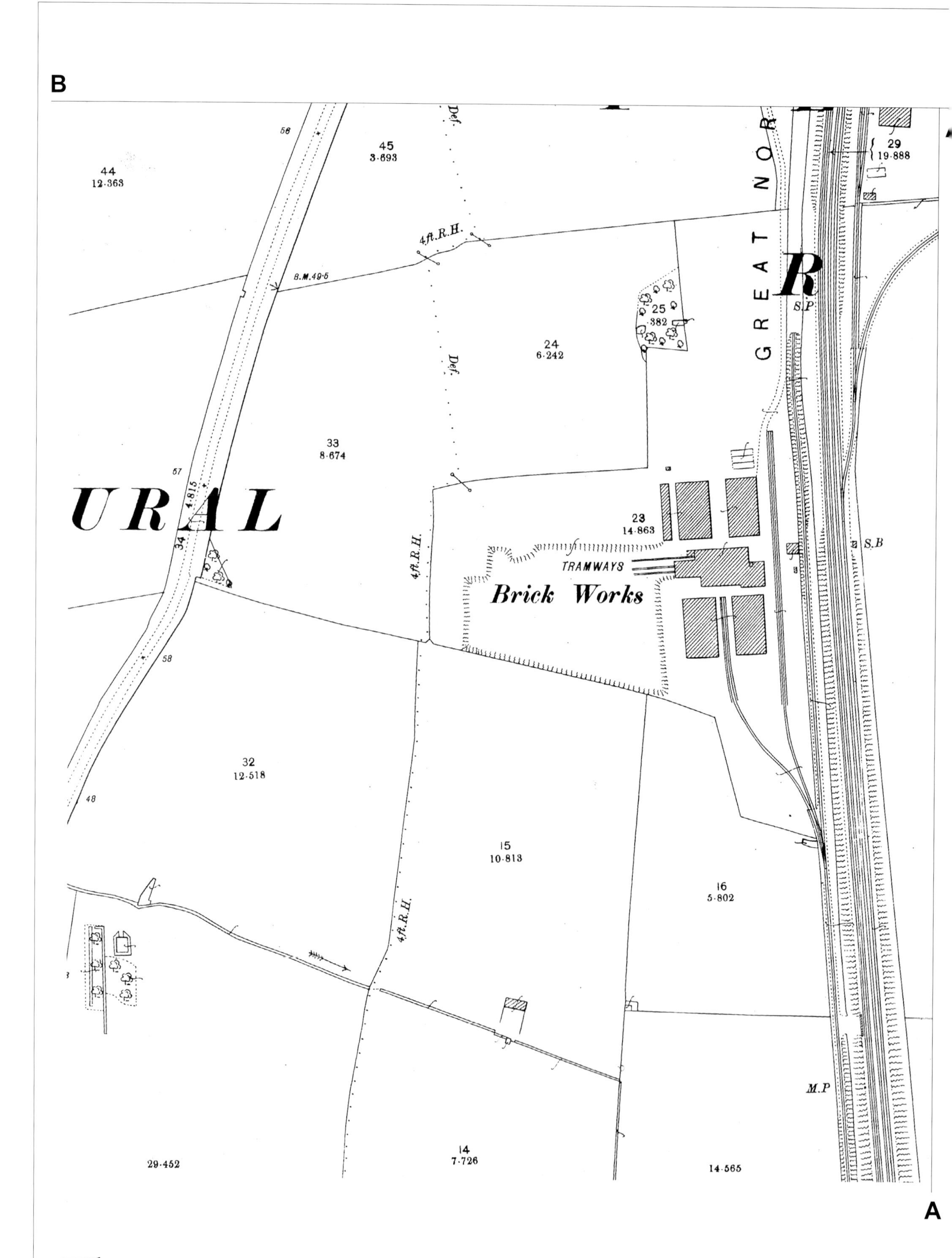
B
44
12·363
45
3·693
Def.
4ft.R.H.
B.M.49·5
25
·382
24
6·242
GREAT NOR
R
S.P
29
19·888
33
8·674
URAL
23
14·863
TRAMWAYS
Brick Works
S.B
32
12·518
15
10·813
16
5·802
M.P
29·452
14
7·726
14·565
A

Fletton

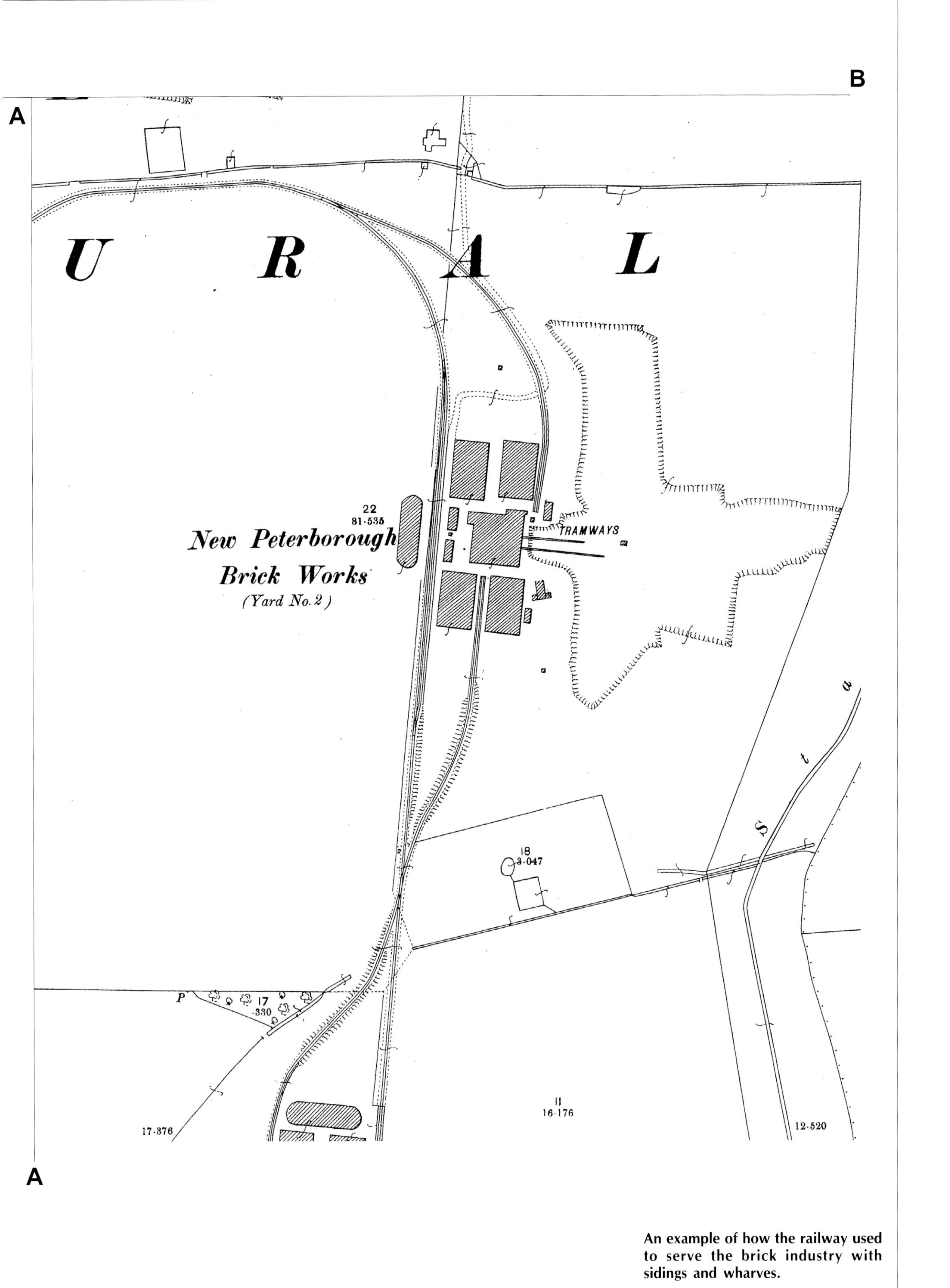

An example of how the railway used to serve the brick industry with sidings and wharves.

C

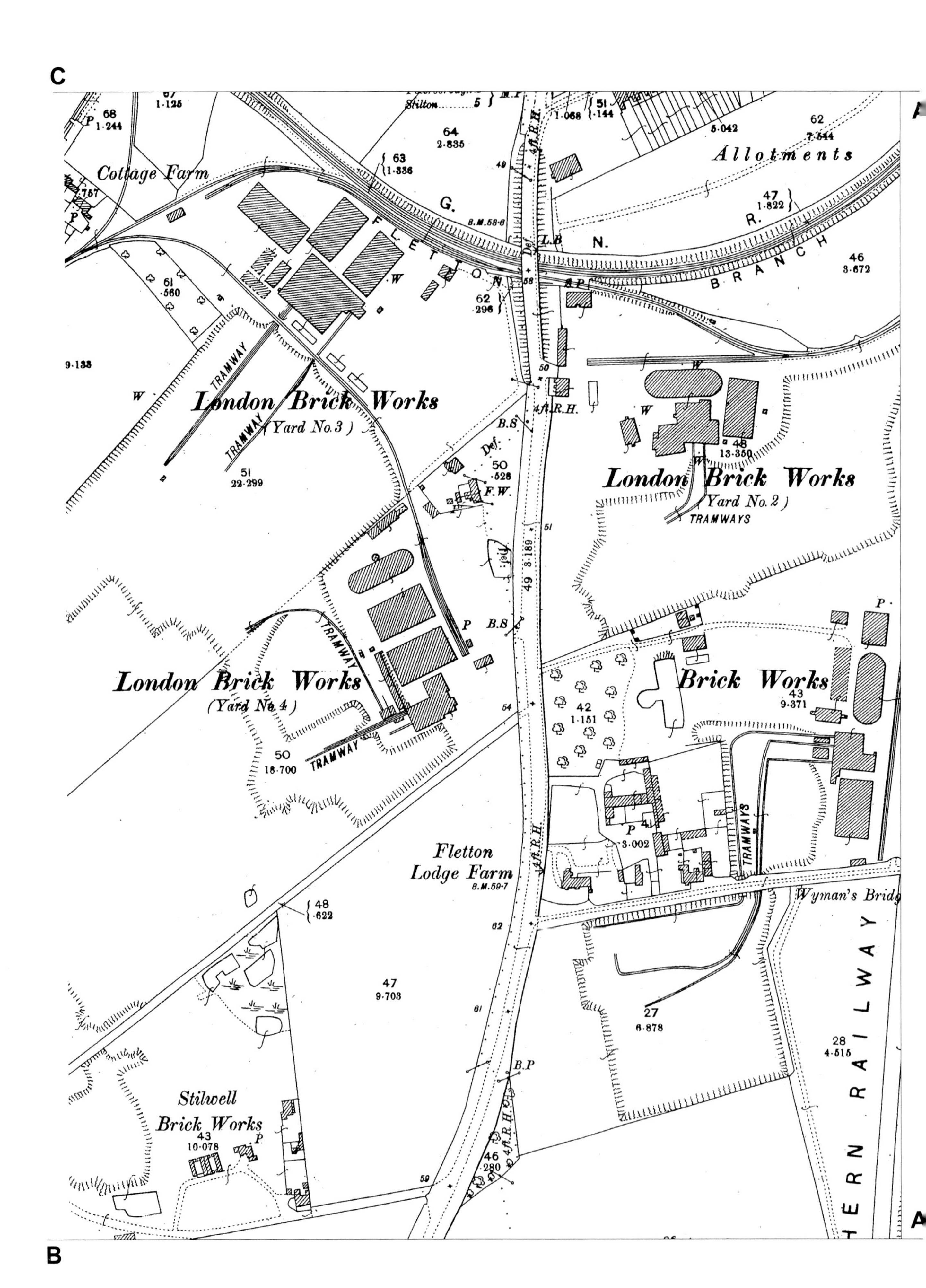
Cottage Farm
London Brick Works
(Yard No. 3)
TRAMWAY
TRAMWAY
FLETTON
G. N. R. BRANCH
Allotments
London Brick Works
(Yard No. 2)
TRAMWAYS
London Brick Works
(Yard No. 4)
TRAMWAY
TRAMWAY
Brick Works
TRAMWAYS
Fletton
Lodge Farm
Wyman's Bridg
Stilwell
Brick Works
HERN RAILWAY

B

C

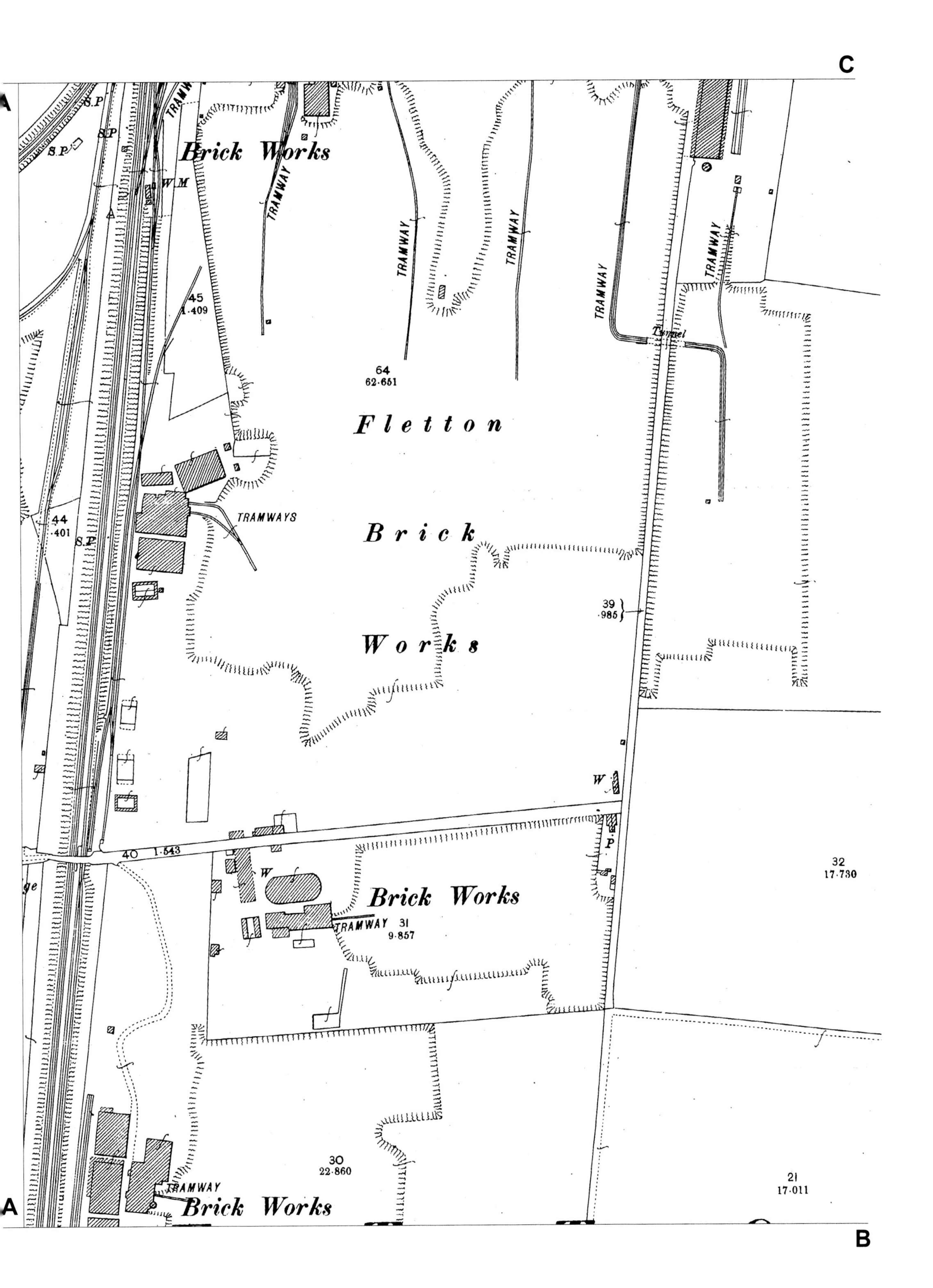
A
Brick Works
S.P
S.P
S.P
W.M
TRAMWAY
TRAMWAY
TRAMWAY
TRAMWAY
TRAMWAY
TRAMWAY
45
1·409
64
62·651
Tunnel
Fletton
Brick
Works
TRAMWAYS
44
·401
S.P
39
·985
W
40
1·543
P
ge
W
Brick Works
TRAMWAY
31
9·857
32
17·730
30
22·860
21
17·011
TRAMWAY
Brick Works
A

B

D

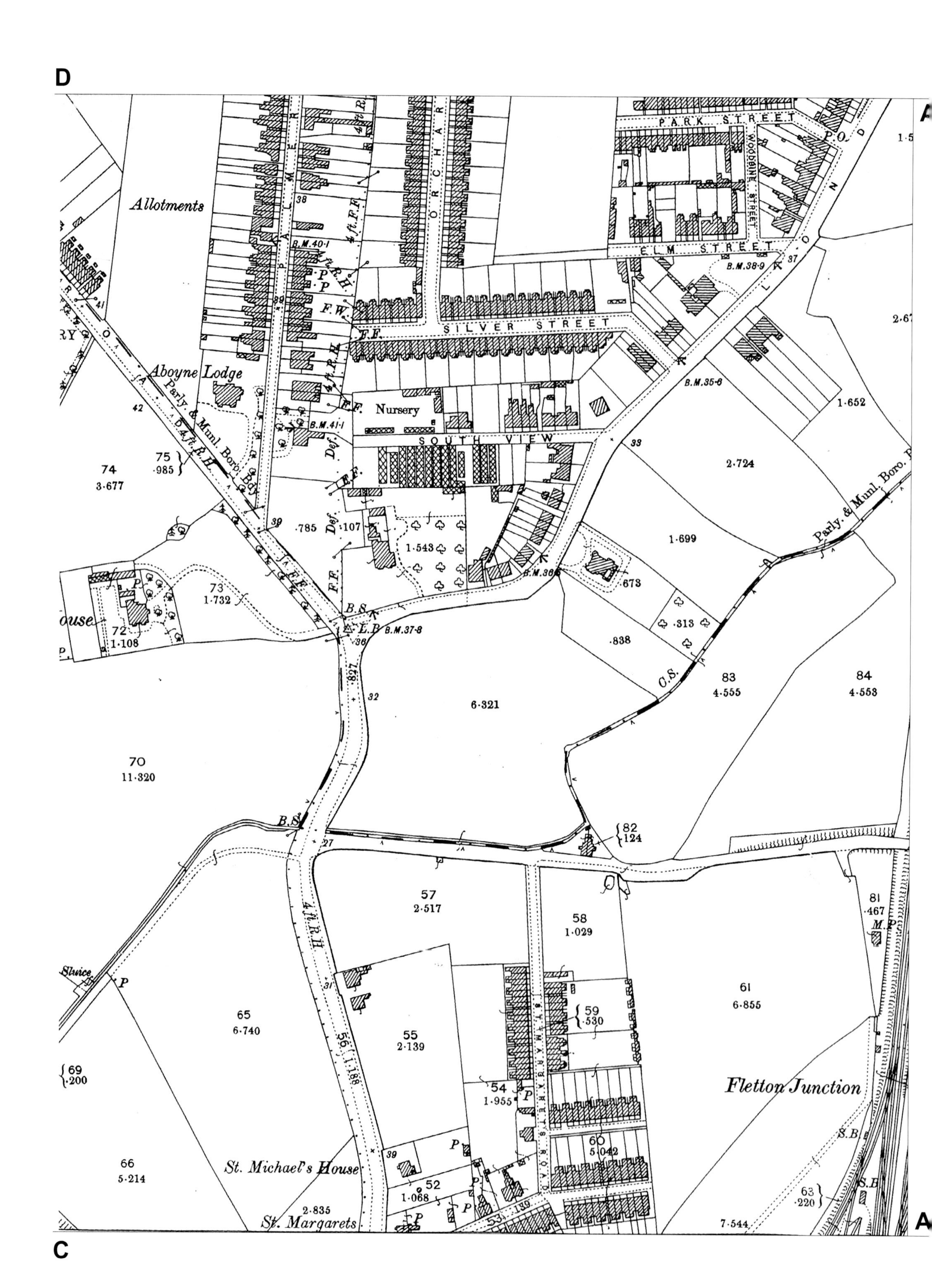
Allotments
Aboyne Lodge
Parly. & Munl. Boro. Bdy.
Nursery
SOUTH VIEW
SILVER STREET
PARK STREET
ELM STREET
WOODBINE STREET
ORCHARD
PALMER
74
3·677
75
·985
73
1·732
72
1·108
70
11·320
6·321
1·543
·785
·107
1·699
·673
·838
·313
2·724
1·652
83
4·555
84
4·553
82
·124
57
2·517
58
1·029
59
·530
55
2·139
54
1·955
56
1·188
60
5·042
61
6·855
81
·467
65
6·740
66
5·214
69
·200
52
1·068
63
·220
2·835
7·544
Fletton Junction
St. Michael's House
St. Margarets
Sluice
B.M.40·1
B.M.41·1
B.M.37·8
B.M.38·9
B.M.35·6
B.M.36·6

C

D

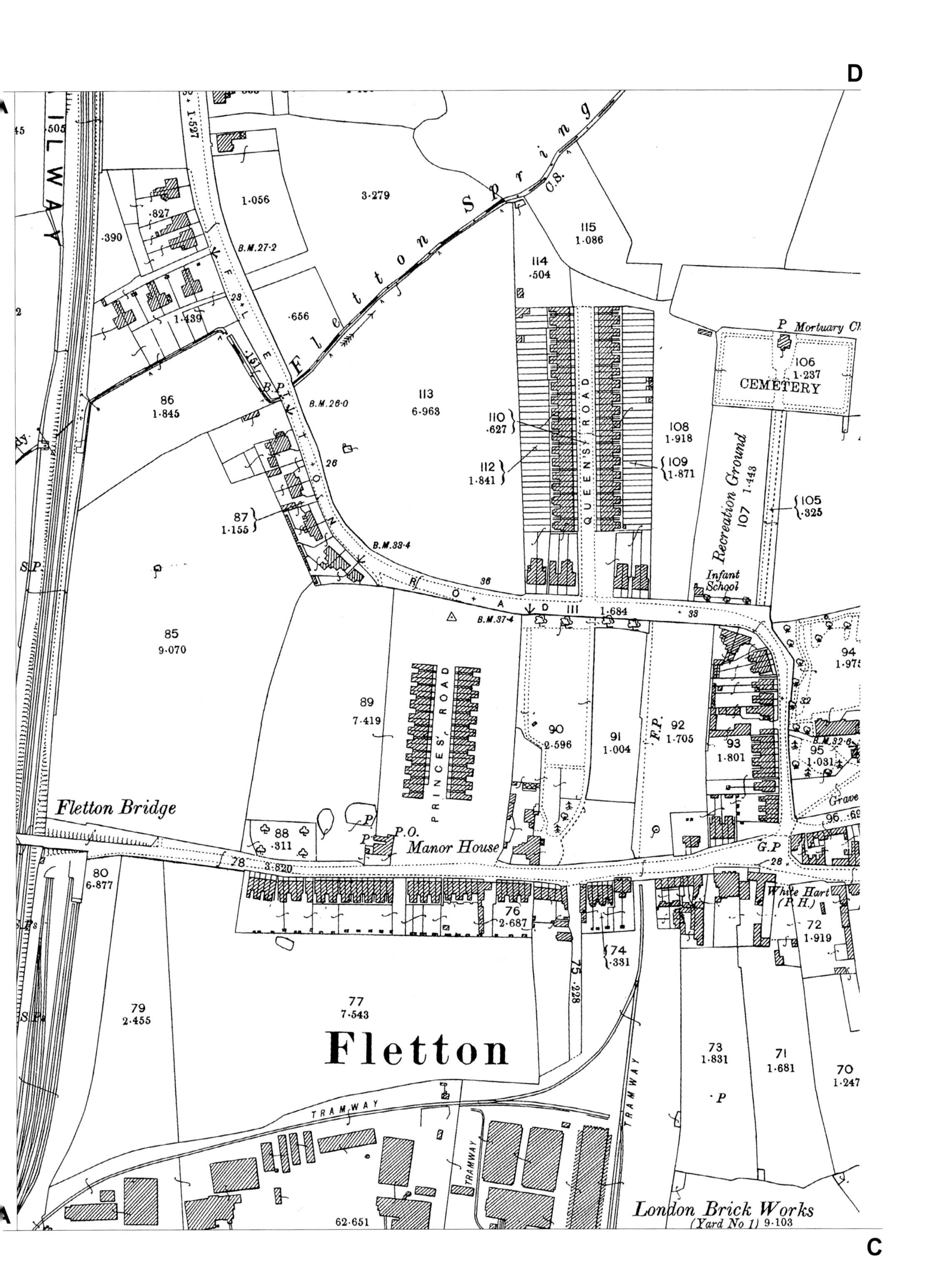

Fletton Spring
FLETTON ROAD
QUEEN'S ROAD
PRINCES' ROAD
CEMETERY
Mortuary Ch
Recreation Ground
Infant School
Fletton Bridge
P.O.
Manor House
White Hart (P.H.)
TRAMWAY
Fletton
London Brick Works
(Yard No 1) 9·103

C

E (Continued in next chapter)

D

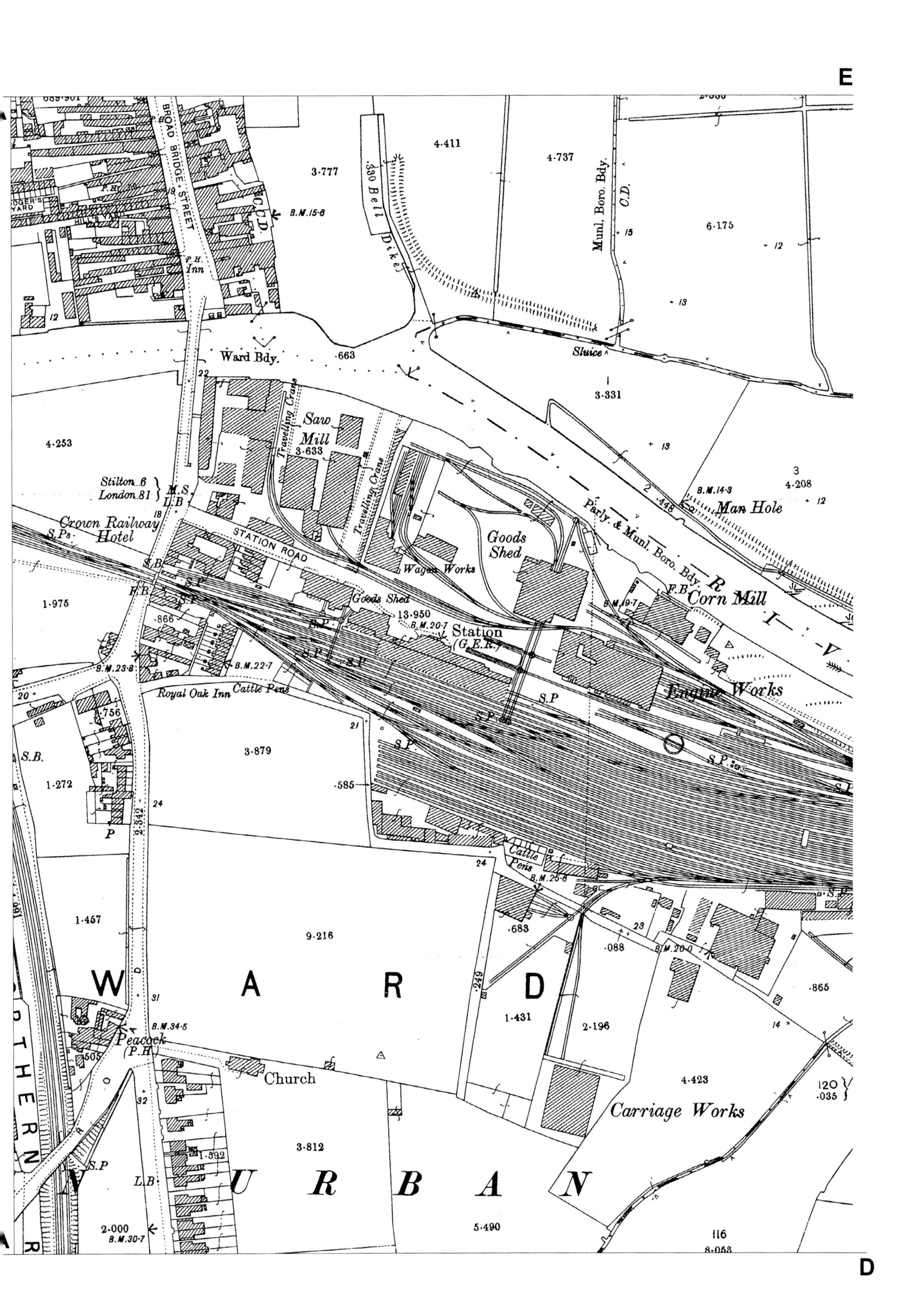
E
D
BROAD BRIDGE STREET
Bell Dike
Mun. Boro. Bdy.
Sluice
Ward Bdy.
Saw Mill
Travelling Crane
Goods Shed
Wagon Works
Stilton 6
London 81
Crown Railway Hotel
STATION ROAD
Station (G.E.R.)
Parly. & Munl. Boro. Bdy.
Man Hole
Corn Mill
Engine Works
Royal Oak Inn
Cattle Pens
W A R D
U R B A N
Peacock (P.H.)
Church
Carriage Works

you could feel the road deflecting under the engine, and the feel varied with the weather. Maintenance of a level and straight road across the Fen was achieved by unloading ashes and 'fettling' the road. Ash had the advantages of being light, resilient, unable to hold rainwater, and freely available. Its disadvantage was that by comparison with ironstone slag, a by-product of the steel industry, it was considerably less strong, and less able to hold the line especially in hot weather. With the drive for higher speed, together with the use of imported iron ore that produced little or no slag, granite was introduced for rail ballast as a replacement in the 1960s. It was stronger, far more abrasion resistant even in wet conditions, but heavier. With a century and a half of compaction, granite ballast was used over the Fen successfully. With diesel and electric traction there is no significant hammer blow or lurching to impose extra loading on the track, and today in a few minutes an express flashes across a section which was an outstanding engineering achievement.

Yaxley & Farcet was the next station, in a cutting, after which the countryside changed abruptly. Yaxley lays above the west bank of the old course of the Nene on a bank of hard clay, excellent for brick making. Two additional goods lines commenced from Yaxley. The next 2½ miles was occupied entirely by the brick industry, principally the London Brick Company, Forders and Eastwoods. The development of the brickfields started in the late 19th century driven by the expansion of London suburbs. The tall chimneys from the kilns were the signature of the brick industry, as indeed was the earthy smell. Sidings went off either side, and as the clay was excavated, the sidings were extended to new excavations. An aerial ropeway was installed so that excavation could continue east of the railway and serve the kilns on the west side. The ropeway had deteriorated steadily and collapsed in the late 1960s on to the main line, fortunately avoiding an accident but blocking the main line. It was scrapped as a result. A number of New England's varieties of 0-6-0 were occupied in servicing the many sidings. The south part of Peterborough, before the Nene was crossed, was called Old Fletton, and here a spur went west from Fletton Junction down to the LNWR at Longueville Junction in 1881. This spur, the Botolph Branch, had a chequered career, having been severed in 1929, restored in 1947, closed in 1961, and finally reopened to link the main network with the preserved Nene Valley Railway.

The Fletton brick has become a part of history, and the means by which the flesh-tinted building brick has become so well-known was the GNR and its successors. Bricks have a colouring which is vernacular, dependent on minerals, usually ironstone, their concentration and behaviour at high temperatures. Experienced bricklayers usually could tell types of brick from their colour. 'Flettons' accounted for a great deal of the building in London and the suburbs, along with the weaker yellow, sandy stock bricks. Brickmaking clay needed to have a low sand content: too much weakened the bricks. The bricks were conveyed to the London area in special large braked bogie wagons. Curiously the building work for the GNR made use of a very distinctive light grey-yellow brick, I believe from Whittlesea, a few miles to the east of Peterborough, where there were more large brickworks.

The bricks from the Peterborough area were for general building work. They should not be confused with engineering quality bricks, which were used to build arch rings, tunnel linings, viaducts, retaining walls, and large load-bearing structures. They were made from carefully selected materials, and the production process was more closely controlled to ensure the maintenance of specified quality, such as the 'Staffordshire Blue' or Southwaters. They had a greater crushing and breaking strength, and naturally, were more expensive. The production process was more closely controlled to ensure the maintenance of specified quality. Some structures used engineering brick and lower quality brick – for example road overbridges had blue engineering brick arch rings, but the spandrels and parapets that were bearing lower loads were built of lower quality bricks with a distinctive red-brown colour. The 1926 Survey shows the considerable extent of the brickworks and the rail network which served them.

Below. **The largely dismantled goods yard at Yaxley at the end of 1963.**

The rear of Yaxley station building – see page 103.

As the GN main line drew near to Peterborough, the depredations and outpourings of the brick industry came into view as is illustrated here. Sidings and additional freight running lines can be seen in the picture, looking northwards towards Peterborough.

The four tracks were carried on two lattice spans over former LNWR route to Peterborough East at Peterborough. Immediately beyond, the down lines crossed the Nene on a second through lattice span, while the up lines parallel the Nene on the original arch girders. This is the up lattice span over the LNWR route. This is a 'through' bridge and the tracks are carried on longitudinal timbers.

CHAPTER FIFTEEN

Peterborough and New England

Just before Peterborough North the GNR crossed the LNWR line from Northampton and Rugby to Peterborough East, where the GER line from March met the LNWR line head on. The MR had constructed a line from Leicester, reaching Peterborough in 1846 through Stamford, opened throughout in 1848. It continued past the site of the North station to cross the Nene, turning eastwards to meet the Eastern Counties Railway at the East station, the LNWR joining just below the GNR lattice girder intersection bridge. The GN main line ran on to an approach viaduct and then crossed the Nene on a three span bridge. The original bridge consisted of cast iron arch ribs of 66ft span. Each span comprised six arch ribs, grouped into three pairs at 3ft centres, each pair being at 7ft 6ins centres. Each rib was cast in two halves, connected at the centre to ease the problems of handling, transport and erection. As mentioned before, cast iron was used generally in railway bridges at first, but after a number of serious failures it was replaced with wrought iron. In the arch form used at Peterborough, and at the original Huntingdon Ouse Bridge, the design was largely in compression. The bridge was widened with three new wrought iron spans west of the old bridge, carrying the down lines. The down bridge was a through type, the tracks carried between the lattice girder trusses.

Peterborough North station was approximately half a mile north of the Nene bridge. A typical tour on an inspection saloon would involve the party leaving the saloon at Peterborough probably for lunch at the GN Hotel, and meanwhile the Atlantic would have shunted the saloon into one of the north end bay platforms. In later years the party would have a cold lunch whilst shunted off the main line. Various matters would have been discussed en route and at lunch, such as the need for retaining or adding facilities, station reconstruction, closing signalboxes, etc. An engineering inspection would have concentrated on the ride and track quality, with individual closer examinations of layouts and structures. Some engineering inspections took place later using the Whitewash Coach, which provided a running analysis of track top and line. If the Permanent Way Inspector for the section was present on the run, it would have been an anxious experience being confronted simultaneously with the civil engineering hierarchy and his sins of omission!

The old GNR station had been enlarged, and remained essentially the same for a century. In 1973 the complete rebuilding of Peterborough was completed, transforming the track and platform layout. The old station was a synthesis of almost all of the shortcomings that operators could experience. Situated on a sharp curve, it was also subject to a heavy PSR, 20 mph. As the station was approached there was a connection between Nene Junction on the MR/LMSR lines and Crescent Junction on the GNR, by means of which trains could pass between the main line and the GE section. Some LMSR trains called at the East station and not the North: the MR had its own station at Crescent Road but this became disused a century or more ago. Crescent Junction was just south of the station, separated from the station by the mass of Crescent Road overbridge, a large bowstring girder bridge ever-present in photographs of the station area. At the north end of the station on the up side was Peterborough North signalbox, a very attractive traditional GNR structure. Beyond on the down side was Spital Junction.

The station itself was an island platform with two faces and bay platforms at the north end, and an up platform face and south end bay. The buildings were on the up side. There was, incredibly, just one platformed up track, and a second without a platform, variously called the up slow, up

The down span on the intersection bridge crossing the LNWR south of Peterborough. Notice the guard rails over the bridge, and continued along the viaduct across the Nene. These prevent a derailed vehicle damaging the structure. The identity of the tank loco on the down goods is a mystery; possibly it is an ex-GE J69.

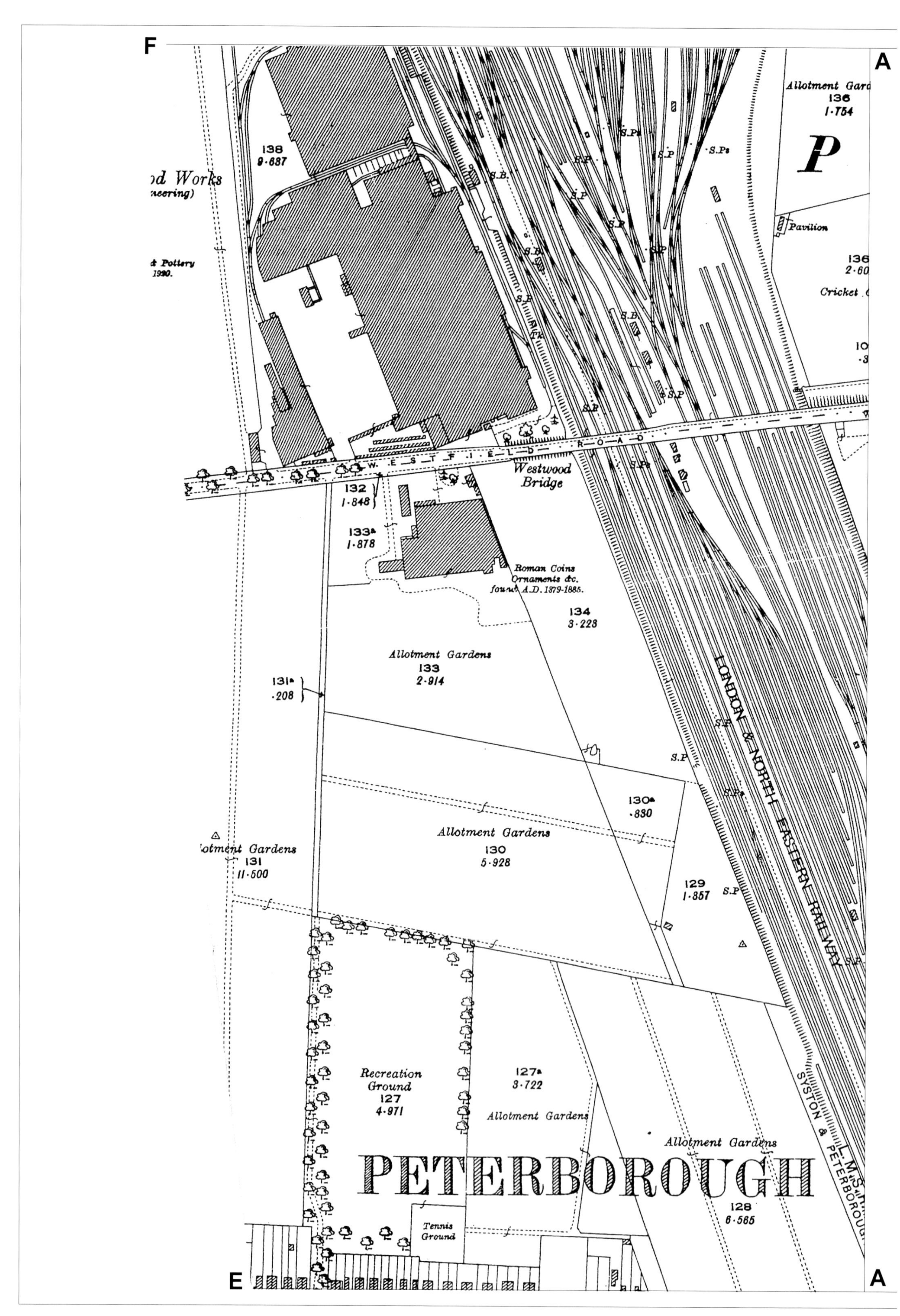
F
A
E
A
od Works
neering)
& Pottery
1930.
138
9·687
Allotment Gard
136
1·754
P
Pavilion
136
2·60
Cricket
S.B.
S.P
S.Ps
W. E. S. T. F. I. E. L. D. R. O. A. D.
Westwood
Bridge
132
1·848
133a
1·878
Roman Coins
Ornaments &c.
found A.D. 1879-1885.
134
3·223
Allotment Gardens
133
2·914
131a
·208
LONDON & NORTH EASTERN RAILWAY
130a
·830
Allotment Gardens
130
5·928
otment Gardens
131
11·500
129
1·357
Recreation
Ground
127
4·971
127a
3·722
Allotment Gardens
Allotment Gardens
PETERBOROUGH
128
6·565
Tennis
Ground
SYSTON & PETERBOROUGH
L.M.S.R.

Peterborough

Plans showing the layout to the south of Peterborough in the 1920s.

Olde Peterborough 5. Further along the up platform in January 1934 we have the Refreshment Room, where 'Luncheons are served daily 12 to 30pm'. Familiar 'BAC' machines are outside dispensing matches, chocolate and toffee. Posters invite you to the England/Scotland Rugby League Final and Crufts Dog Show. The top row is reserved for French Railways. One of the items on the four wheeled barrow is an egg box and a 'Hotels Department Kings Cross' hamper waits its journey home. Everything on the railway, it seems, had to 'Return to Somewhere'. The attractive but inadequate lamp above shows the mandatory 'Peterboro' North'.

Olde Peterborough 6. The interior of North station showing two of the three foot crossings. A large quantity of the mail and parcels being transferred here plus originating or received traffic was manhandled across, there being no parcel bridge or subway. In 1936, something like 3,500 items were dealt with in this way on a normal weeknight – more in the flower or fruit season.

Olde Peterborough 7. We are looking from down to up platform towards London. Refreshment and Dining Rooms are on the Up and both Ladies First and Third Class Waiting Rooms on the down. The gentlemen, it will be noted, just have a 'Waiting Room'. Gloomy it may be, but the place is clean and tidy.

Olde Peterborough 8. This is the view looking from up to down at the country end of the station, December 1933. On the down main platform every available inch of wall space has been used. The whiteness of the posters cheers the place up a bit but in the overall gloom the poster offering the cruise *to Honolulu* might be worth a second look.

Olde Peterborough 9. The 'excursion' platform No.6 on the west side of the down 'island' in January 1934. Separate Booking Offices again – and at the platform Midland trains normally used. Plenty of timetables and an LMS advert for the Leicester-Richmond Rugby match. A smart 'finger post' indicator denotes the next service from Platform 6.

Olde Peterborough 10. Further down the excursion platform, an ornate drinking fountain, another of life's losses over the years, is on display in January 1934. But it is the advert boards that take our attention. There is one for Hungarian State Railways and one for Norwegian State Railways before we get to the M&GN and L&NER – and this is Peterborough. Just how many people from Peterborough did go to Budapest in those days (let alone the Hawaiian Islands)? A fine 'Nestlé's' machine and some smart platform awning complete the scene.

Olde Peterborough 11. The full length of the 'excursion' platform (No.6) in December 1933 with some elaborate brickwork at this end. The two lines this side of the platform line are the Up Slow and Down Goods. Trains using the up slow had to cross the down main line at both ends of the station, part of the operating nightmare. The pilot sits in bay 5 with a van.

Olde Peterborough 12. The north end of the station with the north up side bay to the left, December 1933. The gloom beneath that awning, even if it is December, is it seems, impenetrable. The pilot looks like an Atlantic, in LNER green.

Peterborough North showing the old LMS Spital Bridge engine shed, a Midland roundhouse erroneously labelled 'Engine Repair Shed'.

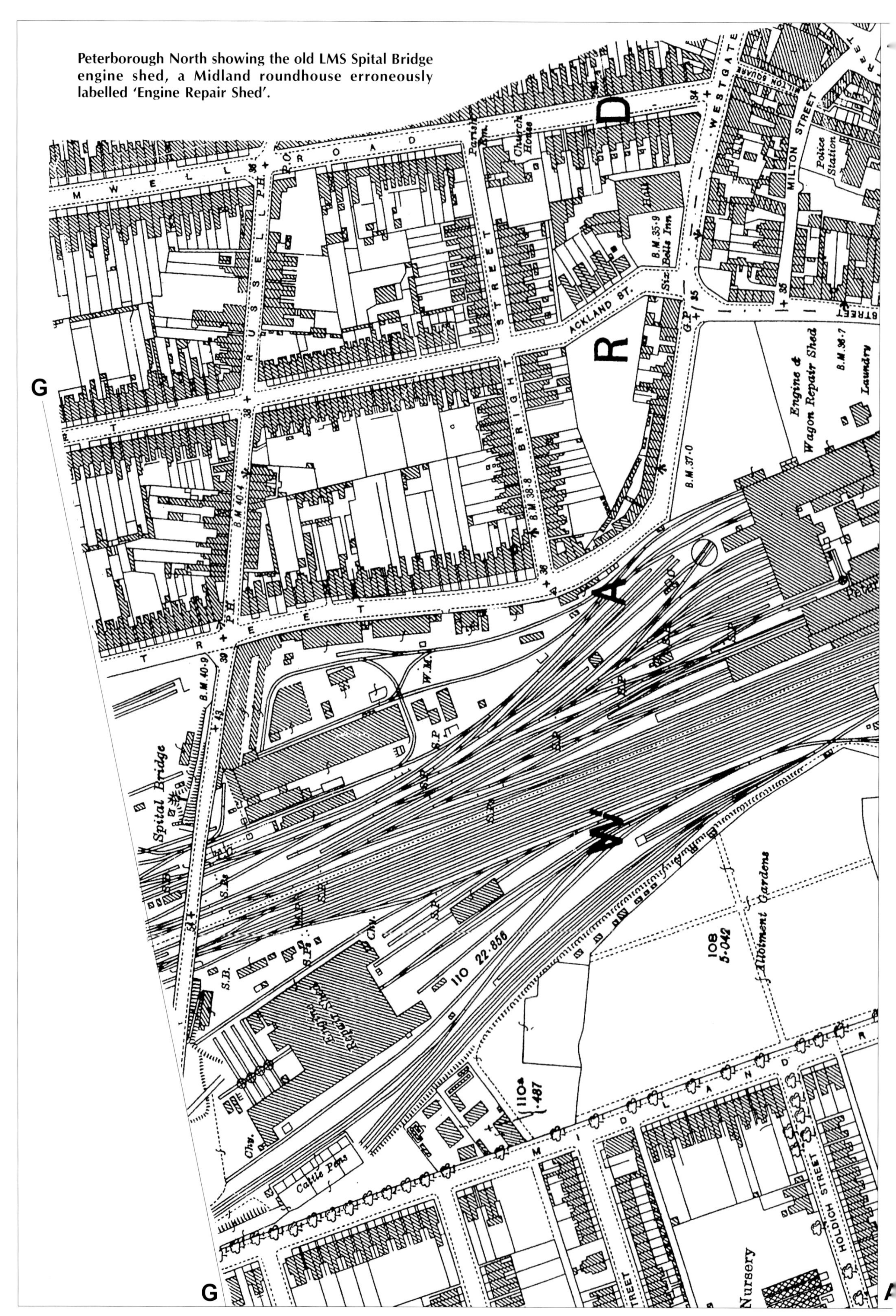

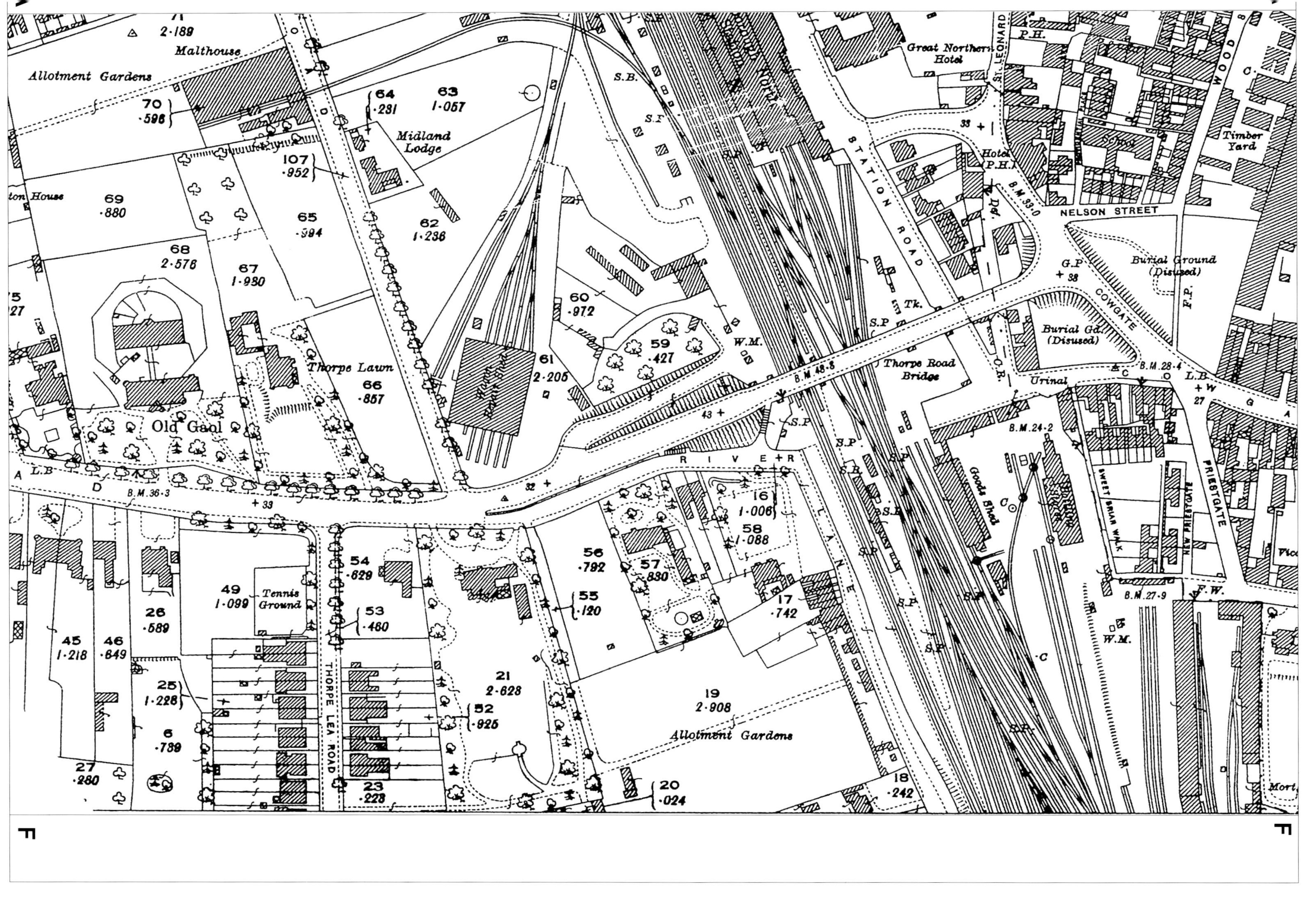
Allotment Gardens
Malthouse
Midland Lodge
Old Gaol
Thorpe Lawn
Great Northern Hotel
Timber Yard
STATION ROAD
NELSON STREET
Burial Ground (Disused)
COWGATE
Burial Gd. (Disused)
Thorpe Road Bridge
Urinal
RIVER LANE
Goods Shed
SWEET BRIAR WALK
NEW PRIESTGATE
PRIESTGATE
Tennis Ground
THORPE LEA ROAD
Allotment Gardens
F
F

Olde Peterborough 13. A loco at last! This is the south end looking north with C1 Atlantic 4431 of Grantham in the up main platform. She already has over 26 years service in and will be around until October 1944. Note the small figures on the cabside. It wasn't wide enough for the standard 12 inch ones. The train will be an 'all stations' from either Grantham or Doncaster. A former Great Eastern Railway coach sits in the up side bay waiting for a service via Peterborough East.

A 1950s interior at Peterborough North, with the up main platform 2 on the right.

A down express pulls away from Peterborough North on 16th August 1958, headed by Ardsley's V2 No.60884. The train is leaving the down excursion (or slow) platform. A curious procession stands on the down goods – a GCR N5 0-6-2T No.69293, a 350HP diesel shunter behind with a Queen Mary brake van, and a V2 with modified front end, tender first. Peter Groom.

independent or even up excursion. The down main used the eastern face of the island, and the trains from the GE or MR used the western face, strangely called the Excursion road. The down and up platform tracks were under an overall roof of simple trussed design, and their length was a coach or two less than the principal expresses. Peterborough was not only host to the expresses and slow services of the main line, services to and from the GE section, occasionally to and from the LMSR, but also to services from the Midland & Great Northern Joint line, and those using the old GNR main line via Spalding, and Boston. The latter two services used the northern bay platforms, while GE section and LMSR services used the excursion road. The northern bay platforms were also used for locomotives waiting to take over down services, and likewise the south end bay was used for up services. The up bay was also used by services departing for the GE section. During the summer and on Saturdays, the main line service was significantly enhanced, and Peterborough North had to cope with a large number of trains. It was difficult to bring the up independent into use north of the station since it was necessary to cross the down road at an even more heavily reduced speed at Spital Junction, only to have to cross back again at Crescent Junction. Not only did the station have to handle this variety of passenger traffic, but there was even more freight traffic to be handled, passing through and not stopping. When the line was quadrupled the extra tracks had to be added on the east side since the MR line and sidings were on the west side. The down freight travelled on the down goods which passed west of the station as far as Spital Junction, where the goods lines crossed over to the east side of the main line to reach the New England yards. Up freight trains, unless in the unlikely event of being routed through the up platform, also crossed from the up side at Spital Bridge, took the up goods to Crescent Junction where it crossed back over the main lines on to the east side for the climb up to the Nene bridge. To describe the layout as difficult was an understatement of heroic dimensions.

Peterborough North was said, in the early 1950s, to be without track circuiting, an alarming prospect. In fact I think that what track circuiting existed there was minimal, since in an hour or two watching operations at different times, there were several moves of considerable complexity that would have been difficult with fully circuited mechanical signalling. Safety required concentration and care. That it was carried out at low speeds helped, indeed it was probably mandatory. The layout would never have passed scrutiny today, although I can see that its rather minimal design might have appealed to our financial brethren. Banking was allowed for down trains, when authorised, within the length of the down platform. Although it was a difficult start with the train on a curve, the start in the up direction with a sharply curved climb to the Nene bridge was considerably worse, for which there was no banking authorisation and no layout provision. The operational pressure was on the up track rather than the down. A Pacific with up express would draw in, and a light J6 0-6-0 would steal, silently, to within 20ft of the tail lamp, leaving room for the Pacific to set back if necessary. Then a D16 4-4-0 with her two or three coaches for the up bay would creep in behind the J6. Pacifics for the northbound expresses would back down, reverse across to the down side and reverse again into the bay. I remember standing in the cab of SIR RALPH WEDGWOOD on the down main as an up express drew to a halt. A tall chimney drew slowly behind it, alongside, and looking down I saw beneath it a 'Little Black Goods', a J15 0-6-0, sporting 'The Fenman' headboard, with three or four coaches, standing behind the express. Not only

An up express headed by the Top Shed favourite, V2 No.60800 GREEN ARROW, runs into the up platform at Peterborough North on 2nd August 1960. K.C.H. Fairey.

The Yorkshire Pullman restarts from an unscheduled stop at Peterborough North on 7th July 1955. A pilot, V2 No.60832 has replaced A4 No.60014 SILVER LINK, and despite her well worn appearance (being three months away from general overhaul) Ted Hailstone brought her back on the 9.50 from Leeds the following day. The A4 failure was easily dealt with and she was back on the Pullman two days later. P. Lynch.

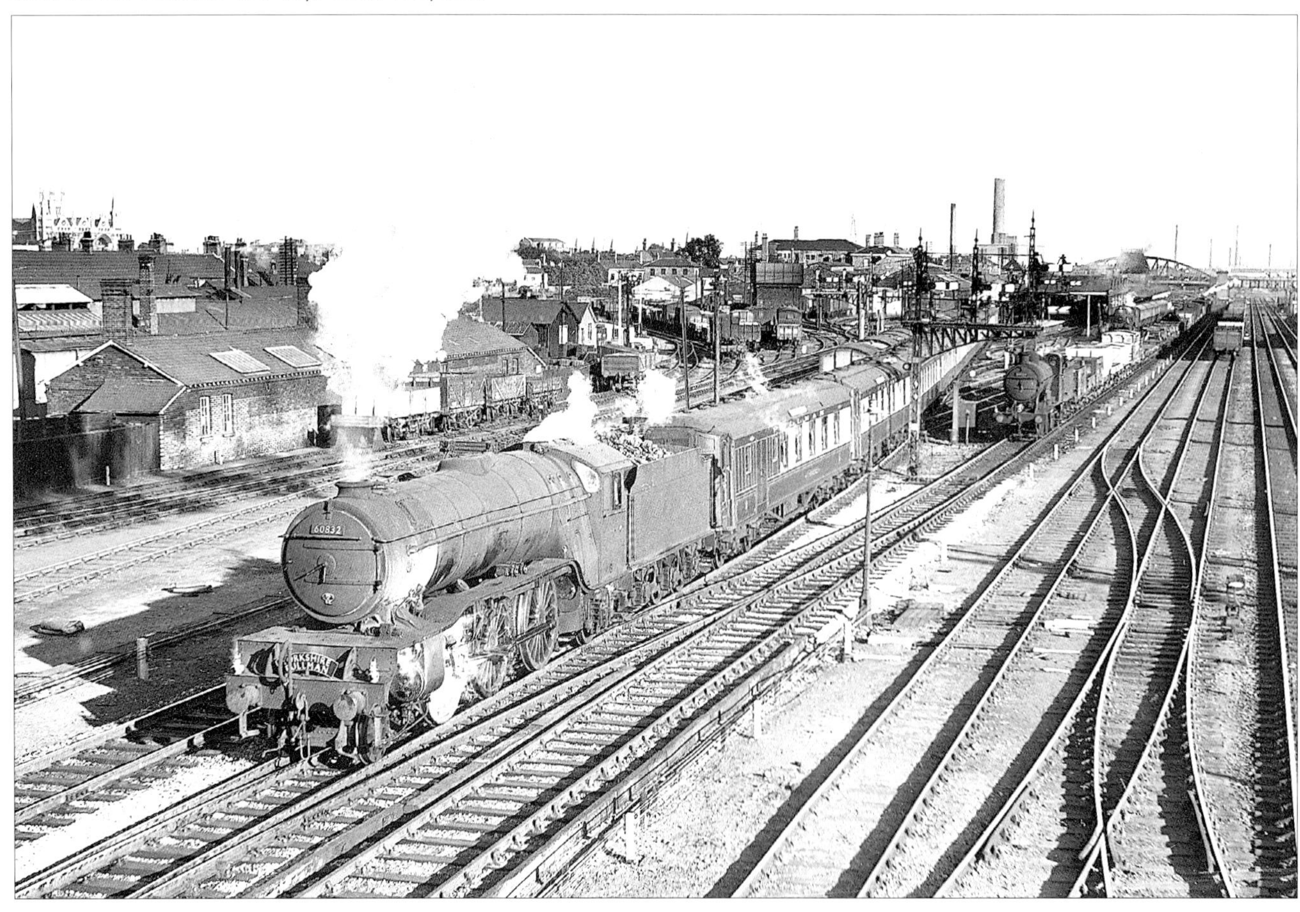

The station pilot, GC 0-6-2T No.69293, has collected some ECS for a down service from Peterborough North on 16th August 1958. The diesel shunter from the earlier photograph on the same day has now gone, but the tender first V2 is still waiting. Three N5s were sent south to work from Hatfield but were little used and went on to work from New England on the Stamford branch and elsewhere. Peter Groom.

The 15.00 for Boston leaves Peterborough North on 16th August 1958 behind one of New England's long term residents, B1 No.61073. The train appears to be breaking new ground for passenger discomfort, as apart from the reasonably comfortable leading composite, it appears to be formed of a quad-art set displaced from London commuter duties. Peter Groom.

The north end of Peterborough North, looking towards Spital Bridge Junction. From right to left starting after the telegraph pole, we have the up main, down main with the down bay road joining immediately, the down slow or excursion on the photographer's left, then the up excursion road with its trap point protecting the junction, and then the down goods.

The view north of Spital Bridge with a Thompson A2 coasting in from the north on the up main. The vast expanse of New England marshalling yards spreads to the north, with a 9F drawing forward towards the southern outlet.

The expanse of New England was, largely, an immense monument to the coal industry. A J6 0-6-0 arrives tender first with a transfer freight. A characteristic of marshalling yards in those days was the oil that encrusted the sleeper ends, from a myriad of coal wagon axleboxes.

delightful to see but unique in the operational sense, as well as a unique mixture of railway equipment and rolling stock.

The 1973 rebuilt station is similar in that the main station buildings remain on the up side, and the remainder of the station comprises two island platforms. The slow lines are paired on the east side, with the main lines next, a down platform loop, and two bi-directional lines, one used by LM and GE section services, and the westernmost by goods services. On the east side, the slow lines platform faces are used by services to and from Kings Cross, and slow or stopping main line traffic. The up platform has the station buildings and serves only the up slow, while the eastern island platform has only one face, serving the down slow. The main lines have no platform faces. The western island platform has two faces, serving the down platform loop and bi-directional line. The sharp reverse curves were slued to a much reduced curvature, so much so that the 20mph PSR became 105mph after the realignment and relaying had been completed. This was part of a comprehensive overhaul of the main line with the objective of raising speed limits generally. As a result, with the enormously enhanced power to weight of expresses, it became possible to achieve times that were beyond the wildest dreams a decade or so earlier. The Peterborough reconstruction, overall, was one of the major contributions to the high speed main line that the old GNR has become.

One looks back to the old station with affection for some experiences, although the new one is so much better. Apart from the eccentricity of the operation and the interest in its operation, running the service must always have required great concentration at times with the numbers of different conflicting movements. At holiday times the merely routine became difficult, and at times impossible, with passengers on queuing expresses left to contemplate the hundreds – perhaps thousands – of wagons standing in New England yard for a few minutes or more.

The area was thick with sidings. Down from the Nene Bridge there were carriage sidings on the down side, and on the up side, the south yard, goods station and the power station beyond. Beyond the station, behind the North box, on the east side were the remains of the original engine shed, the short 60ft turntable and some sidings. In steam days, the Peterborough main line pilot was a V2 that could just be squeezed on to the turntable. To the west, the MR had a number of sidings, including access to Spital Bridge engine shed, just across from the north end of North station. North of Spital Junction was Eastfield signalbox on the up side and Westwood Junction on the down. At Westwood the Midland &Great Northern Joint diverged to join the MR lines, and after passing the MR Wisbech sidings it swung through a right angle to head east, flying over the main line on an intersection bridge.

The 'Muddle & Go Nowhere' was closed pre-Beeching in 1959, a sad loss to the romantics among us. In managerial terms it didn't stand a chance, without any traffic of any significance outside the main holiday period, in an area where little existed once motorised road transport arrived. It was not robustly built, nor commercially exploited very well, and as a result could not be economically operated. The introduction of the effective if utilitarian Ivatt class 4MT 2-6-0s had brought an end to the M&GN's delightfully attractive and eccentric motive power. Incredibly, a

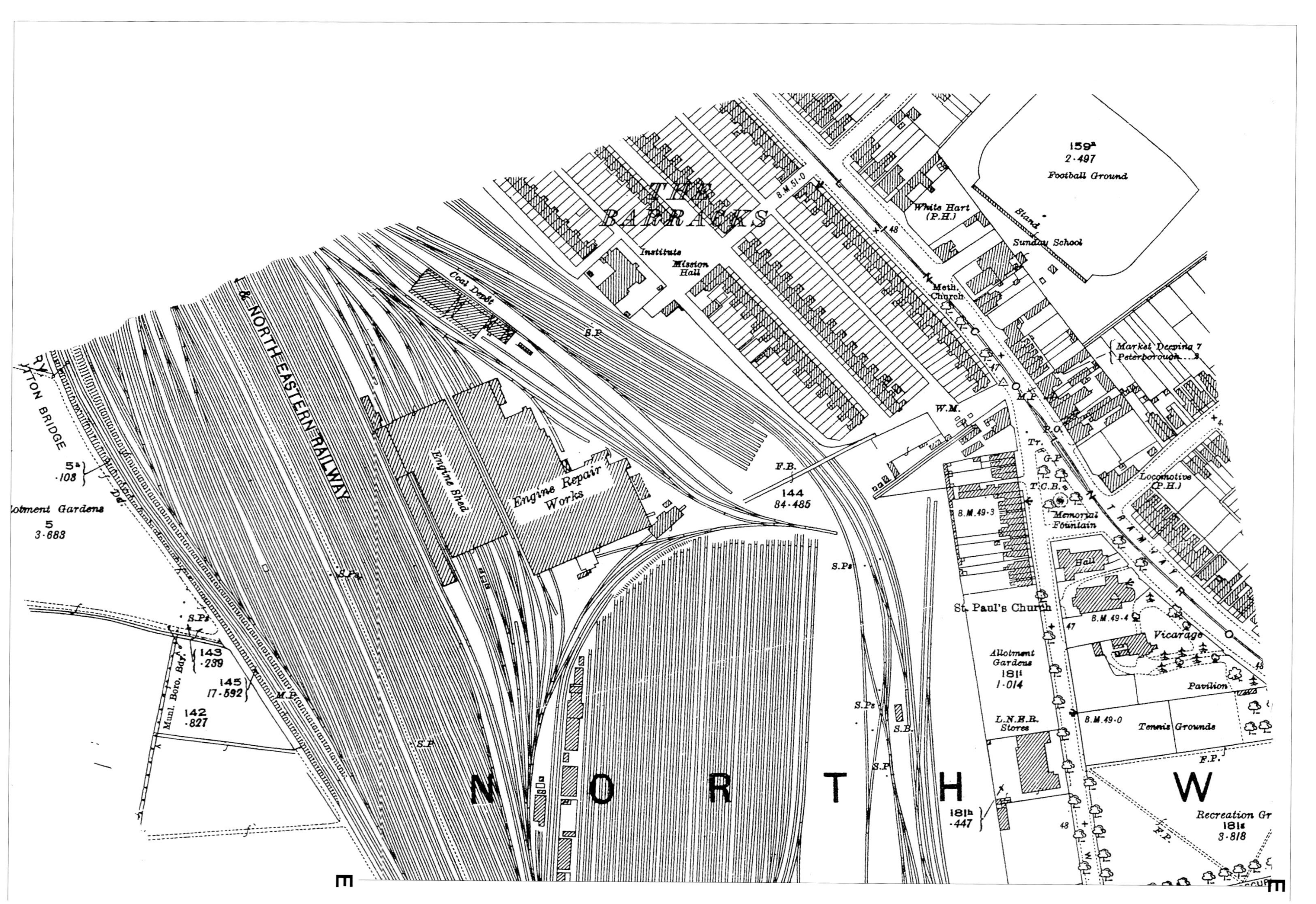

159a
2·497
Football Ground
Stand
Sunday School
White Hart (P.H.)
THE BARRACKS
B.M. 51·0
48
Institute
Mission Hall
Meth. Church
Coal Depot
S.P.
Market Deeping 7
Peterborough 3
M.P.
P.O.
W.M.
Tr.
G.P.
T.C.B.
Memorial Fountain
Locomotive (P.H.)
TRAMWAY
& NORTH EASTERN RAILWAY
Engine Shed
Engine Repair Works
F.B.
144
84·485
B.M. 49·3
Hall
St. Paul's Church
B.M. 49·4
47
Vicarage
Allotment Gardens
181l
1·014
Pavilion
L.N.E.R. Stores
B.M. 49·0
Tennis Grounds
F.P.
S.Ps
S.B.
TTON BRIDGE
5a
·108
Allotment Gardens
5
3·683
143
·239
145
17·892
142
·827
Munl. Boro. Bdy.
N O R T H W
181h
·447
Recreation Gr
181s
3·818
E
E

E
G
G
E
WALPOLE STREET
CLARE
B.M. 51
B.M. 50·5
B.M. 50·1
B.M. 49·2
49
48
47
136
·797
S.B.
S.P
Arklos Sidings
138
3·374
Allotment Gardens
139
28·531

The prospect north from Westwood Junction and Eastfield, with New England shed and its attendant smoke haze in the far distance.

New England, looking south from the South box towards Westwood Junction. The S&C (switches and crossings) layout near the signalbox is interesting in that the geometry of the diamond crossing has necessitated a sharp curve immediately beyond.

number of new diesel multiple units were ordered for the M&GN before it closed, but they were diverted to replace prototype diesel and steam power on the London suburban services. In this role they rapidly gained the nickname of 'Flying Greenhouses' in the London area.

Between Eastfield box and the M&GN flyover on the up side as the OS maps show, there were four major yards and numerous sidings together with a large loco depot, all embraced in the name 'New England'. The maps illustrate well the enormous spread of the marshalling yards. Traffic came in from the north, from Nottingham and the industrial district beyond, and from South Yorkshire via Doncaster and Retford. It was mainly coal. The fast freight that came from Grimsby, Hull, Northumberland and Scotland ran through, with a pause for a Carriage and Wagon examination and often to change crews and/or engines. Most of the slow freight continued southwards, remarshalled into trains for Ferme Park and lesser destinations, but some continued to March to supplement that which had travelled south via Lincoln, for onwards movement to East London and the docks. The goods lines continued on the eastern side of the main line, serving New England, continuing to Werrington Junction before taking up their normal position either side of the main lines. There was another mailbag pick-up point nearby by the side of the down main.

At New England in steam days lay the large and important motive power depot, home to large fleets of eight coupled and six coupled tender and tank freight locomotives. Apart from the long hauls, there was an enormous number involved in serving and shunting the dozens of brickworks sidings. All stopping freight and siding work to Stoke in the north and south to Huntingdon as a rule was worked by New England. Later, the GNR 'Long Tom' 0-8-0s were superseded by Gresley two and three cylinder 2-8-0s, and the ubiquitous J6 0-6-0s replaced most of the Stirling and earlier Ivatt engines. Gresley introduced his P1 Mikados in 1925, but they were not able to use their considerable haulage capacity successfully. Their longer trains were difficult to recess to make way for expresses, and the option of faster running was well-nigh impossible due to the lack of fitted vehicles and robust rolling stock.

After the war, in LNER and BR days, there was a large fleet of WD 2-8-0s and J6 0-6-0s to deal with the freight traffic, six Pacifics and a number of B1 4-6-0s to handle the passenger turns, and another large fleet of Green Arrow V2 2-6-2s for both passenger and freight. It was unusual in that a triangle was used for turning locos rather than a turntable, a device which was also used at Grantham. New England was primarily a freight depot and Grantham, which was also part of the Peterborough District, was primarily a passenger depot. Later the LMSR depot at Spital Bridge came within the Peterborough District. Later still Peterborough District itself was absorbed into Kings Cross District.

As referred to above New England worked duties of all sorts, from the up 'Aberdonian' to the goods trip down the Benwick branch from Three Horse Shoes Junction. Its large fleet of Green Arrows meant that almost every main GN depot made free with New England's V2s, and they could appear on almost anything, anywhere. Moreover one never knew quite what to expect, since they were usually at least dirty if not plain filthy, whether two months or two years from general overhaul. They were usually an adequate substitute and no more, but with an enterprising crew going home one could be pleasantly surprised. With such a wide range of duties for the district to cover of course any cleaners recruited at the main depot would soon have found themselves firing somewhere. The loss of coal traffic, the intervention of road transport and the use of freezing techniques in the food industry led to the loss of almost all rail freight, which hit New England hard, and the use of diesel traction led to closure. The large land holding north of Peterborough was sold off, and the lineside of 2000 looks very different from 1852, or 1952 for that matter.

New England depot looking south with its perpetual haze. Many of the old Midland sidings have been lifted by this time.

New England shed, with the North box in the foreground, and the freight lines passing by either side, looking south. One feels for the residents of the houses to the left. Washing day must have been something of a trial.

The south end of New England depot, with a J6 0-6-0 to the right and a 350hp diesel shunter near the South box.

Two views at New England South with Spital Bridge in the distance. One feels for the unfortunate lengthman whose task it was to oil the slide chains/baseplates of the hundreds of switches!

Right. Panoramic view of the north end at Peterborough North, overlooked by the rather nice GN signalbox. The curvature of the layout can be appreciated. The ex-MR lines are to the left while on the right, out of sight, is the old engine shed and turntable where the main line pilots stood. Beyond the signalbox are the sidings for empty stock, locos, and so on.

Below. The back of New England shed yard, from the main line, with Lincoln Road houses to the left.

Below right. Westwood bridge spans the layout. Westwood Junction allowed departures from the North station to cross to the MR and M&GN routes. The signalbox is, I think, Westfield, at the south end of New England.

NORTH BOX

The view north from Tallington footbridge. A down train heads north in the distance. The continuation of the down slow can be seen, and on the up side there is a typical pre-war long crossover, three slips and a diamond crossing.

CHAPTER SIXTEEN

Peterborough-Grantham

North of New England originally the GNR turned sharply north-east towards Boston before turning north-west at Spalding and heading for Lincoln. This was the original GNR loop line, built earlier than the southern section to London. The GNR had powers to extend their line on to Gainsborough, and on to join the present main line at Bawtry, but they were reluctant to commit the necessary funds to complete the route via Lincoln. As a result of various agreements the GNR's Doncaster-Retford line was linked to Lincoln via Retford. The resulting alignment was anything but direct, but construction of the present Peterborough-Retford route was under way by then. It seems certain that the GNR was intent on a direct route from Peterborough to Doncaster from the start. In order to compete for coal traffic the loop line was brought into use as early as possible and the GNR had earned at least two years' revenue before the direct route was opened. The Werrington-Boston section was as long a straight and level section as any in the country, sadly truncated in the Beeching era. The loop line was opened by 1848 between Peterborough and Lincoln, and by 1850 it was opened south of Doncaster to Maiden Lane. Two years later the main route, 'The Towns Line', was opened.

The direct route north of Werrington was relatively straight, cutting through the limestone country and reaching a summit at Stoke, from where it descended gracefully to the Trent Valley through the country town of Grantham. Just like the route from Hitchin, the major engineering works were the river crossings. There were two tunnels, Stoke and Peascliffe, and a third that was scarcely more than a long bridge, although built to a tunnel profile, the 57 yard Askham Tunnel at Markham summit. The route had crossed farming country from the Eastern Chilterns to Doncaster, and only Peterborough and Retford had been locations of industry, albeit far less than today. There were originally many level crossings, but as roads became more important, an overbridge was built later, leaving only the lineside signs of the earlier level crossing. The new railway crossed earlier railway routes on flat crossings at Newark and Retford where speed was restricted by a PSR. Apart from these, two sets of water troughs and the heavy curve at Grantham, it was a fast section.

In the steam era, one could be at the lineside north of Peterborough and see a succession down trains pulling away, the driver carefully balancing the need to get up speed for the troughs at Werrington without expelling his mate's fire from the chimney. It was the arrival of the Deltics that made Peterborough a special experience. While countless crews accelerated their steam locomotives away steadily from the restrictions of the station area, it was the Deltics with their astonishing power to weight ratio that gave us an entirely new dimension in acceleration. To hear TULYAR, ALYCIDON or their sisters opened out clear of Spital Bridge was something very special, even to a hardened steam man. The noise of the exhaust of a big two stroke diesel engine for three hours or so was hard on the driver, and the cab had thick insulating panels to keep noise levels down while the crews also had the curiously named 'ear defenders'. The cab windows were normally tightly shut, but if they were open, one could experience – as near as possible – the enormous roar of a Deltic at full power, reminiscent of a wartime Lancaster bomber taking off. As the speed rose past New England, the engines quietened a little, and by Werrington they had settled down to the familiar high-pitched exhaust, and one could enjoy the thrill of speeds that were still a novelty; almost incredible, and unlimited by the speed of the fireman's shovel. The Yorkshire Pullman, for example, used to make its stately way north to its unchallenging schedule behind its top link

Lolham level crossing as it was in 1957.

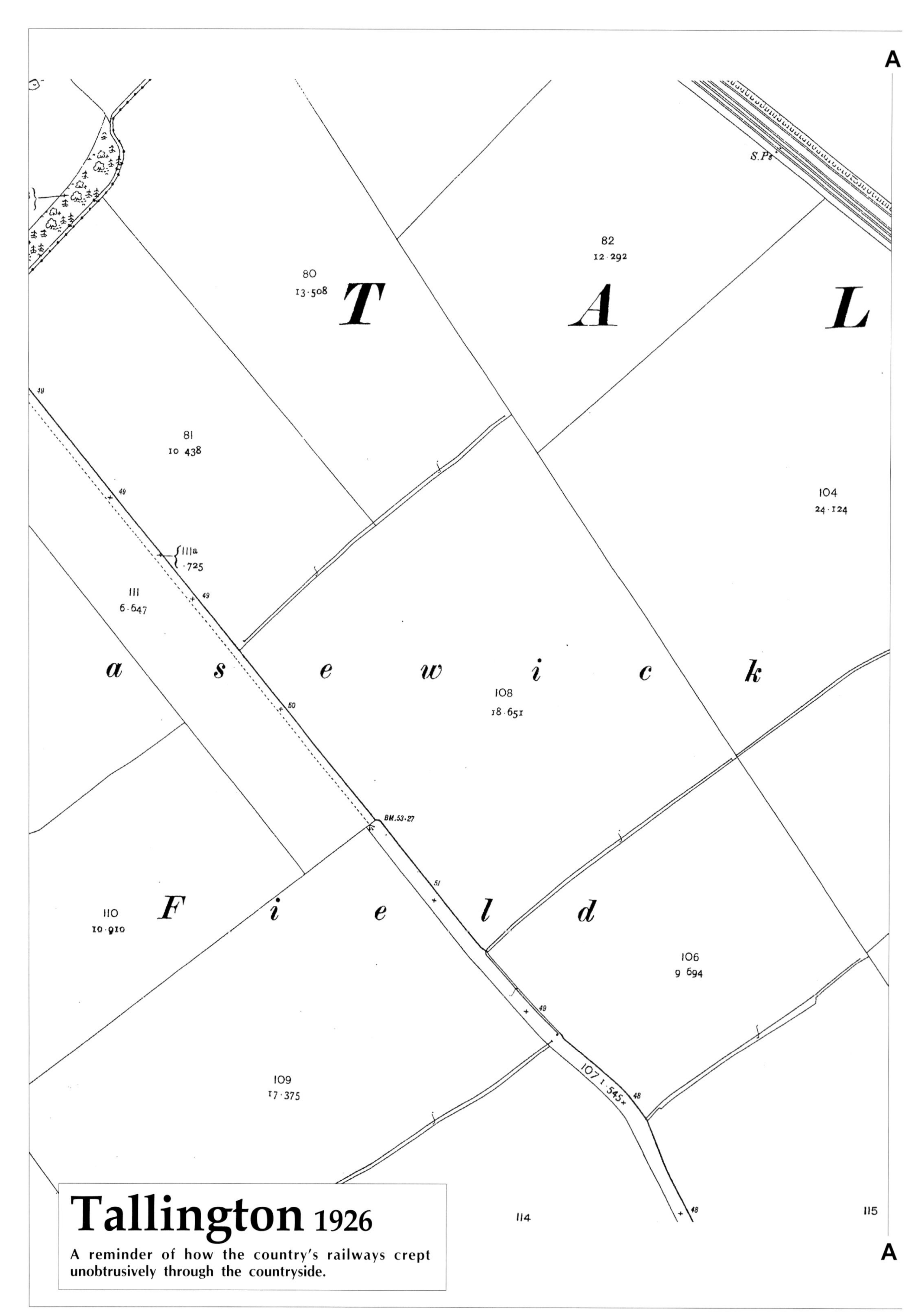

Tallington 1926

A reminder of how the country's railways crept unobtrusively through the countryside.

A

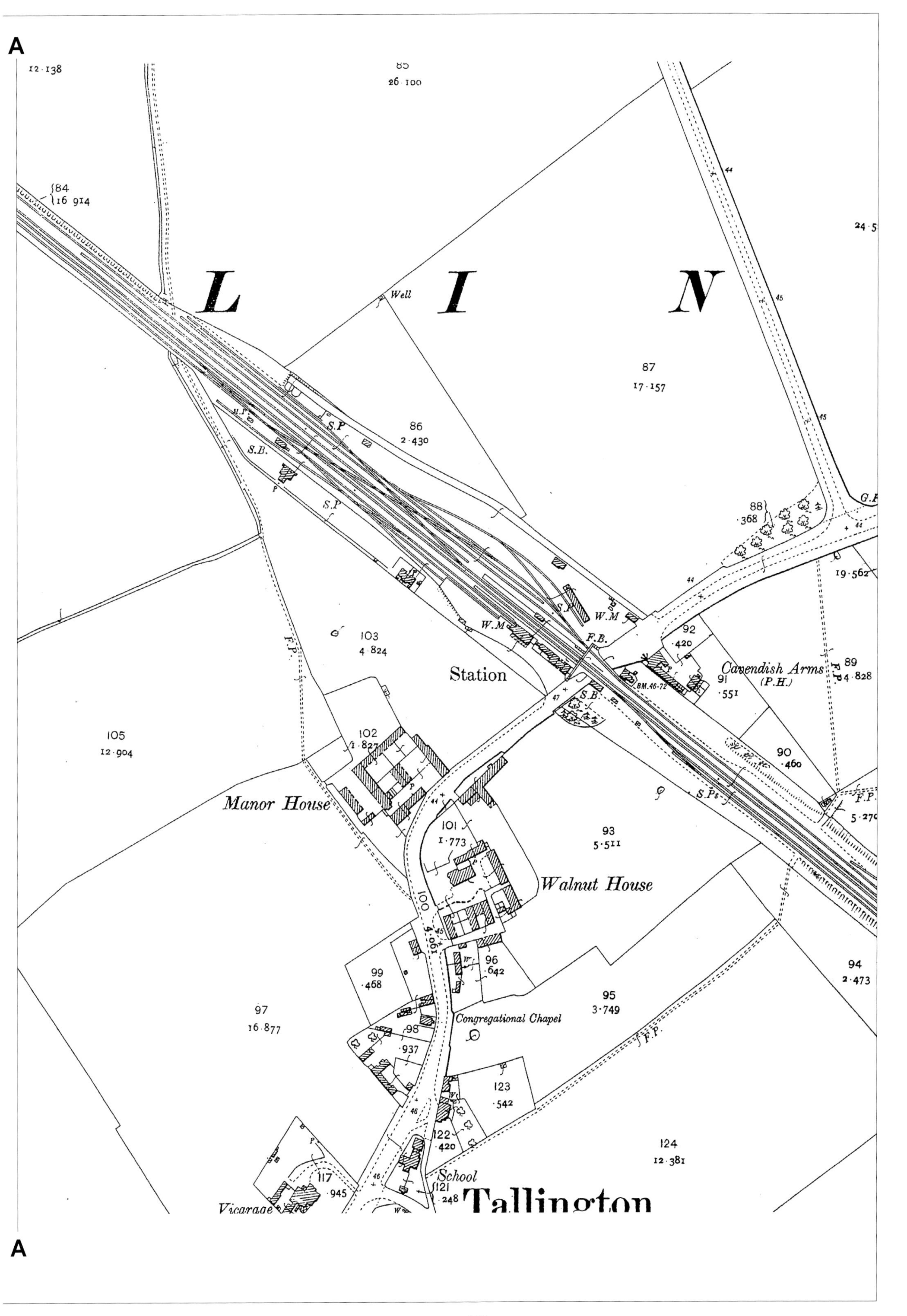
LIN
Station
Manor House
Walnut House
Cavendish Arms
(P.H.)
Congregational Chapel
School
Vicarage
Tallington
Well
S.P.
S.B.
W.M.
F.B.
F.P.
G.P.
BM.46·72
85
26·100
12·138
84
16·914
24·5
87
17·157
86
2·430
88
·368
19·562
92
·420
91
·551
89
4·828
103
4·824
105
12·904
102
1·827
90
·460
101
1·773
93
5·511
5·270
100
4·061
99
·468
96
·642
95
3·749
94
2·473
97
16·877
98
·937
123
·542
122
·420
124
12·381
117
·945
121
·248

A

Tallington station with its elegant footbridge and level crossing (now very busy) in 1957. Below shows the station with the down slow and siding connected into the down main. Above is a closer view of the level crossing.

A general view of the station from the down side.

The up goods line passed behind the back of the up platform at Tallington. Observe how flat the country is by now.

Pacific, breasting Stoke at say 45-50mph unless the driver was one of the more spirited runners. On my first trip on the Pullman with BLACK WATCH, the speed was doubled, 100mph on the approach, and she tore past Stoke at 90mph! In 1959 Bill Hoole topped Stoke Bank at 82 mph with the 295 ton SLS Jubilee special: five years later the Deltic-hauled Aberdonian passed Stoke box at exactly the same speed with exactly twice the load. The Deltics may have been hard on engine life, on maintenance, and on costs, but they gave that irreplaceable thrill of brute power. They gave the East Coast expresses an enormous increase in speed, away from the best of the steam age, towards the speeds of today.

The MR line from Peterborough to Stamford and Leicester was on the western side, running parallel to the main line after the divergence of the M&GN. Leaving the New England complex behind, Walton was the first of a number of level crossings on the climb to Stoke summit. The line needed to cross a limestone ridge at the 100th milepost, but otherwise the countryside was fairly flat. The lower part of Stoke Bank had a surprising incidence of level crossings – five – which rarely intervened on operations in the form of signal delays.

The crossing gates at Walton at one time suffered a number of collisions or glancing blows from up expresses overrunning. As explained with the signalling of the level crossing at Arlesey, the operation of absolute block signalling through level crossings was cumbersome unless adjacent signalboxes gave early warning of approaching trains. While the Rule Book and Regulations made no reference to road traffic, assuming that the gates were simply closed when necessary, in fact life was often different, and the signalman was often made very aware of the displeasure of road users for presuming to delay their journey by a few minutes!

At Werrington Junction, the line to Boston diverged to the east, and immediately after the junction there lay a set of water troughs. The MR line continued alongside as far as Helpston before diverging to the west, and the main line swung to the north over Maxey curve. The down slow ran from Werrington to south of Tallington, and from that station to Greatford. Otherwise the additional down road reverted to goods status to Stoke box, apart from station platforms. The up slow ran from Stoke to Little Bytham and from Essendine North to Tallington; elsewhere it was the up goods. At Helpston there is another level crossing, a third at Lolham, a fourth at Tallington on the A16, and a fifth at Greatford. With the introduction of power signalling and 125mph running, Helpston and Tallington were retained as gate boxes, the crossing keepers supervising Maxey and Lolham, and Greatford respectively with CCTV supervision. The crossing keeper at the 'gate box' actually controlled barriers rather than gates, despite the name.

The descent from Stoke was the fastest section of track in the country during the steam era, where the highest speed with steam traction was achieved, on July 3rd 1938. Although Stoke Bank figures extensively in East Coast steam mythology, the ascent was nowhere near such an obstacle as Beattock, Shap, Honiton, Dainton and Hemerdon. It was a long, gentle ascent, and it was the speed maintained over its length with the streamliners and faster express services post-war that was important. With the descent. it was necessary to watch the speed, for a Pacific in good condition not calling at Grantham would reach 100mph without too much difficulty. With Deltic, HST and electric power, Stoke Bank is no more, and expresses regularly achieve the maximum speed permitted, 125mph, in either direction. The line rose gently to Essendine before the gradient sharpened a little more over the last ten miles. Its fame in the steam era derived from its 20 mile length, the superb quality of the track and, with fast approach to Stoke from the north, the achievement of truly magnificent bursts of speed 'down the hill' when one could enjoy the thrill of a Gresley A4 Pacific at full speed.

The main line north of Peterborough was specially engineered as part of the BR East Coast electrification of the late 1980s for 140mph running by specially authorised test trains. It was hoped at the time to introduce 140 mph maximum speeds, and the Cl.91 AC electric locomotives were designed with this objective. For a short while BR InterCity marketed the 'Electra' trains as InterCity225, the diesel electric

Essendine station from the south end, down side. The Stamford branch ran into the down slow, and the branch service is in the platform with a C12 4-4-2T at the head. An up express is no doubt speeding through on the up main, headed by the W1 4-6-2-2 No.60700. Dr Ian C. Allen, www.transporttreasury.co.uk

Essendine station looking north from the up side. The old Bourne branch bay was by then used as a siding.

HSTs of the 1970s originally being InterCity200. The Railway Inspectorate, concerned for the safety of on-track staff, would not give approval to 140 mph running until a satisfactory train-operated warning system had been installed. There were a few designs in existence at the time, but the commitment in investment and resources over the route, signalled as it was with equipment of differing vintages, was unlikely to be justified by the additional income arising from 140 mph running. The 140 mph section was indicated by the use of a flashing green aspect. With normal running, drivers ignored the flashing aspect. The arrival of powerful electric locomotives required crew training, and with growing confidence, drivers occasionally could not resist testing the capabilities of their new traction. At this time a colleague returned to London from Peterborough, and in passing, mentioned that as the train seemed to be travelling rather fast, he noted that it had only taken 22 minutes to pass Hitchin from a Peterborough start!

Stoke signalbox was the northern boundary of the Peterborough Resignalling carried out in the 1970s and completed in 1975, and most of what was encountered in bringing the Kings Cross Resignalling into being was also encountered at Peterborough. From Stoke onwards the line is under the control of Doncaster power box. Ten satellite relay rooms were controlled from the power box. The decrepit electrical detection and safety systems of the old GNR/LNER boxes were a liability, and it was the excellence of manual operation and system maintenance that enabled the signalling to give such good service in terms of safety. The control of the level crossings was more of a problem at Peterborough. Where a crossing had no adjacent road junction nearby to cause a tailback on to the railway, automatic half-barriers (AHBs) were installed. If there was or is a danger of a tailback preventing the crossing being cleared, then CCTV monitoring has to be provided so that the signalman can inspect and clear the barriers, ensuring that no vehicle is trapped on the crossing. Together with correct road profiles to prevent long vehicles from grounding, warning signs and alarms represent a considerable advance on the old gated crossings despite the visual assurance that the latter gave. That is also despite the tendency of otherwise perfectly rational people to drive their vehicles round the lowered barriers into the path of an approaching train at speed, and then blame the existence of the level crossing when they are caught. Or worse. The strike-in point, where the detection equipment to drop the barriers of an AHB is located, is a good way in the rear, although over the years it has been moved to and fro as a result of accidents and subsequent recommendations. With 125mph running, I believe that the Railway Inspectorate required AHBs to be replaced by bridges, CCTV supervision, or the road had to be diverted.

The East Coast main line had an enviable reputation for the quality of its track, and Stoke bank and the York plain were the showpieces for fast running. Aspects of track maintenance have been touched on already, but while maintaining the basic geometry remained the objective, the means has changed radically from the days of the GNR. The GNR would have had length gangs maintaining typically a mile or two of the line on foot, although with more tracks and S&C (switches and crossings) that distance would have been less. It was patrolled daily by the ganger who noted where attention was required. Alignment was corrected by slueing, 4-8 men using sluing bars under the ganger's direction. Correction of the 'top' was achieved by packing ballast or chippings back under the sleepers, in one of three ways. The original method was 'beater packing' in which the ballast or ash was hammered back under the sleepers with a special beater, a cross between a pickaxe and sledge hammer, until the correct rail level was reached. The second method was 'fly packing', where the track was lifted to level by jacking, and suitably sized ballast put under the sleepers. Here the ganger's judgment was vital. 'Measured shovel packing' (MSP) was third, the

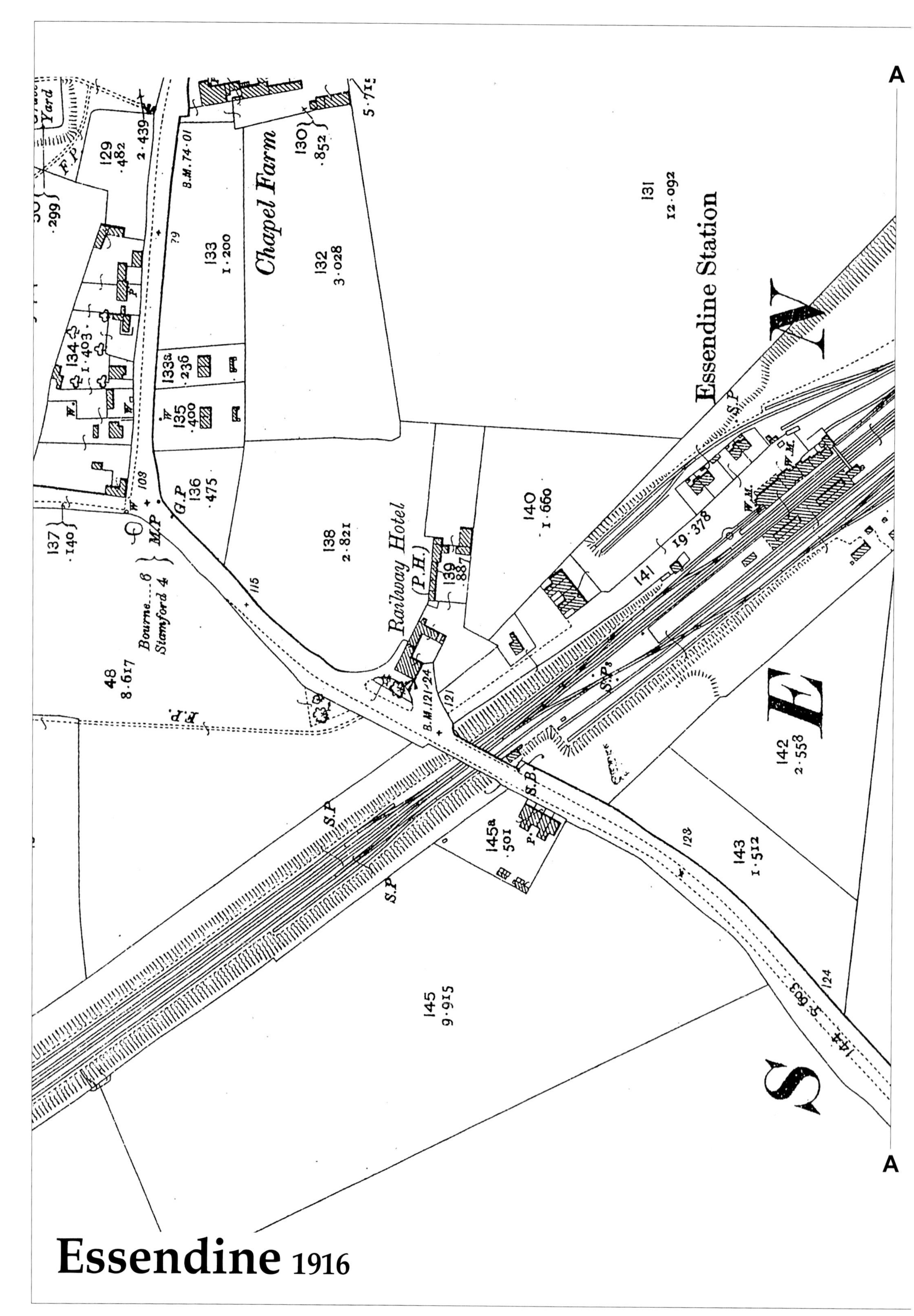

Essendine 1916

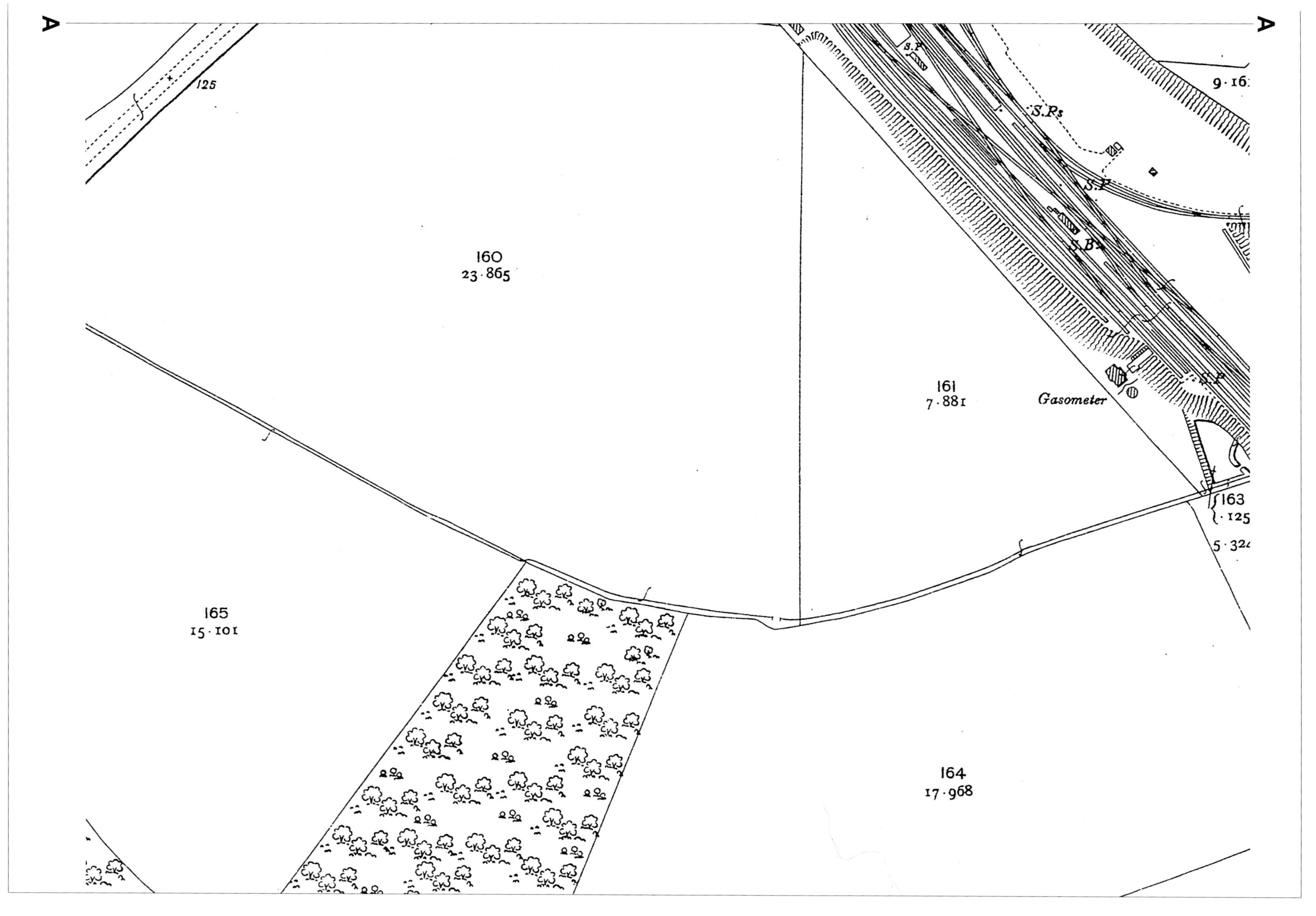
A
A
125
160
23·865
161
7·881
Gasometer
S.P.
S.Ps
S.B.
9·16
163
·125
5·32
165
15·101
164
17·968

Little Bytham station looking north towards the M&GN lattice girder bridge.

bespoke method that was displaced by tamping. The cavity under the track was measured under traffic, the track was then lifted and a measured amount of chippings spread beneath the sleepers. Chippings were unloaded into bins by the track side. The bins survive, though I doubt whether many are used now with the advent of tamping. It was slow, but properly repaired track would stand for at least many months if not much longer and give a good ride. The SNCF, while proclaiming the undoubted excellence of their traction and rolling stock, kept quiet about their use of MSP to maintain a superb track. Photographs could not disguise the presence of regular heaps of chippings every 60ft in the six-foot between the tracks, even into the 1980s!

By the 1950s, gangs had weakened seriously since men were reluctant to work hard for poor pay in uncongenial and, let it be said, primitive and occasionally dangerous conditions. In the suburbs gangs had to double up to form an effective working team. With the development of machines that would tamp the ballast, notably from Matisa of Switzerland at first, then Plasser & Theurer, it was decided to reorganise with mechanised maintenance as the basis. Gangs were then placed in charge of lengths some 4 to 6 times greater, and the grades were renamed. Patrolling became the responsibility of patrolmen (leading trackmen) in place of the ganger (track chargeman) who were expected to make a written record of their patrol in a notebook. Alas for armchair reorganisation, for many could not or would not write while some were not British and were unfamiliar with the language, and so made their report verbally and simply ticked their notebooks, which told the reader nothing.

The effort to bring track maintenance into the world of machines, office administration, work study and personnel management was successful but there were serious and ultimately expensive mistakes. One was to assume that men who would otherwise be in basic agriculture thought like office clerks – wrong. Another was to assume that all track was ready for tamping – also wrong. Tamping itself took several years to become established, with unreliable machines, even more unreliable operators, and maintenance undertaken inadequately by BR staff rather than employ skilled contractors. One could go on, but there was no alternative but to make it all work. The main lines, well ballasted and drained, gradually improved with the new system. With the advent of CWR, the level of patrolling was reduced. The safety of staff became more important as speeds rose; for example, when working on a high speed curved location the number of lookout men alone could rise to at least four.

Management has always given priority to the maintenance of high quality as well as safety on the main line. With the CWR, granite ballast replaced blast furnace slag as mentioned already, but the ballast profile for the track was enhanced to avoid buckling in hot weather, or distortion in cold weather, and the consumption of ballast increased considerably. The main line tracks have been patrolled in more recent times by a recording car, which also records rail examination. Manual maintenance has almost been replaced now, but it is still required at individual trouble spots. I remember riding on a Deltic, and only finding two places between Kings Cross and Doncaster that required any attention, in embarrassing contrast to my own patch to the south of the Thames! But I digress.

Tallington was the first intermediate station with its level crossing, opened in 1853 with the others on this section, with a down platform face and an up island platform. There was no down slow through the station and the stopping services, albeit few, had to block the down main. The second up line became the up goods south of the station. Fortunately for express passengers, there were few stopping services. However, it passed through the Uffington estate, owned by Lord Lindsay, who had the reputation of driving a hard bargain. To pass over his land the Directors had to agree that Lindsay and any of his staff had the right to stop a train at Tallington for their use.

By 1883 the GNR found that the number of expresses being stopped at

Tallington had become unacceptable, and negotiated an end to the concession. That it cost £1,000, an enormous sum in those days, was testimony to Lindsay's commercial acumen! When the route was quadrupled, the down slow/goods line was not continued through Tallington station, since additional land would have been required on the down side. I would not be surprised if the GNR Directors accepted this inconvenience rather than risk another passage-at-arms with Lord Lindsay! The Dowmac factory on the east side of the line has supplied at least half of the millions of concrete sleepers used on the national network over the years. The stations in the area were all closed in 1959.

At Essendine, two branch lines once converged, from Stamford in the west, and from Bourne in the east. Essendine was a mirror image of Tallington, with a down island platform and an up slow platform face. It had a North and South signalbox prior to the Peterborough Resignalling. The Stamford branch used the outer, down slow face, while the Bourne branch trains used an up bay. The up main had no platform. The Bourne branch was closed in 1951, usually worked by an elderly 0-6-0 from Boston or New England depots, latterly a J6. The Stamford branch was worked by the GNR C12 4-4-2Ts, although these were replaced up to closure by the GCR N5 0-6-2Ts. The branch closed in June 1959. One of the happy memories of Essendine was running in on the 10.40 slow service from Kings Cross with its top link A4 alongside the 12.15 from Stamford with, in contrast, the unmistakeable shape of its C12 at the head.

Just north of Essendine is the fastest place, usually, on the 20 mile descent from Stoke, and any visit there used to be rewarded by the sight of expresses at full speed. It is difficult a century later to imagine the sight of such as Patrick Stirling's single wheelers at speed in GN days. In the last days of the GN and during pre-war LNER days, the superheated Ivatt Atlantics often made fast runs down the bank, especially the Copley Hill engines with the Yorkshire or Queen of Scots Pullmans before being displaced by Pacifics. O.S. Nock, travelling on the footplate, recorded a remarkable 93mph with No.4456 on the Queen of Scots, which knowing the reputation of the Atlantics for wild riding, must have been a feat of note-taking whilst holding on for dear life! As at Hitchin, it was neither the diesel nor electric traction that impressed so much as the older single blast engines, driven harder than usual, that created the more vivid impressions. On a summer Saturday, with New England's V2s pressed into express duty, the sight and sound of a grimy black V2 being driven hard downhill was a sight to relish! I remember the vivid impression made by New England's No.60893 hurtling south with a Leeds express, more memorable than the A4s that were probably travelling even faster. When Kings Cross men with their A4s took over the up Flying Scotsman at Grantham, often late, there were some mighty efforts made, especially down Stoke Bank. It was an opportunity to be grasped, for after a hard five mile start uphill, the A4 had to be driven hard up to speed to get time back. With full regulator, the cut-off would be reduced a little to avoid the risk of wheelslip at speed through Stoke Tunnel, and then it was 25-30% down the bank to get this heavy 500 ton train flying. Several Kings Cross top link men such Ted Hailstone, Joe Howard, Harry Willers and Bill Hoole managed to exceed 90 mph at Essendine, and the best effort I recall was 96mph just north of Essendine with just over 500 tons. Later, with lighter loads, as well as the A4s, several of the Peppercorn A1s and double Kylchap A3s were recorded at 100 mph from the Grantham start.

Thinking of those days, I remember meeting Ted Hailstone off the up Flying Scotsman at Kings Cross with SILVER LINK, having arrived early on a lodging turn from Newcastle. His fireman, up on the A4, was a stranger, and having asked who he was, I learnt that he was a senior fireman, redundant from somewhere in the remoter recesses of the GE. On his second day he had gone to Newcastle with Ted. It

The southern approach to Great Ponton station and goods yard.

Little Bytham

Little Bytham in 1914. Note the formation of the branch to Edenham, long since lifted. As at Essendine the addition of goods lines has started but has some way to go before the 1950s layouts were achieved.

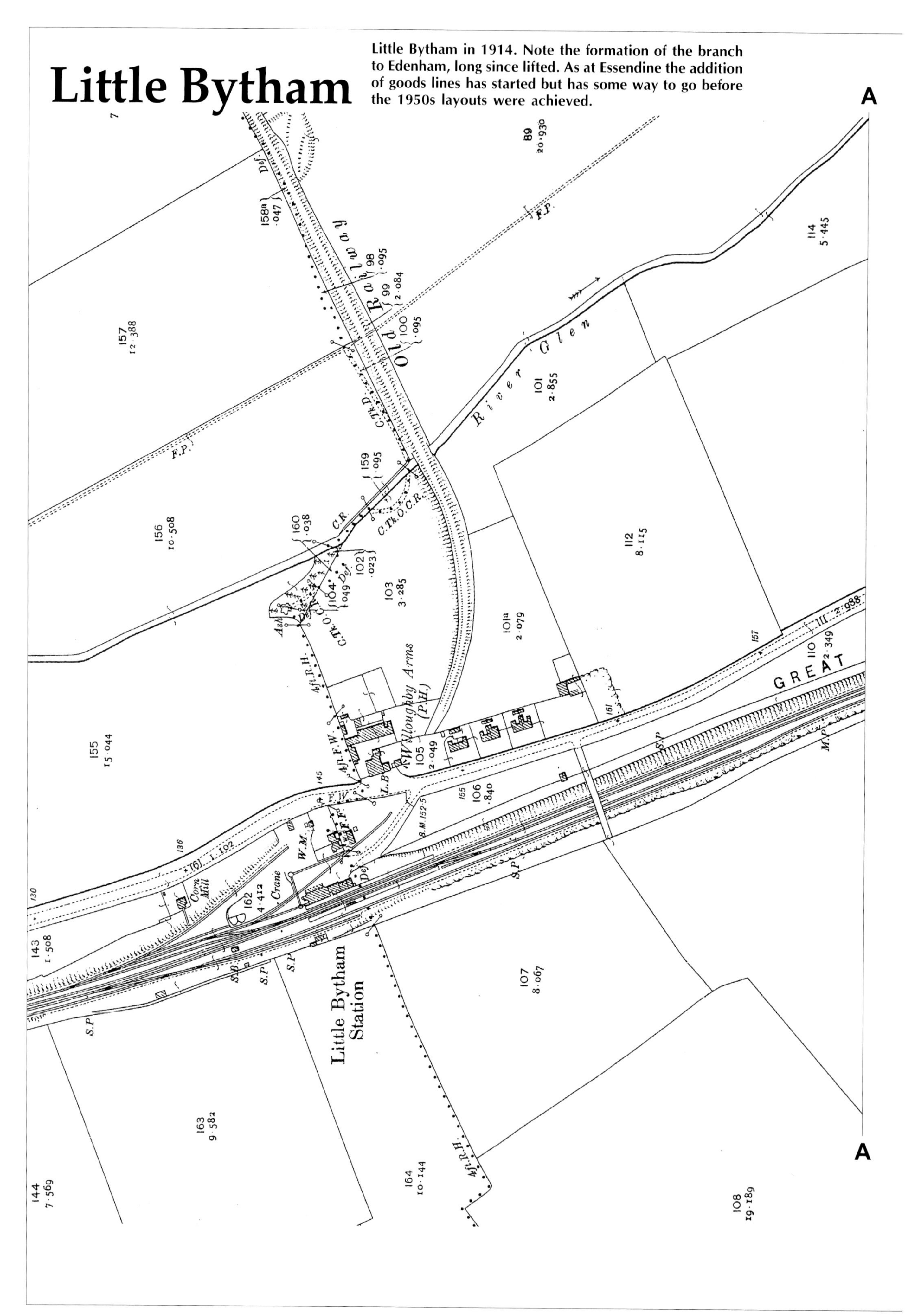

A

NORTHERN RAILWAY
Ca
School
Smy.
P.O.
S.Ps.
Spring
B.M.144·0
B.M.142·5
B.M.156·8
B.M.206·5
109
31·165
113
13·273
115
16·211
116
·633
117
1·370
118
16·702
119
13·258
120
42·450
122
3·364
123
4·081
124
·152
125
·786
126
·534
127
1·970
128
2·728
129
2·758
131
9·702
137
12·196

A

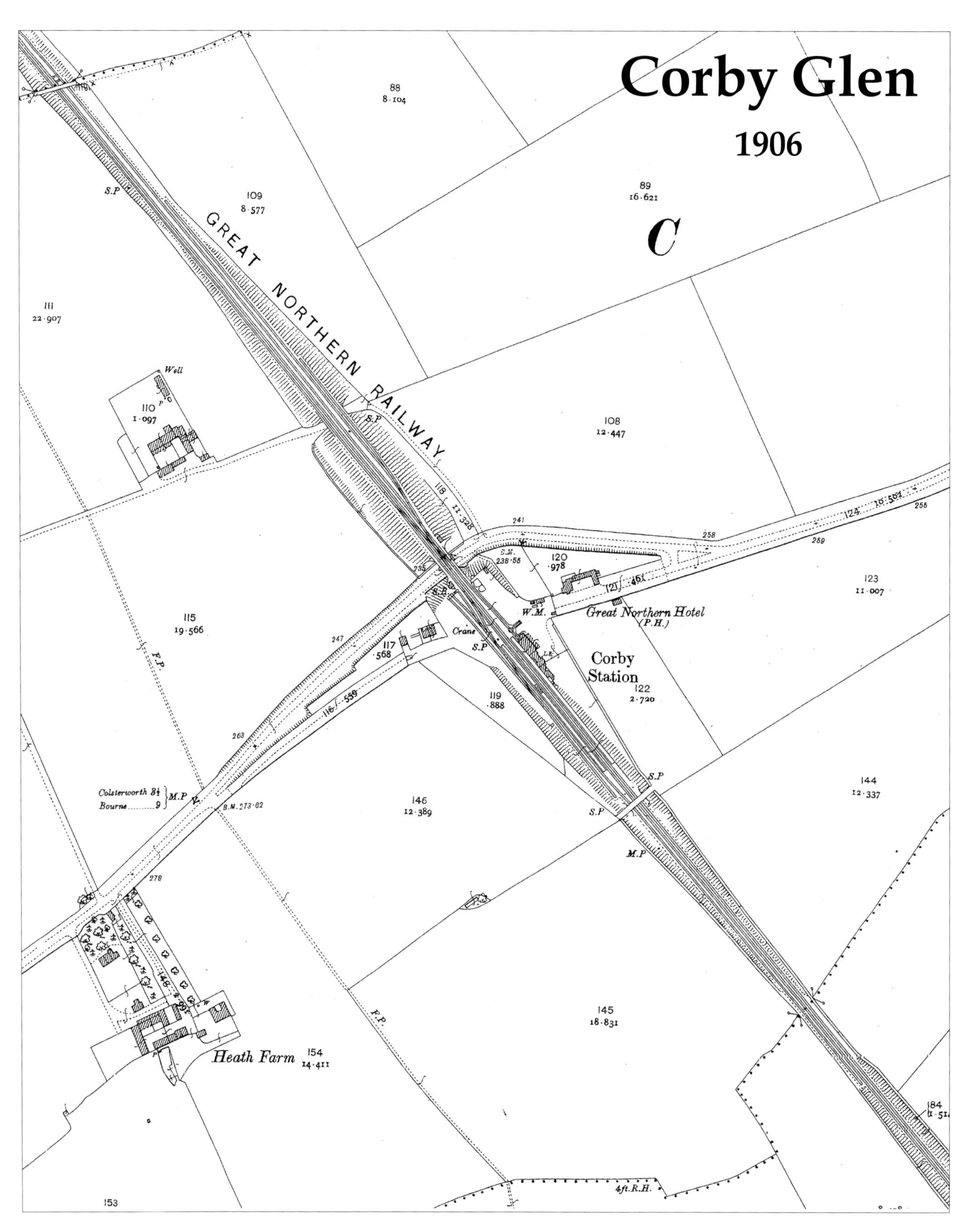

was his third day, and his first experience of Stoke Bank at high speed. He had never travelled so fast in his life – much to the driver's amusement! I remember Bill Watts' horror in similar circumstances, firing to Bill Hoole on SEAGULL with the Elizabethan. Bill Watts was a lad from Kings Lynn, raised on Clauds and Little Black Goods, and a wide open regulator at 30-35% cut-off at 80-90mph was not to his liking! One could see the sense of BR/ASLEF rules for promotion, but sometimes they were a bit hard on country lads.

Over the years some strange locomotives were pushed hard down the hill, for no better reason than it was a lot easier than pushing hard uphill! The Pacifics and V2s dominated overwhelmingly, but before the 1939-45 war in LNER days one might have seen a K3 2-6-0 at speed, no doubt a mildly terrifying prospect for a fireman new to express work on the main line. In the early 1950s, an A1, No.60122 CURLEW was failed at Highdyke with the up 14 coach West Riding. By way of replacement, Grantham could only supply a rebuilt class B12 4-6-0, No.61553, which continued to lose time with this heavy train, but must have been quite a sight being pressed somewhat harder than three coaches to Nottingham or some such. In the middle 1950s the engine with the 13.52 Saturday express to Leeds came off at Grantham,

The up Yorkshire Pullman headed by A1 No.60118 ARCHIBALD STURROCK climbing south of Grantham towards Stoke on 2nd June 1959.

turned, and returned to Kings Cross with one of the up expresses such as the White Rose or Heart of Midlothian, probably about 470-480 tons. By Saturday lunchtime, Top Shed had usually used most of the available power, and on one occasion, one senses in desperation, a rebuilt class B16 4-6-0 off a York freight lodging turn, No.61420, was sent out with the 13.52, which Grantham happily sent back! Remarkably, it was not far off right time running in to London. It must have been an unforgettable sight at Essendine. However, still more remarkable, for much the same reason, Shedmaster Peter Townend was reduced to a class 9F 2-10-0, No.92184, for the 13.52. 9Fs had been used for the Saturday 12.38 lunchtime service to Biggleswade and the 13.35 to Peterborough, so it was a calculated risk. Grantham were asked to provide something more appropriate for the return duty. Maybe they were, but maybe they were short as well, or perhaps took the view that a 9F for one of their prize A1s was a poor bargain. Another Pacific took the 'White Rose', but the 9F came back with the equally heavy up relief to the Heart of Midlothian. No doubt the 9F climbed with ease to Stoke, but it reached an amazing maximum of 90mph at Essendine. The presence of enthusiasts timing the run ensured its enduring fame, and the attention of senior management was also ensured as the Line Manager, Gerry Fiennes was returning on the train. It was said locally by way of attempted clarification that Driver Baur thought he had a Britannia Pacific, but I doubt whether anyone believed it. I often wondered quite what the crews concerned thought about the unconventional steeds that management occasionally presented them with.

Just over two miles or so to the north, on July 3rd 1938, the fastest steam locomotive in the world, MALLARD, reached 125 mph on the up main, possibly 126 mph for a few sleepers. This historic feat is commemorated by a lineside sign in the style adopted by the LNER, placed by the Gresley Society Trust. This was not the only record breaking descent from Stoke: a special run with a specially prepared HST attained 148.4mph, a world record for diesel traction. A class 91 electric locomotive reached 162mph in 1989, exactly the same as that reached by the prototype APT down Beattock bank some years earlier.

Between Essendine and Little Bytham an early signalling scheme introduced automatic IB signals sited on the main lines at Monkswood, near the 90½ milepost, breaking the new block section in two. In the same way another set was at Counthorpe, by the 94¾ milepost. Just before Little Bytham the climb to the summit starts in anger, and the lineside begins to show traces of limestone. The station had two island platforms and extensive facilities for agricultural traffic. In 1856 a short private railway from Little Bytham served Edenham on the Grimsthorpe Estate to the east. The M&GN line from Leicester to Bourne passed over the GNR just north of the station on a simple through lattice girder bridge.

The 1906 and 1914 Surveys show the line before the full widening. The down goods/slow had been built, but the stations were unaltered and the up slow yet to be built. A mile north of Little Bytham on the down side lay Lawnwood Sidings, serving a small brickworks off the down goods. The next station was Corby Glen, which took its name not from a nearby valley but the small River Glen that followed the line down to Greatford before turning east to join the Welland. Corby was another two island station with a large goods yard. The down slow extended north just over half a mile to Burton IB signals, which were only on the down lines. Corby had two short level sections before the last three miles to Stoke rose at 1 in 178. It was the point where the steam drivers lengthened the cut-off to hold speed on the final three miles, and usually there was a spurt of 2-4mph so that the minimum speed before the

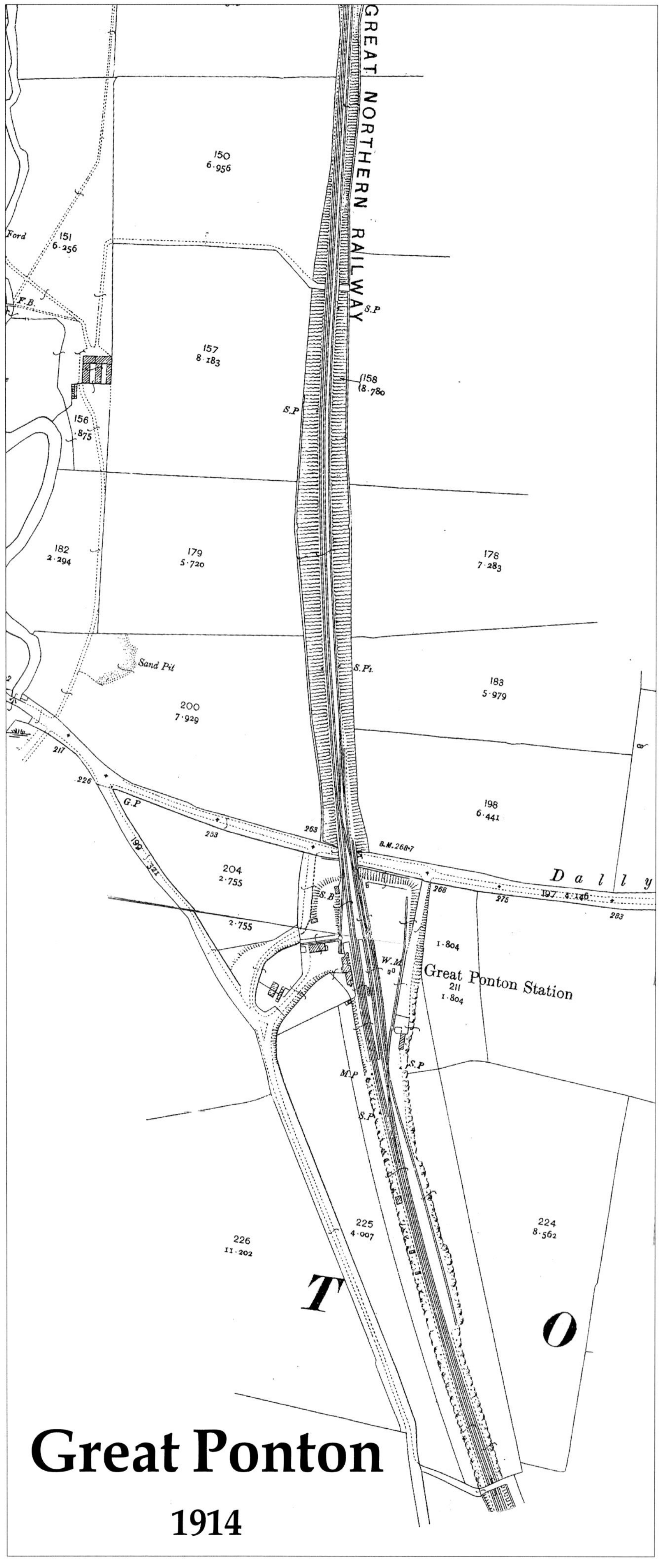

Great Ponton

1914

station, with a light train such as the Talisman, was the same as at Stoke.

As we approach Stoke summit, on the down side of the line, there are long cutting slopes with characteristic markings at right angles to the line that can be seen in various cuttings on the main line. These are counterforts, a method of stabilising cutting and embankment slopes, and there are few lengths of cutting through clay that do not have a section of counterforting that was introduced to stabilise a slip in earlier times. The problem goes back to drainage, once again. The behaviour of soil is imprecise but some very general rules have been determined. Clay slopes have an inclination at which they are generally stable, 2 to 3, which approximates to just under 40°. The Great Central used a flatter slope, 3 to 5, obviously better in avoiding slippage if more costly in land purchase. It was a balance between cost and safety, for the cost implications in the excavation of a deeper or flatter cutting were huge. Water, seeping into the ground at the top of the cutting slope, was a potential lubricant that could eventually render the slope unstable and bring it down. It was rarely very dangerous in fact, but one could never tell. The slipped material had to be removed, and the water drained away, and this was achieved by counterforting. It was a series of deep trenches laid to drain into the track drains, backfilled with blast furnace slag lumps of about 12ins, or later, granite. The stones interlocked and reinforced the slope as well.

The alternative was sheet piling, which was expensive in first cost and difficult to install, particularly if the counterforting previously tried had not been successful. Correct driving was essential if the piles were to interlock as a retaining wall. It is difficult to drive piles plumb through boulders. Either one brought a crane and pile driving equipment on a train and unloaded it, or it came in by road. In recent years Network Rail has improved road access enormously, but rarely was there a convenient road access to the foot of the slip in the past. It usually meant shutting one of the slow lines for a week or so.

Slips occur with embankments too, although they should drain freely, but their consistency is variable, made up with ash, clay or stone. As with other parts of the railway, the records of how the line was built, and with what, do not exist. Where the balance of cut and fill had not been achieved, extra fill was obtained from 'borrow' pits at the lineside. The later treatment for cutting or embankment slips was the injection of grout – cement mortar slurry – into the bank, a process that was very successful and had the advantage of continuing under traffic, protected by a TSR. The slurry was a mixture of cement, sand and water, assisted by additives. Grouting proceeded to a plan. The injection tube is driven into the embankment to a depth of 6-10ft, a quantity of grout pumped in, then the tube is withdrawn 3ft, another quantity injected, and so on. Too great a concentration of grout could actually bring the bank down, so a plan was important. Where property was endangered at the foot of the bank, one had to look at different methods such as a dwarf retaining wall or, as a last resort, sheet piling. In the early days of grouting some unfortunate incidents occurred with the grout emerging in quite unexpected places, largely due to inadequate control over quantities used. This sometimes led to considerable agricultural correspondence at harvest time!

As we near the top of the bank, the line runs into a deep cutting, spanned near the 99th milepost by a splendid high arch bridge built in brick. A photogenic location, the purpose of the bridge was, and as far as I know still is, to link two parts of a farm property severed by the construction of the railway. It was a very expensive solution to a modest problem, but of course one is not aware of the subtleties of land negotiation at the time of railway construction.

Stoke summit was at the 100th milepost, with the signalbox just nearby. The down goods and up slow terminated here, and the two tracks curved to the west and fell at 1 in 200 to Grantham down through Stoke Tunnel which, at 880 yards, was a very useful means of measuring the speed precisely. The change from 1 in 178 rising to 1 in 200 falling required a very slight vertical curve: these were of large radius in railway work where gradients are nearly always relatively gentle. It was the arrival of the Deltics that brought this matter to the fore, since speeds of 90mph and more at the summit were quite unprecedented – even with a crew and a light Pacific returning home! The slight uplift was discernable, and with the overhaul of the main line, Stoke was remodelled and the summit eased to a flatter curve for the higher speeds.

From Stoke to Doncaster the East Coast main line was double track with the occasional additional loop lines for overtaking slow-moving freight. At the north end of the tunnel the railway swung to the east past Highdyke signalbox. At Highdyke there were two sets of sidings on the down side, one south of the box and one north, both leading in towards the box. A mineral branch came in from the west, from the open-cast iron ore mines at Sproxton and Stainby. Ironstone mining in the area started in the 1890s, with links to the Midland and M&GN, and the GNR branch was completed in 1909 when the steel industry at Scunthorpe was in its infancy.

The branches from the two mines ran east and combined at Skillington Road, a small signalbox with a splendid array of GN somersault signals. The branch then ran east down a 1 in 40 gradient over the A1 road, and up 1 in 40 before descending another 1 in 40 towards Highdyke. It joined the main line on a sharp curve past the box running into Highdyke north sidings, which rose towards the north. This was a precaution in case of a runaway. The loaded wagons were shunted into the south sidings, marshalled into trains for Scunthorpe. Empties travelled in the reverse direction.

As the branch had severe gradients in its length, it required a powerful locomotive. It was probably worked by GNR 'Long Tom' 0-8-0s, succeeded soon by Gresley 2-8-0 of classes O1 (GNR) and the three cylinder O2 2-8-0s, one or two of which could be seen from a passing train in the days of steam. The O2 was a strong locomotive usually seen rolling along slowly with a big train, but freight locomotives were not kept in pristine condition, especially three cylinder ones. On the branches from Highdyke, it was necessary to take a run at 1 in 40 with a loaded train in order to climb it, and the O2s showed a surprising turn of speed. To hear one being urged up to speed was very uncomfortable to hear. Diesel traction was, I believe, tried out, but the traffic ceased as a result of the import of superior/cheaper ore from Sweden. From Grantham Yard box to Highdyke there was an additional up goods line to relieve the up main from delays caused by slow moving freight.

Just beyond was the station at Great Ponton, comprising a down platform and an island with a platform face only on the up main. The goods yard was on the down

The approach to Grantham from the south. An up goods line ran from Grantham Yard to Highdyke, and the water column allowed trains to stand clear of the up main while taking water.

Grantham down yard in 1958 with ex-GNR C12 4-4-2T No.67352 as station pilot. K. Cook.

side, and there also were up sidings connected into the goods line. The small signalbox was rebuilt as a brick structure with a concrete slab roof, an architectural style used post-war throughout the East Coast main line, Potters Bar signalbox being the best-known example. The limestone scenery was similar to that farther west in the Cotswolds, looking quite out of place on the eastern side of the country. The next signalbox was at Saltersford, north of a deep cutting, halfway between Great Ponton and Grantham, but that was removed by another early IB scheme. A down goods loop capable of holding an 80 wagon freight was installed at Saltersford during the 1939-45 war, later recovered in the 1950s. The deep cutting slopes north of Saltersford had given trouble in the past, and heavy counterforting is evident.

Grantham was virtually a three-quarter sized version of Peterborough with only one up line and platform face, and a down island with two platform faces. Bay platforms were located at the north end of both down and up platforms but not the south. There were three signalboxes, South, Yard, and North. Yard stood at the south end of the up platform, so relief engines for the up expresses ran through beforehand and reversed into the loco spur behind the box. Both the down slow and goods were signalled for bi-directional running. At Grantham South on the up side there was a large iron works shown in the 1931 Survey, later replaced by an engineering works producing both Aveling Barford agricultural equipment and Ruston & Hornsby products. Services came in from Nottingham, Lincoln, Sleaford, Boston and before the war, from Leicester, to terminate at Grantham. Grantham had also been a calling point for many expresses since its very beginnings. Its position became more important with the arrival of Gresley A1 Pacifics in LNER days, as an engine changing point.

Grantham has a long and distinguished history in East Coast locomotive affairs. Of the first twelve A1s ordered by the GNR, Grantham had three. With the delivery of the 20 LNER A1s, Grantham received another seven. The condition of Grantham's fleet, even in days when locomotives were usually scrupulously clean, was immaculate, and it was said that Grantham's A1s were still wonderfully clean after 211 miles to London and back with heavy trains. As through working between London and Newcastle increased, Grantham's role reduced, and the introduction of the streamliners passed the depot by. During the war some of Top Shed's A4s were sent to Grantham and in wartime duties were exported down country to avoid the bombing. After the 1939-45 war, the number of locomotive transfers increased enormously, and it was impossible to be specific about allocations without relating to a particular date.

In 1951, the Chief Motive Power Officer, L.P. Parker ,decided to increase the extent of engine changing at Peterborough and more importantly, Grantham, to avoid the risk of overheating and steaming troubles with the single chimney Gresley Pacifics. This restored Grantham as an important part of East Coast operation. The depot had a dozen or so of the A3s, and with the introduction of the Peppercorn A1s, four went to Grantham, with the prototype A1/1 GREAT NORTHERN. By September 1951 the fleet had increased to 10, and the Grantham top link of 12 men shared six A1s. The standard of reliability and running, with the A1s often clocking up over 400 miles a day, was on the high side for steam locomotives, and remarkably good, as good as anything achieved in steam days and substantially better than most. Even after the reintroduction of through working on a larger scale with the Talisman in September 1956, the depot continued in good style with fewer A1s and double Kylchap A3s. With diesel traction on the main line the end was not far away, and Grantham is now reduced to manning rural DMU services.

The local services were catered for with elderly GN classes, strengthened post-war with B12 4-6-0s from the GE section. The J6 0-6-0s were a good light mixed traffic locomotive, used extensively on all manner of services, both passenger and freight. Locomotives from Colwick, Doncaster,

A wartime Grantham station, 17th April 1944.

Grantham shed from a passing down train, 3 July 1960. Stephen Gradidge.

B

A

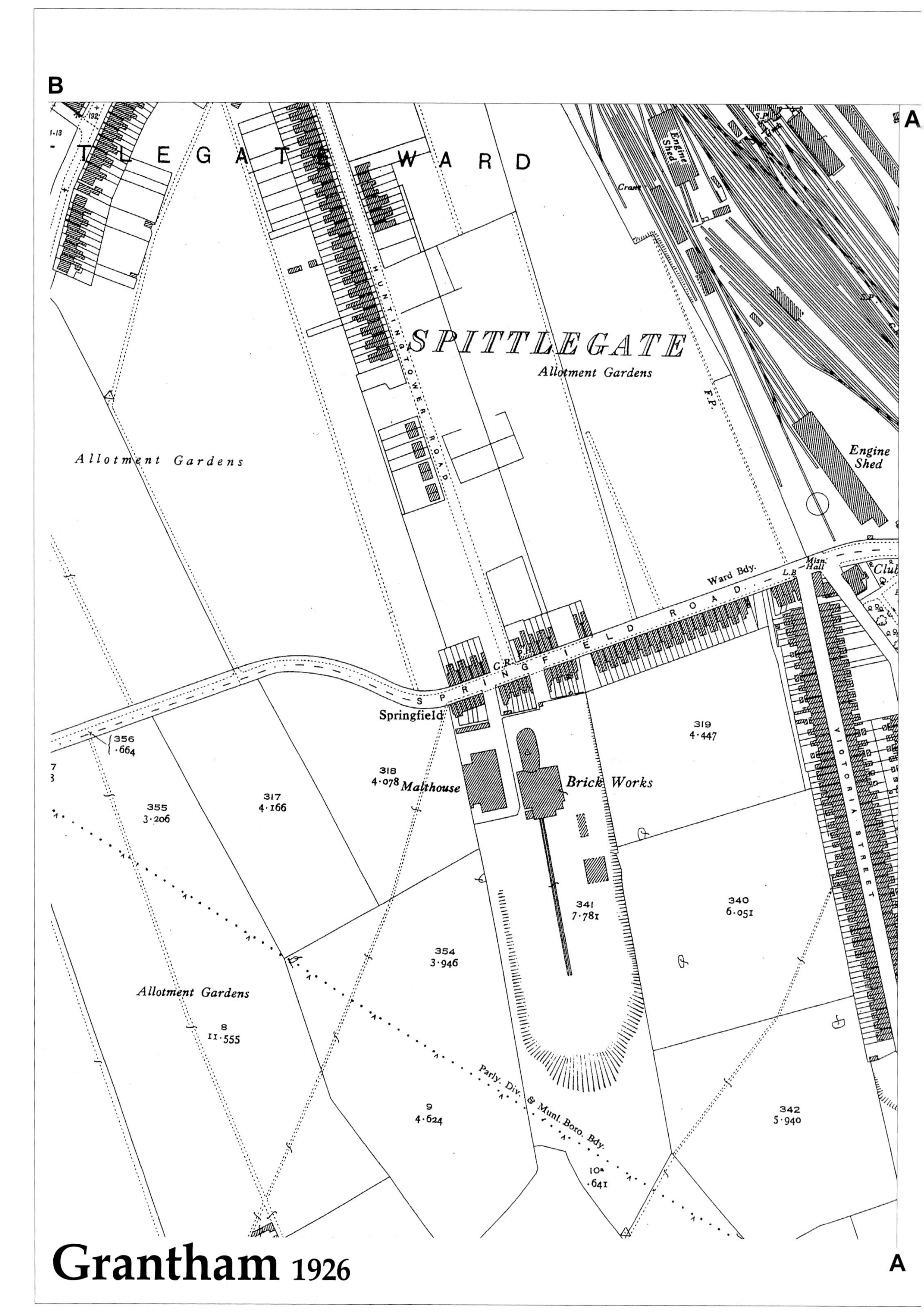

A

Grantham 1926

B

A

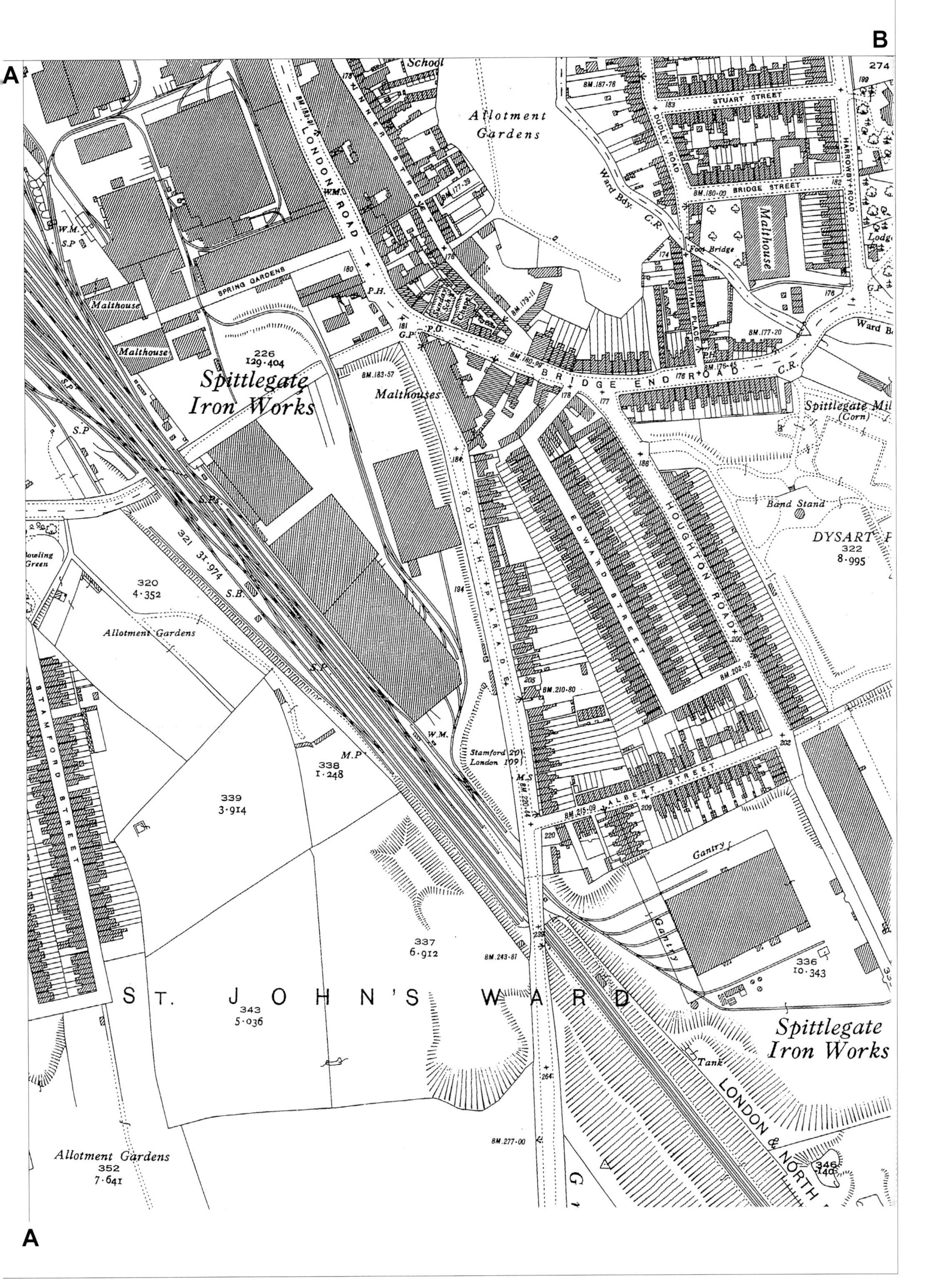

School
Allotment Gardens
LONDON ROAD
SPRING GARDENS
Malthouse
Malthouse
226
129·404
Spittlegate Iron Works
Malthouses
P.H.
P.O.
G.P.
BRIDGE END ROAD
STUART STREET
DUDLEY ROAD
BRIDGE STREET
HARROWBY ROAD
Malthouse
Foot Bridge
WITHAM PLACE
Ward Bdy.
Spittlegate Mill (Corn)
Band Stand
DYSART
322
8·995
274
Lodge
SOUTH PARADE
EDWARD STREET
HOUGHTON ROAD
ALBERT STREET
Bowling Green
320
4·352
321
31·974
Allotment Gardens
STAMFORD STREET
338
1·248
339
3·914
Stamford 20
London 109
Gantry
337
6·912
336
10·343
ST. JOHN'S WARD
343
5·036
Spittlegate Iron Works
Tank
LONDON & NORTH
Allotment Gardens
352
7·641
346
·140

A

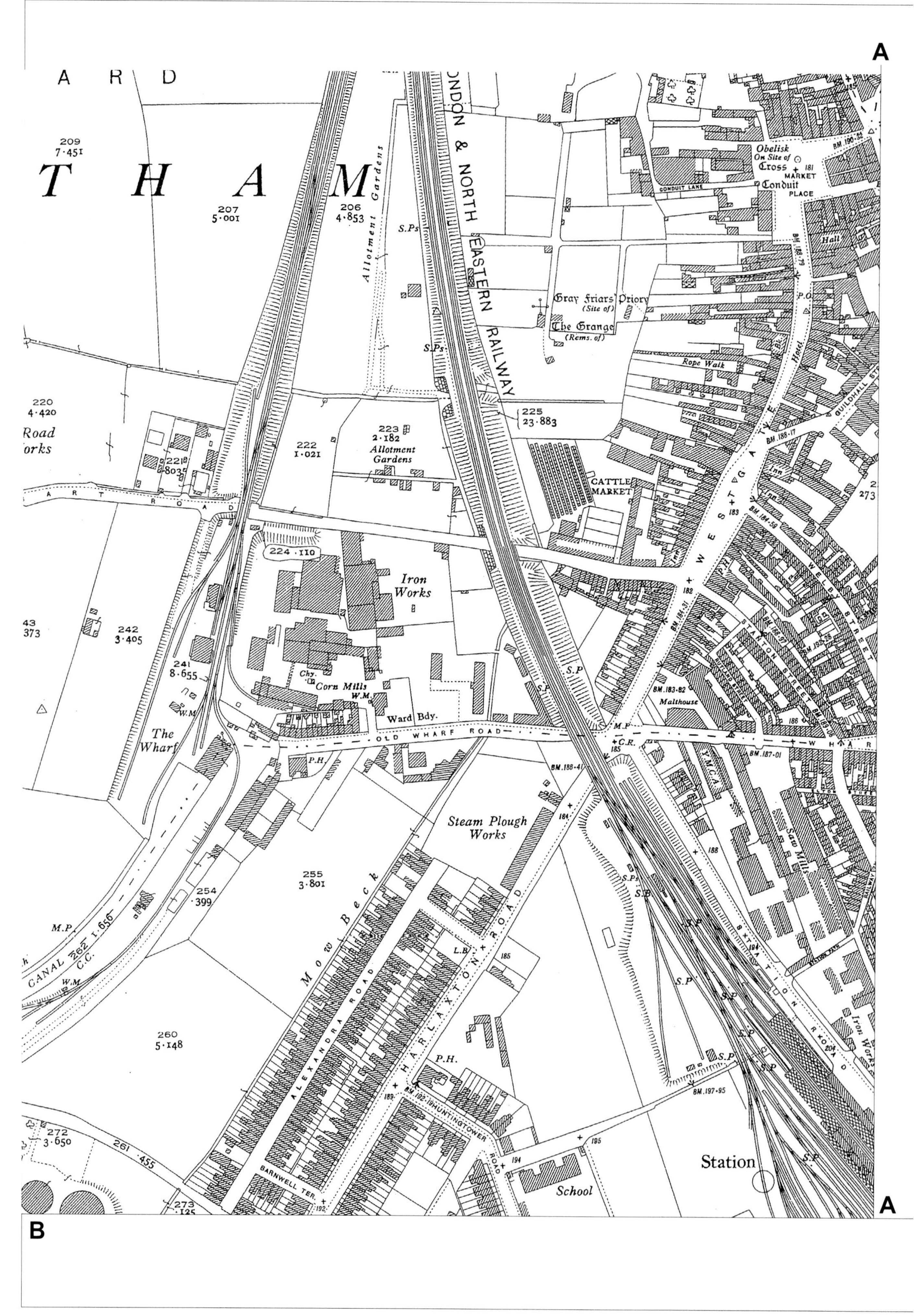
A
A
B
T H A M
ONDON & NORTH EASTERN RAILWAY
Allotment Gardens
Gray Friars' Priory (Site of)
The Grange (Rems. of)
Rope Walk
Obelisk On Site of Cross
Conduit
MARKET PLACE
CONDUIT LANE
Hall
P.O.
Hotel
CATTLE MARKET
Iron Works
Corn Mills
Ward Bdy.
OLD WHARF ROAD
The Wharf
Steam Plough Works
Mow Beck
CANAL
ALEXANDRA ROAD
HARLAXTON ROAD
HUNTINGTOWER ROAD
BARNWELL TER.
School
Station
Malthouse
Y.M.C.A.
Saw Mills
Iron Works
STANTON STREET
WELBY STREET
GUILDHALL STREET
WESTGATE
STATION ROAD
Road Works

A

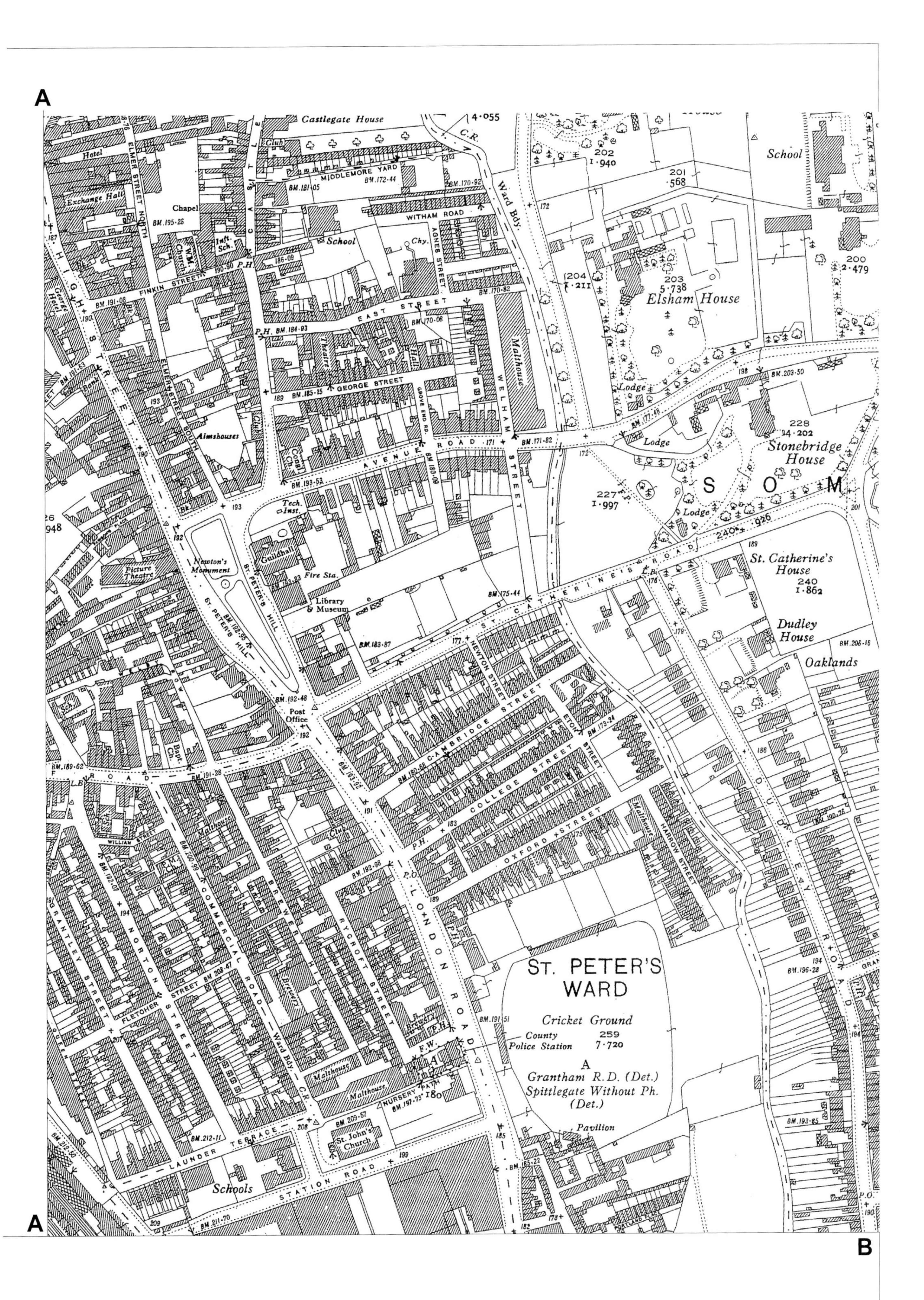

Castlegate House
Club
Hotel
Exchange Hall
Chapel
School
MIDDLEMORE YARD
WITHAM ROAD
Ward Bdy.
FINKIN STREET
EAST STREET
GEORGE STREET
AVENUE ROAD
WELHAM STREET
Malthouse
Theatre
Almshouses
Tech. Inst.
Guildhall
Fire Sta.
Library & Museum
Newton's Monument
Picture Theatre
ST. PETER'S HILL
Post Office
Elsham House
Lodge
Stonebridge House
S O M
St. Catherine's House
Dudley House
Oaklands
ST. CATHERINE'S ROAD
NEWTON STREET
CAMBRIDGE STREET
COLLEGE STREET
OXFORD STREET
ETON STREET
HARROW STREET
DUDLEY ROAD
LONDON ROAD
COMMERCIAL ROAD
BREWERY HILL
RYCROFT STREET
NORTON STREET
FLETCHER STREET
GRANTLEY STREET
WILLIAM STREET
ST. PETER'S WARD
Cricket Ground
County Police Station
Grantham R.D. (Det.)
Spittlegate Without Ph. (Det.)
Pavilion
NURSERY PATH
St. John's Church
LAUNDER TERRACE
STATION ROAD
Schools

A

B

A J6 0-6-0 waits for the road by Grantham Yard box. These fine little 0-6-0s were maids of all work in the area.

Lincoln and Boston worked in as well. Various other classes such as A5 4-6-2Ts and L1 2-6-4Ts were used as well at times. A GNR 4-4-0, D3 No.4075, rebuilt and allocated to Grantham for special duties just after the end of the 1939-45 war, finished in full LNER apple green and numbered 2000, an extraordinary use of scarce funds. One of the strange features of the GN Section was that traffic from the Grimsby area for the south travelled via the East Lincolnshire line and Boston and not Lincoln, doubtless because of history, but also the poor layout and plethora of level crossings at Lincoln were always a problem. As a result, while Immingham's many B1 4-6-0s and K3 2-6-0s were a familiar sight, those from Lincoln were unheard of down south. In the mid-1950s, the first generation DMUs arrived, which improved the quality of travel for passengers on the Lincolnshire routes considerably.

Grantham also enjoyed a place in GNR history for another, less happy reason. On September 19th 1906, Ivatt Large Atlantic No.276 with the 20.45 Kings Cross-Edinburgh, due to call at Grantham, approached the station at excessive speed. Anticipating the need to change locos, Grantham North had set the road for the Atlantic to come off on to the Nottingham branch. Sited where it was, with a heavy right-hand curve, no doubt there was some cant of a sort on the track. The connection would have been limited to 15mph and on a left-hand curve off the back of the main it would have had reverse or negative cant. Estimates of the speed of the express vary from 'high speed' to 50 mph or so, but whatever the speed, it was far too high and the engine and much of the train overturned with tragic results. In such cases the first action was to hold a joint inspection and then enquiry at which the appropriate people were questioned. Normally, although some of the evidence conflicts, a reasonably clear pattern emerges. In this case there was a mass of conflicting evidence which could have suggested a number of different causes. Much of it pointed to a braking failure, but this accident has been examined in fine detail by a number of experts without reaching a clear conclusion.

It was on the busy days before bank holidays in the 1950s that Grantham was at its most interesting. In truth, the provision of services was probably excessive if not in frequency certainly in capacity. New England, Doncaster and York had their large fleets of V2s plundered, and most Pacifics that were available were pressed into service. Shackled by the self-

On 23rd April 1958 a special train of agricultural machinery, chartered by Aveling Barford, pulls out of Grantham Yard behind B1 No.61113, specially cleaned for the occasion.

Grantham at the southern end, by the Yard box, 17th April 1944; MALLARD is on an up express, while Ivatt Atlantic No.4407 waits in the engine bay. The unusual platform starter gantry was originally equipped with somersault arms, but by now upper quadrants had replaced them. It was later replaced by a colour light signal with a 'feather' (the four light route indicator above the aspect).

cleaning apparatus that impaired the steaming of some V2s, punctuality fell off later in the day. Grantham had little freight activity other than the fast freights that ran through, but this and the Highdyke iron ore traffic were suspended on summer Saturdays.

The extensive layout of steam days has receded considerably in extent; the basics remain with three platforms, but the western platform is now fully bidirectional. Grantham remains an important calling point but without the necessity to change crews or engines, some of the principal expresses no longer stop there. A mile north on a heavy right-hand curve lays Barrowby Road Junction, where the branch to Nottingham diverged to the west. It was the curve that restricted speeds to 70mph, if I remember correctly, in steam days. A 1937 scheme replaced the main line signals with IB signals, and the junction was moved to Grantham North, and the box at Barrowby Road was left to control the branch and the entrance to the goods yard at the old station at Ambergate. The old station had a wharf at the end of an arm of the Grantham canal. Later the site was occupied by an iron foundry.

***Below*. The north end at Grantham, 17th April 1944. A filthy unidentified A4 is about to set off for the north, and a Gresley O3 2-8-0 is coming off shed. The down platform starter is, like the up starter, equipped with 'sky' arms to enable crews to read the aspect from a distance. Given the relatively small number of trains running through non-stop the provision seems excessive, but it may have been associated with the operation of the streamliners.**

The staggered platforms of Barkston station, looking south, in 1957; the phrase 'rural outpost' comes immediately to mind. The upper view is of the up platform and that below is the down..

CHAPTER SEVENTEEN

Grantham-Doncaster

The Grantham-Doncaster section was very agricultural with many road and foot crossings, some of which were replaced by bridges. Lineside buildings and road layouts hint at how things once were. A century or so later, the railway has modernised but essentially the agricultural nature of the countryside remains. Leaving Grantham a fast section was entered with the descent to the Trent, continued down a long straight through Peascliffe Tunnel (967 yards). The tunnel, although not through London clay was like that at Stoke, of standard shape and construction. After a cutting there was Barkston. The station had staggered platforms and a small goods yard. The importance of Barkston was that the Nottingham-Sleaford line passed underneath the GN just north of the station, and there were connecting double track spurs towards Sleaford from the main line from either direction, joining at Barkston East Junction. As a result there was a triangle between Barkston's South, East and North Junctions, and although services used the southern chord and the Nottingham-Sleaford line, the northern chord was used mainly by locomotives running-in from Doncaster Works. They ran light to the triangle, turned, then were examined before returning to Doncaster. The triangle was used before the war both for trial runs for new locomotives such as the GN Pacifics, the Mikados, the three streamliners and for test and braking trials, MALLARD's being the most famous.

The downgrade continues through Hougham and Claypole to Newark. At one time there were intermediate boxes at Westborough before Claypole, then Balderton and Barnby before Newark. The route from Grantham to Doncaster runs through flat country, and today has 19 level crossings of various types supervised from five gate boxes plus the power box at Doncaster. In addition there are five farm or foot crossings protected by miniature warning lights. When the operator sets a route in the power box, in this case, Doncaster, the signals protecting the crossing do not clear until the crossing keeper has lowered the barriers, aided by CCTV in most cases to ensure that the crossing is clear, and given the release to the power box. As technology develops, the possibility emerges of concentrating crossing supervision into fewer gate boxes. One crossing keeper or signalling position was considered able to supervise five crossing in BR days, but their location was an important consideration. For example, in 1998 Grove Road crossing was transferred to Ranskill, which supervised four other crossings. A pity, for the box at Grove Road was a fine old GNR building.

Just before Newark the main line was joined by a line carrying mainly freight from the ironstone area to the south-west of Grantham. At Newark, the main station was named North Gate, as distinct from the old MR station, Newark (Castle). The buildings were on the down side, with a down platform and an up island. Bay platforms were at the south end. There were three signalboxes, South, North and Midland Crossing. The last named was controlled by the LM route. The North box controlled a connecting spur to Castle station, with sidings at each end, trailing into the GN main line, by a large brewery.

A colleague of mine had an inspection of his relaying proposals arranged in the days before the car had displaced the Engineer's saloon. He was held up and the District Engineer in his saloon had reached Newark by the time he had caught up. Lunch was programmed to be taken at Newark, and the saloon was stabled on the spur. As he walked up to it, it was obvious that it had become derailed, leaning at an angle. Now for the Old Man's saloon to be derailed on one's patch was just about as bad as it gets, but on boarding the saloon with some trepidation he found the DE and assistants enjoying their lunch, albeit at an angle. 'We've sent for the Breakdown

Barkston South Junction was, for some reason that only a professional timetable compiler might understand, a timing point in the Working Timetable (WTT). All expresses had to be reported to Control; perhaps it was thought that the Barkston men had time enough for this.

Barkston South and East Junctions

1914

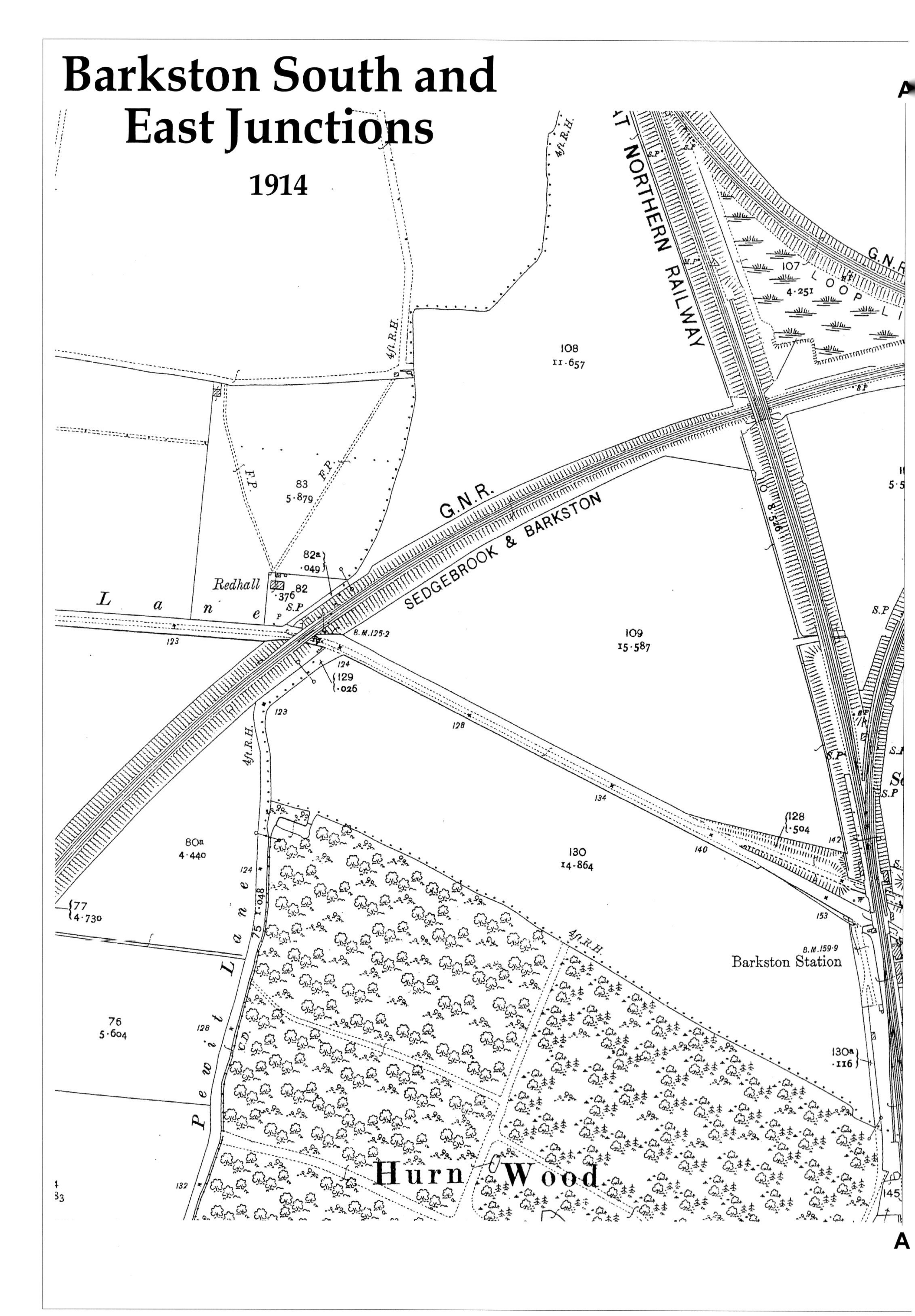

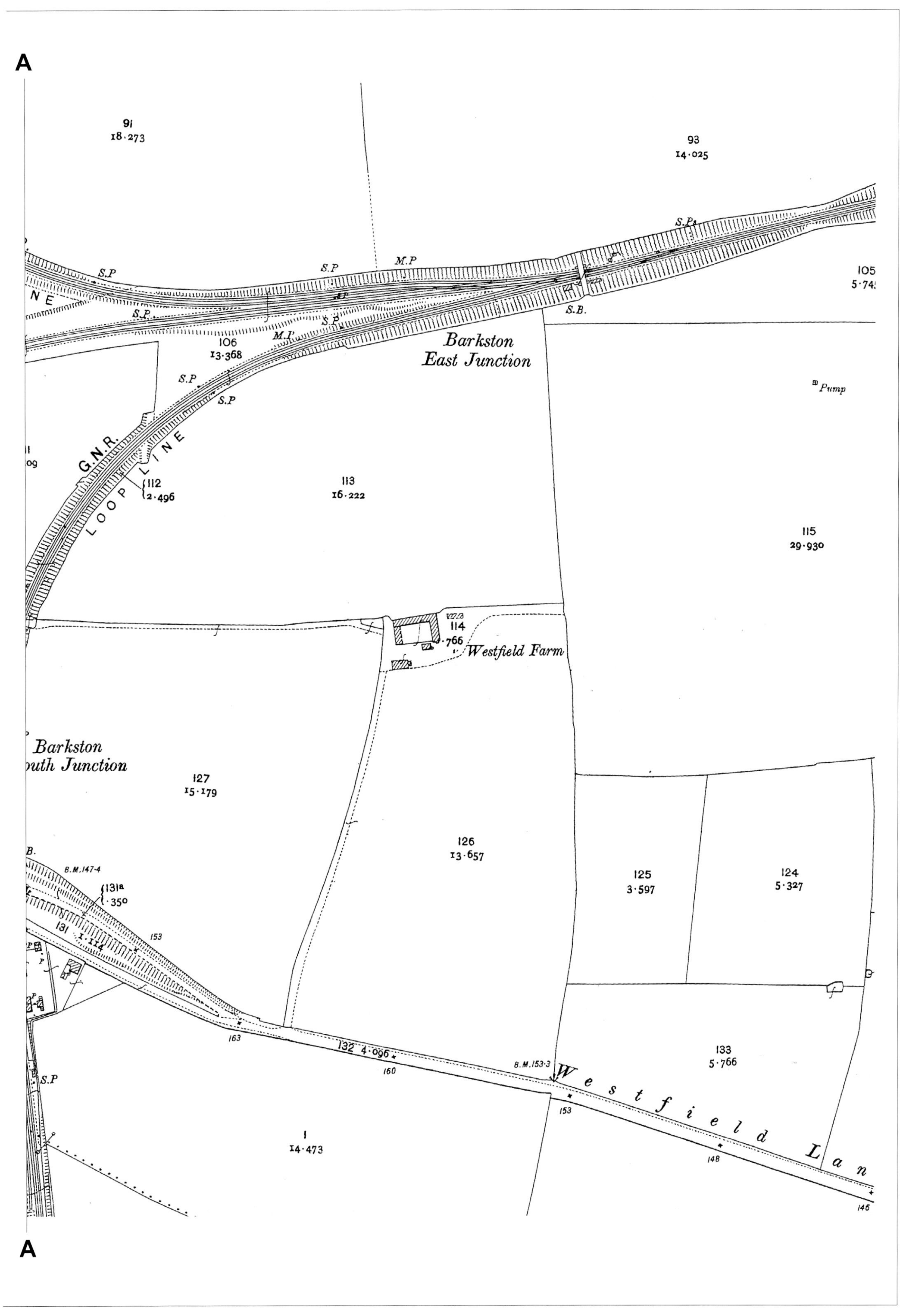
A
91
18·273
93
14·025
105
5·74
S.P
M.P
S.B.
106
13·368
Barkston
East Junction
Pump
G.N.R.
LOOP LINE
112
2·496
113
16·222
115
29·930
114
·766
Westfield Farm
Barkston
outh Junction
127
15·179
126
13·657
125
3·597
124
5·327
B.M.147·4
131a
·350
131
1·114
153
163
132 4·096
160
B.M.153·3
Westfield Lan
133
5·766
153
148
146
1
14·473
A

Barkston South Junction signalbox, seen from Westfield Lane.

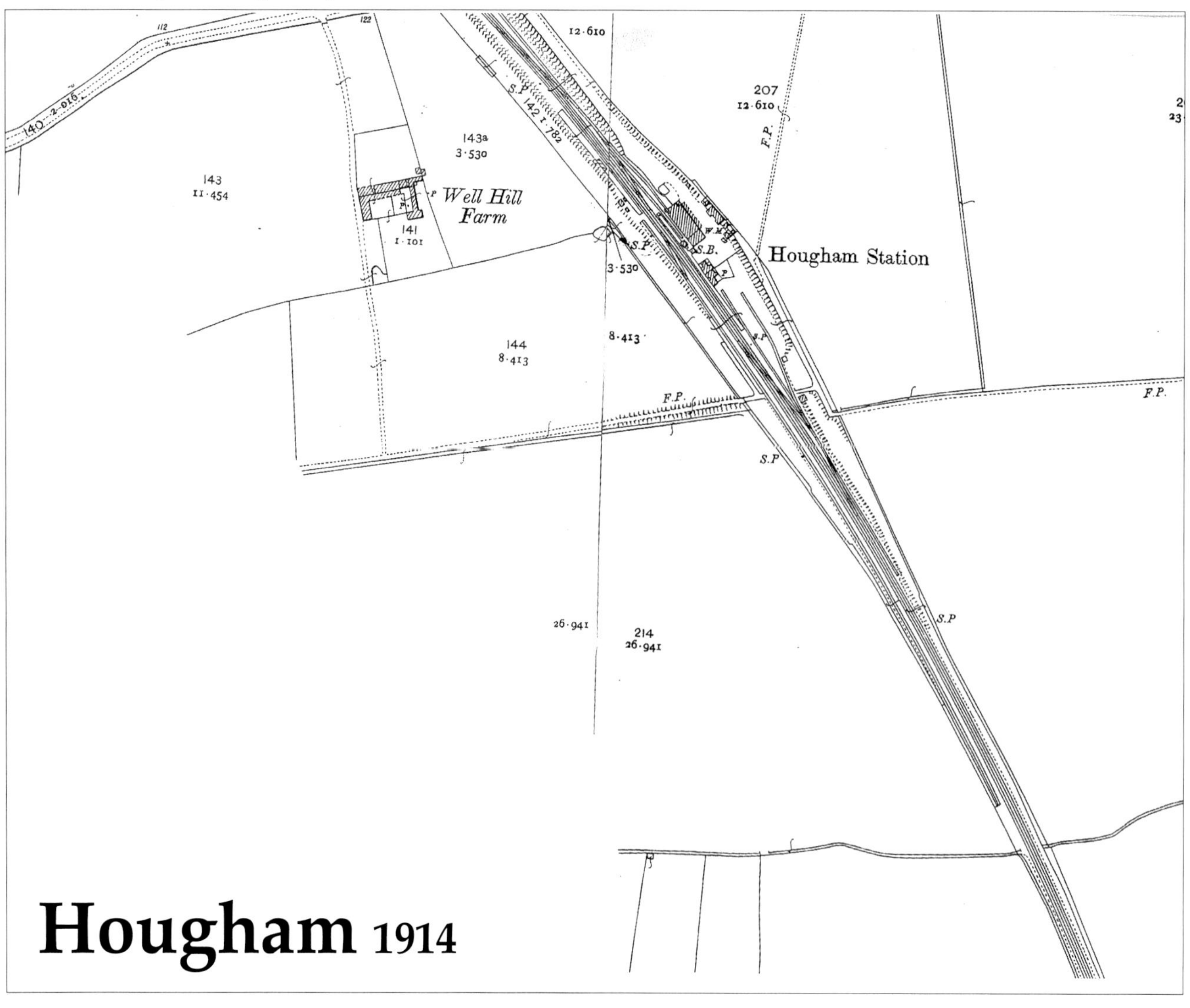

Hougham 1914

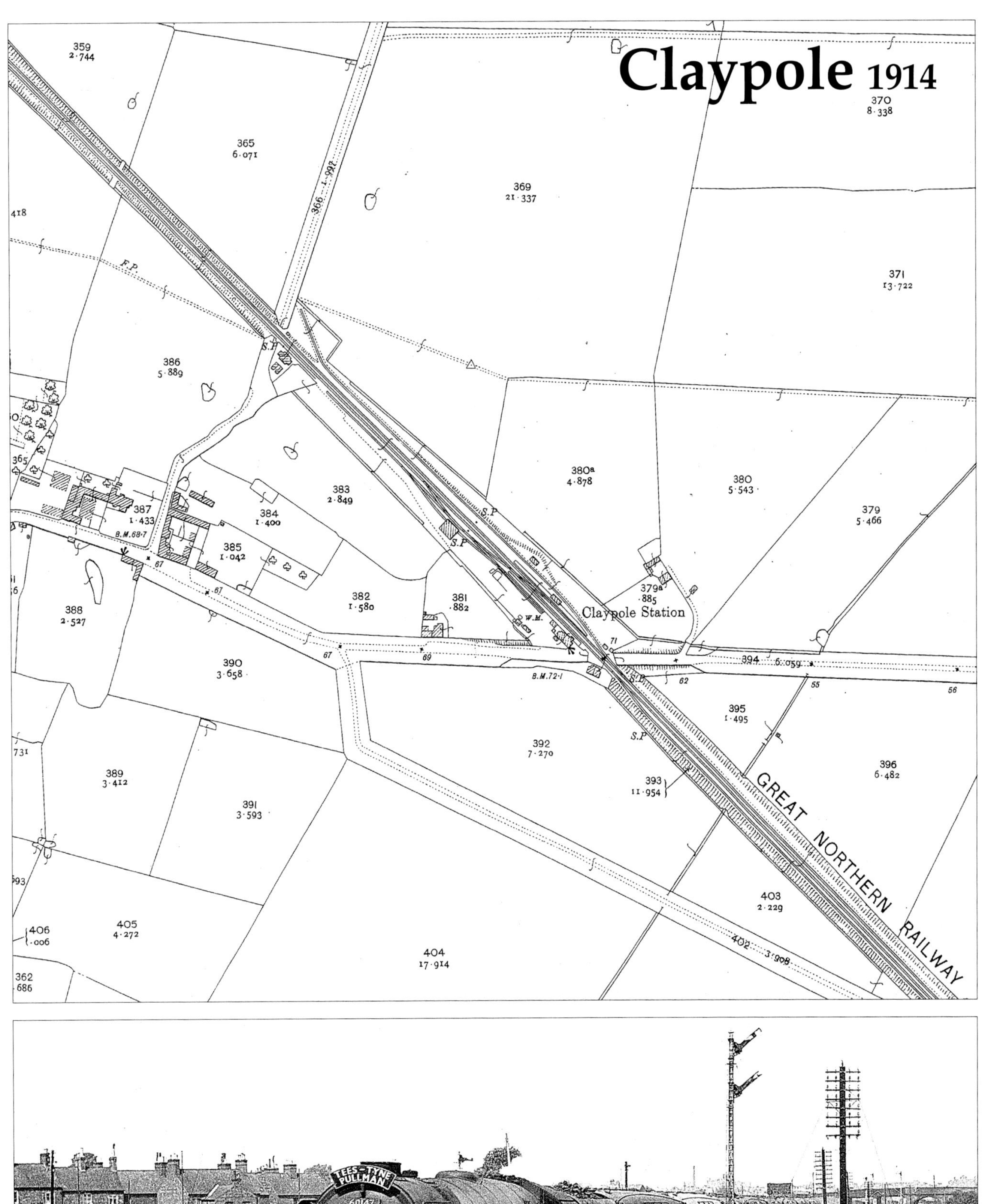

The up Tees-Tyne Pullman south of Newark on track recently re-laid. Heaton, which worked the Pullman in each direction at the time, have borrowed Gateshead's A1 No.60147, unnamed. The period would be about 1950/51.

Newark station, looking north.

Train, so while we're waiting we decided to have lunch'. It reminded me strongly of an event early in my career when Albert Toms, District Engineer Blackburn, was inspecting a single line branch in his saloon, and was propelled straight off the road – an incident hugely enjoyed by everyone else. That the PW Inspector had omitted to secure the catch points only made a bad situation infinitely worse!

Beyond North Gate station, the East Coast main line crossed the MR line from Nottingham to Lincoln on the level. The crossing was unlike the normal diamond crossings where tracks intersect at 6-8 degrees, the angle of intersection being nearer 70 degrees. Where a flangeway gap occurs, normally on the opposite rail there is a check rail to hold the wheelset. In this case, the flangeway gaps in both rails were close, which meant that there needed to be a continuous check rail. Until the 1990s the assembly was a bolted high manganese layout, the first cost and seubsequent maintenance of which hardly bears thinking about. The last renewal replaced it with a cast assembly, simply because the greater robustness was essential, and the components of the earlier layout did not last very long due to the hammering of expresses at 70 mph. The assembly was cast in high manganese steel that was very hard wearing and supported on long timbers, usually hardwood timber. Newark was the first of three flat crossings on the East Coast route, the others being at Retford and Darlington, although part of both York and Newcastle Central's layouts contained a number of similar flat crossings. Speed over the level crossing was limited to 70mph in steam days. In 1965 a new spur was laid between the main line and the Lincoln route that provided a direct route to Lincoln and Cleethorpes, and allowed the closure of the East Lincolnshire line from Spalding to Cleethorpes.

Just beyond the flat crossing the main line crossed the Trent. At this point the river is divided into two streams, the southern navigable stream known as Newark Dyke and to the north the Kelham channel. The first bridge is the Dyke Bridge, a single span of 259ft. Originally built in 1852, the down and up spans were through type truss girder single track bridges, 17ft deep. The top compression boom of the truss was a cast iron tube, and the bottom tension boom comprised wrought iron bars. In 1889 it was replaced by a pair of riveted steel spans of greater depth, 26ft. In the last few years, the bridge has been renewed again, now with a welded truss bridge. This was followed by an arched viaduct carrying both tracks over the Kelham stream.

Beyond the two channels of the Trent lay the water troughs at Muskham, the third set travelling north, 705 yards long. Muskham and Werrington were both laid in 1900, and Scrooby in 1902. The line, after a level section, climbs steadily to cross a ridge at Markham, a high speed section for up expresses, followed by a downhill section to Retford. At Egmanton, the first trial length of CWR was laid on the old Eastern Region of BR. This was installed in the mid-1950s, approximately a mile in length, and was carefully put in place on a good foundation, then fettled until it was near perfect. Nine years later, with no significant attention, it had stood perfectly. It demonstrated the truth that if installed correctly on a sound and well drained foundation, track will stand for long periods and demand little attention.

Unfortunately the times allowed for engineering work were often too short to achieve such a high standard, although nowadays Network Rail achieves greater success in this respect. Often, the rush to complete heavy programmes of relaying, urged on by financial considerations, resulted in tracks that would not stand without constant attention, and which one regarded with trepidation as the autumn rains poured down. Egmanton was inspected some 8-9 years later by the CCE, Sandy Terris, who famously declared that he would issue a disciplinary charge against anyone who dared to contemplate tamping it. There was nothing that could be done to improve it. Eastern Region engineers dined out on this for years, but I can vouch for its truth if not its precise accuracy, having heard it from the horse's mouth!

Relaying in GNR days was by hand, occasionally assisted by a rail crane. Some were steam powered but off the main lines hand cranes were used, often referred to, sarcastically, as 'Armstrong' cranes. Materials were unloaded on site, a 20mph TSR applied and the track was 'opened out'; that is, the ballast was removed by hand. The new track was pieced together, eyed in for

The north end of Newark, with the station behind the camera and the signalbox in mid-picture. The road bridge behind is an early reinforced concrete structure.

The southbound Flying Scotsman approaches Newark behind A4 No.60030 GOLDEN FLEECE in 1949/50. The A4 was at Grantham shed at the time, and was a regular sight on the Flying Scotsman. The old headboard was replaced in 1951.

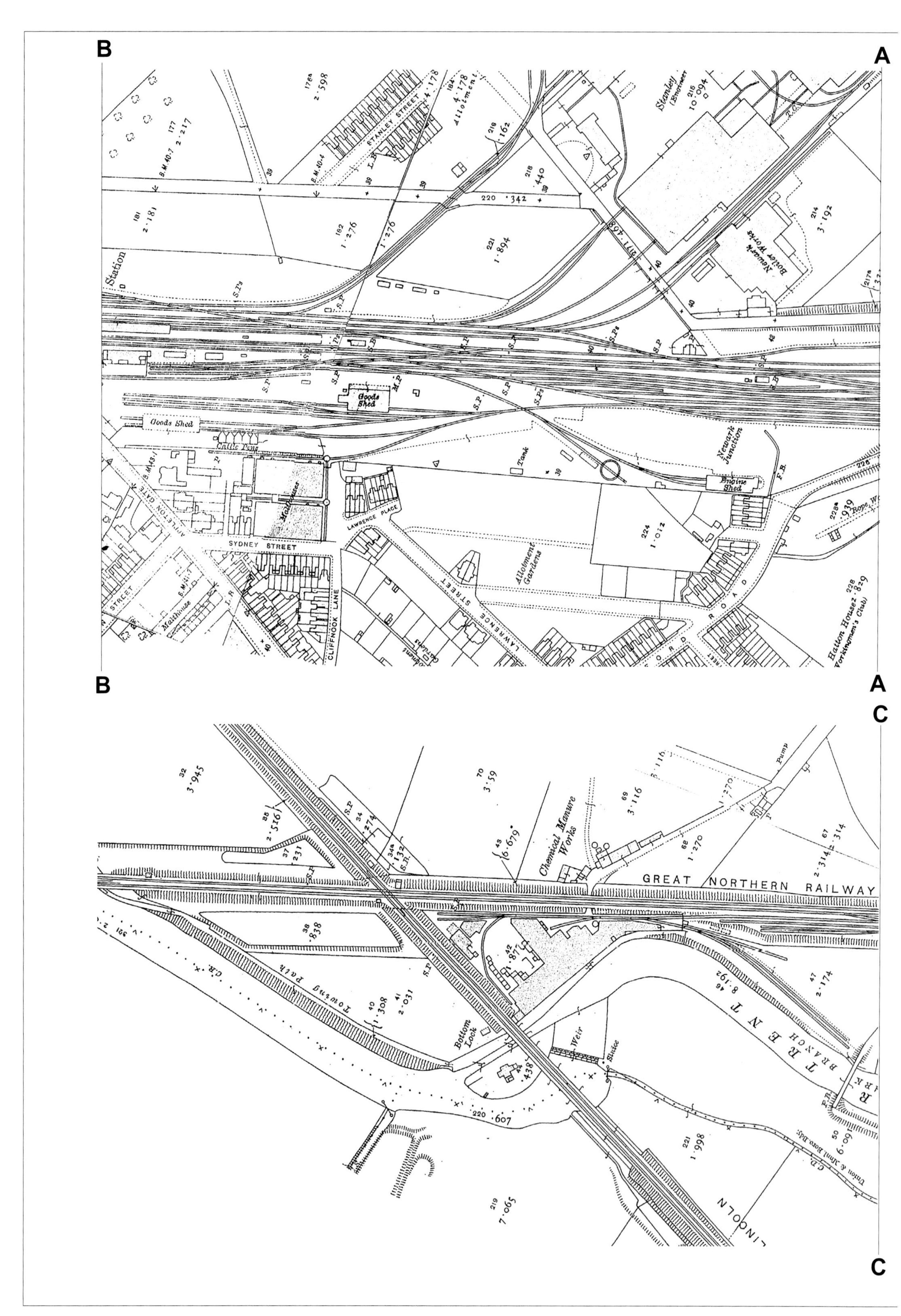
B
A
B
A
C
C
STANLEY STREET
Allotment
Station
Goods Shed
Goods Shed
Cattle Pens
Malthouses
Maltinouse
SYDNEY STREET
LAWRENCE PLACE
LAWRENCE STREET
CLIFFNOOK LANE
APPLETON GATE
Allotment Gardens
Tank
Engine Shed
Newark Junction
Newark Boiler Works
Hatton House
(Workingmen's Club)
Rope Wk
ROAD
GREAT NORTHERN RAILWAY
Chemical Manure Works
Towing Path
Bottom Lock
Weir
Sluice
Pump
TRENT
BRANCH
LINCOLN

Newark 1914

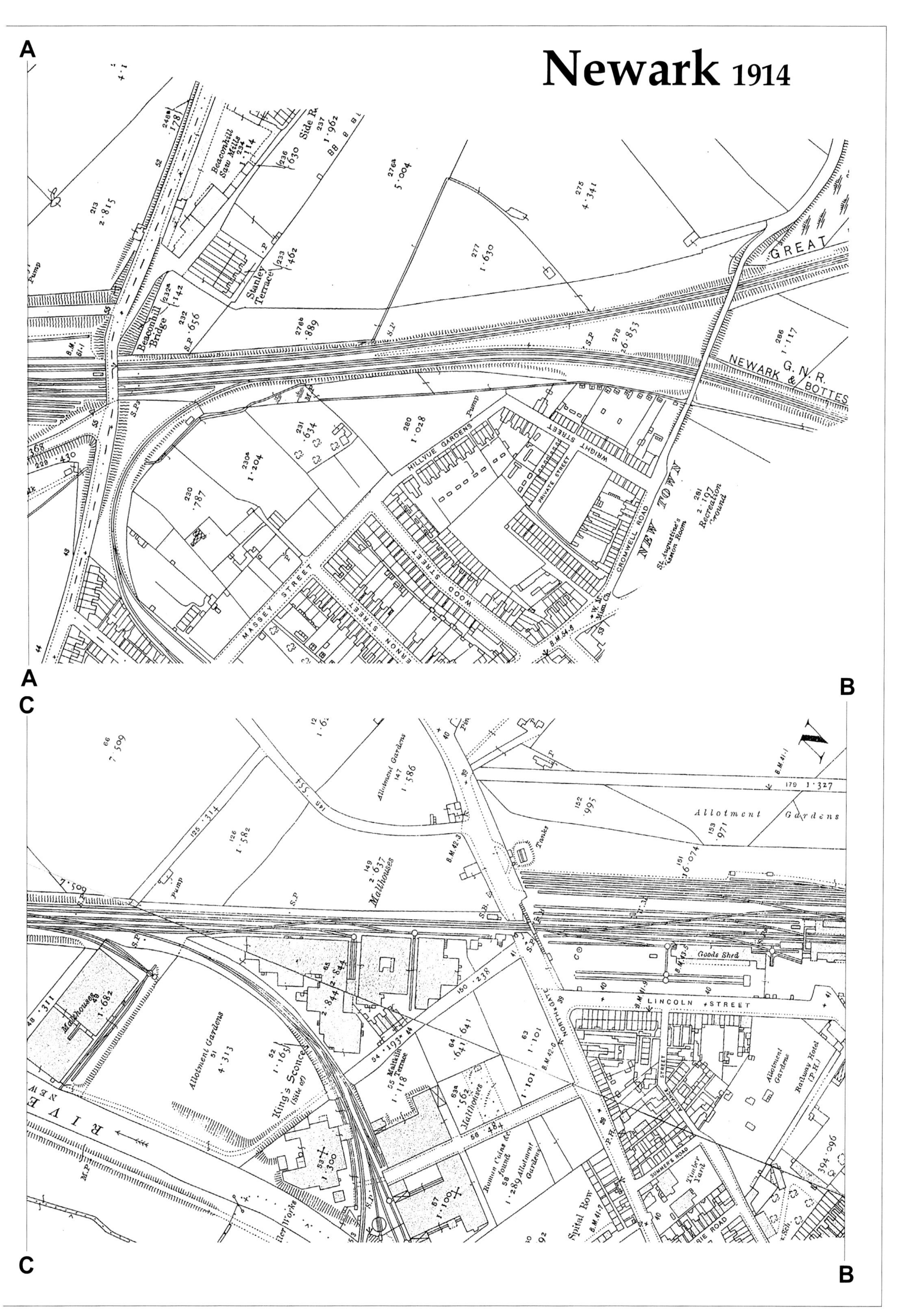
A
A
B
C
C
B
Beaconhill Saw Mills
Side R
Stanley Terrace
Beaconhill Bridge
GREAT
NEWARK & BOTTES
G. N. R.
Pump
HILLVUE GARDENS
WRIGHT STREET
PRIVATE STREET
WOOD STREET
MASSEY STREET
CROMWELL ROAD
NEW TOWN
Recreation Ground
St. Augustine's Mission Room
Allotment Gardens
Allotment Gardens
Maltings
Tanks
Goods Shed
LINCOLN STREET
NORTHGATE
Malthouses
King's Sconce (Site of)
Maltkiln Terrace
Malthouses
Roman Coins &c. found
Allotment Gardens
RIVER
Spital Row
SUMMERS ROAD
Timber Yard
Allotment Gardens
Railway Hotel (P.H.)

The flat crossing with the MR Nottingham-Lincoln route lies just north of Newark station. In this view, the robust construction of the crossing and the timbers on which it is laid are clear. The rail components are of manganese steel, and the fastenings are Mills 'C' clips which, with the approaching A3 fitted with German deflectors, sets the date at 1961-64.

line, and the ballast was returned using ballast forks or sometimes through sieves, supplemented with new stone. It was then checked precisely to a datum, usually the other road or reference pegs if on an independent alignment, followed by a period of fettling to achieve safe running at 20mph. Fettling under traffic to 40mph followed, and then a last fine tuning to get the top and line right before the TSR (Temporary Speed Restriction) was lifted.

Flat bottomed rail (FB) was used experimentally before 1939 war, and in 1949 the Railway Executive adopted the FB rail as standard, replacing the bullhead sections (BH) used hitherto It was not popular with the senior engineers of the day who were bullhead men by and large. The performance of FB rail was not good on jointed track, partly due to the cheap fastenings often used, and partly due to the fact that rail ends crippled, i.e. took a permanent downward set. In the 1950s, BR developed prefabricated relaying, so that 60ft track panels were built at specific depots and loaded 5 high on bogie bolsters. The 60ft track panels, built up at a depot such as Chesterton at Cambridge, used new sleepers and fastenings. The TSR and opening out were the same, but a vastly greater length of track was removed and replaced. This made the amount of opening out and fettling work much greater, requiring more manpower. The whole process gradually forced BR to improve its equipment. The rail cranes were replaced by purpose built track relaying machines (TRMs), and ballast cleaning machines (MABC) ensured a bed of clean ballast for the new track. The process of unloading new ballast called for hopper wagons, and the fettling was greatly aided by the introduction of tampers. The latter were primarily maintenance machines, but their ability to pack stone tightly under the sleepers was invaluable in restoring the track after relaying.

The process of installing CWR on BR was similar to jointed track, except that instead of new rail, service (scrap) rails were used with new sleepers and fittings on most Regions. The service rails were replaced by new welded rail a week or so later. In terms of rail weight the service rails were probably about 10% worn, but the rail ends were usually badly battered, and it was harder to fettle to a good standard. Generally, the following week saw the new long welded rails (LWR) unloaded on to the sleeper ends, and at the weekend the service rails were tipped into the four-foot, and the LWR slued into the rail seats. The LWRs were welded in to full lengths and de-stressed so as to be stress free, originally at 60-70°F, later modified to 65-75°F, then tamped until the TSR could be lifted.

Whereas it was commonplace on the London Midland Region to use service FB rails for the new panels, the Eastern Region used new rail. Where the ER differed, at least in the initial years, was that the jointed track panels were left in the road for some six months or more, during which time they were fettled for full speed running. The ER was still using slag ballast, which although not fully satisfactory for high speed running, was far better than the soft, cheap limestone that Dr.Beeching's cohorts urged on us. By the time the LWR was unloaded and transposed into the track, the latter was in first class condition. By good fortune – for the ER – the West Coast electrification had consumed a large proportion of the pre-stressed concrete sleeper production available from industry. As a result the ER had to make recourse to jarrah hardwood sleepers with Mills C clips, which although more costly was a significantly better quality road at the time. As a result, the quality of the East Coast main line became a byword, whereas that of the West Coast was a constant worry and remained so for some decades. Of course the ER approach to the installation

The two lattice spans of Dyke Bridge, down and up, seen broadside and from (probably but not certainly) the southern end.

Above. The overbridge at Bathley Lane with its massive proportions was a relic of the era when reinforced concrete was the cutting edge of civil engineering technology. It was constructed as part of an improvement scheme to the A1, in one of that road's earlier incarnations.

Top right. The former LD&EC intersection bridge at Dukeries Junction, an example of a continuous wrought iron plate girder bridge. This is the site of Dukeries Junction station, where there was once an up island platform (see page 185). There was also a high level island platform.

Bottom right. The connecting chord line from the LD&EC ran alongside and then joined the GN main line near Tuxford station at Tuxford North Junction. The bridge is a conventional three span segmental arch overbridge. The up side has slipped in the past, and is supported by a gabion (a gabion is a weldmesh 'box' full of hardcore) dwarf wall.

Carlton-on-Trent 1914

Carlton-on-Trent was a small station on the Trent flood plain, a fast section on the up road.

Crow Park 1914

Crow Park, like other wayside stations on this section, was closed in the mid-1950s. It was famous, at the end, for having one (down) train stop there but none on the up. No wonder there were few passengers!

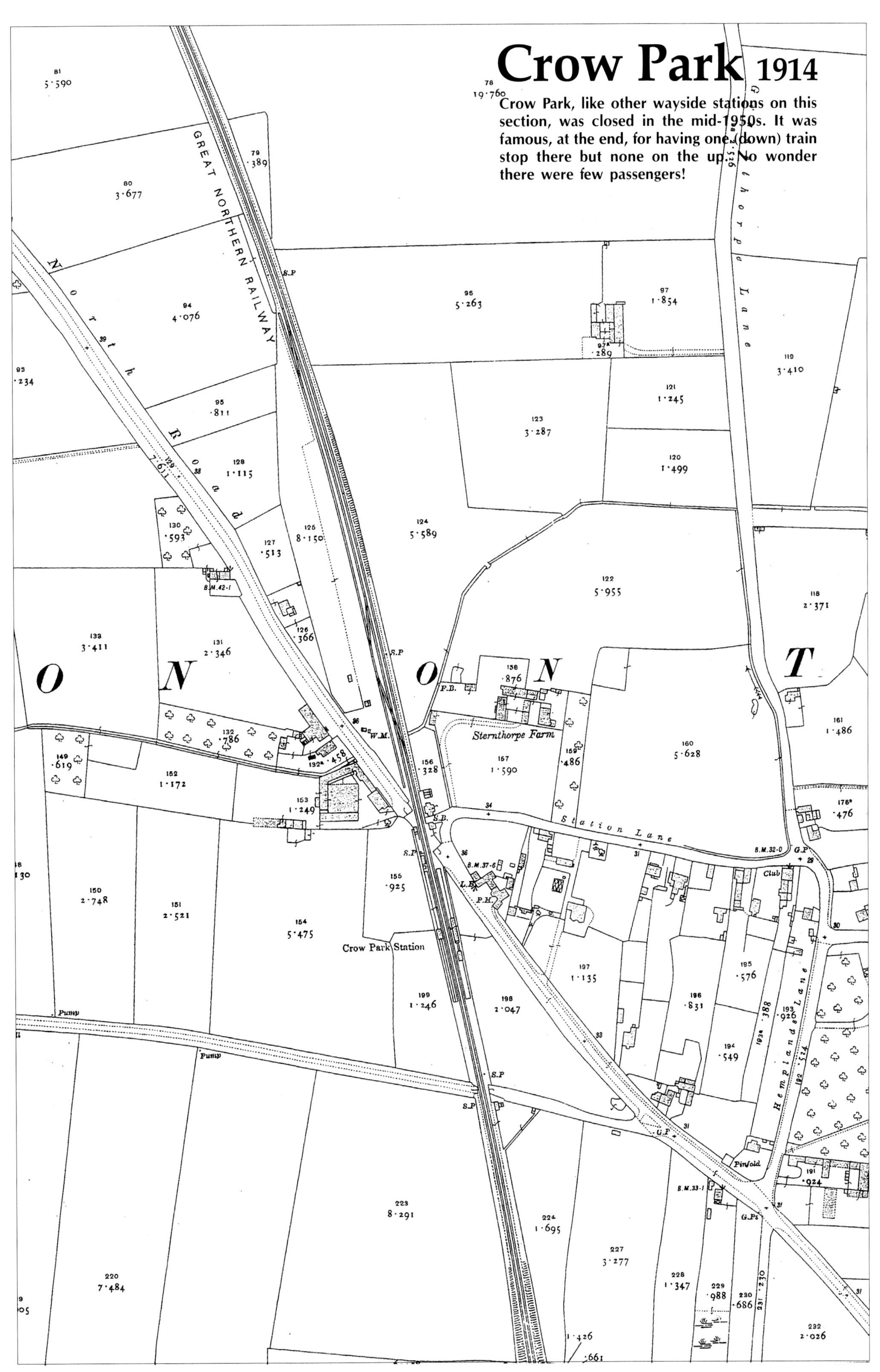

Tuxford station looking north.

Askern Tunnel, just north of the summit at Markham, was very short at 57 yards length. This view is taken from the south. In view of the expense of the tunnel and portal construction, one wonders why the cutting was not continued. No doubt special excavation and cartage was dearer than bricklayers!

Trains travelling south of Retford had to climb Gamston Bank. Here a typical plate girder bridge, probably in wrought iron, spans the main line and the up goods loop. The latter is laid with reinforced concrete sleepers, which rode poorly and lasted for ever! In the second view, taken from the bridge, K3 No.61974 heads an up freight.

Tuxford and Dukeries Junction 1914

At one time an important junction but post-war most traffic was on the main and cross country routes and not on the connecting spur line.

A

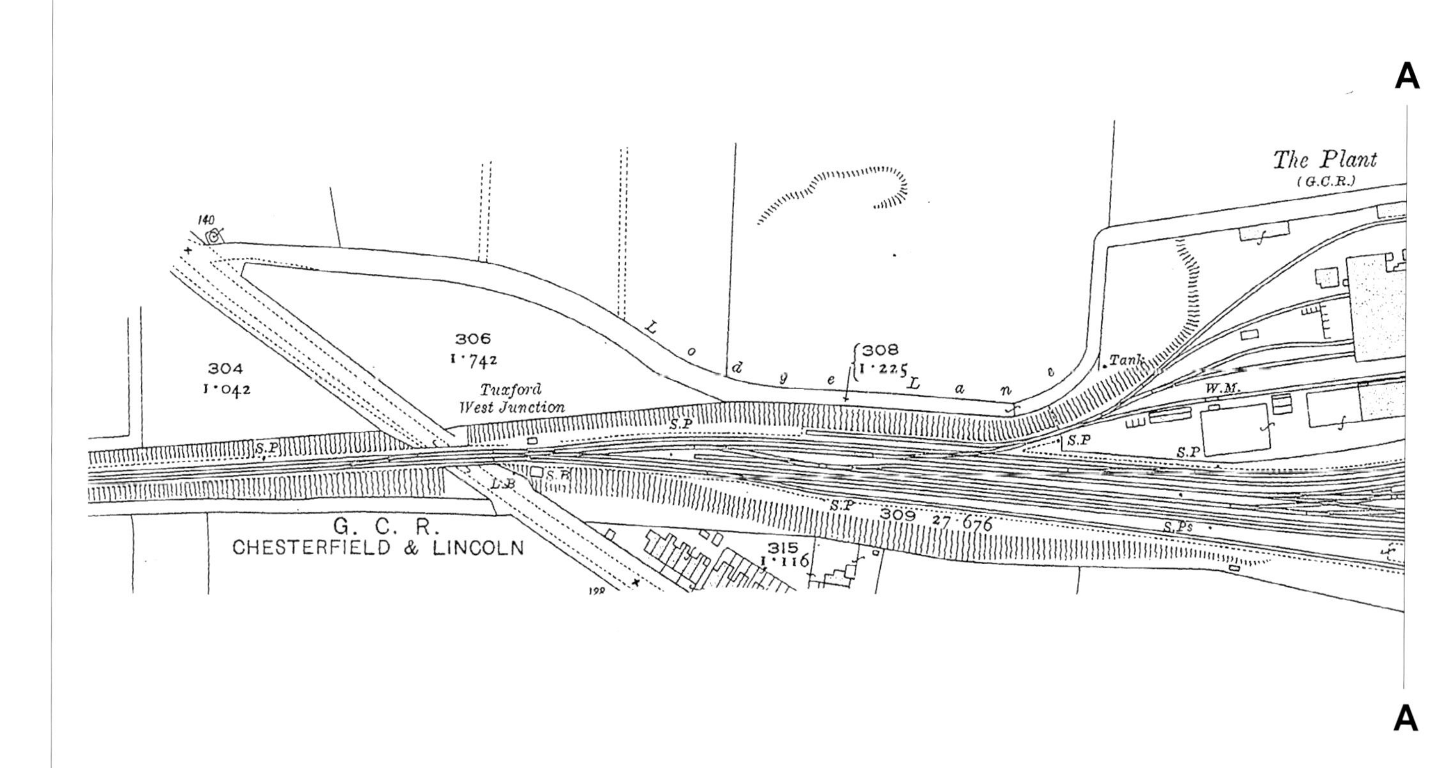

A

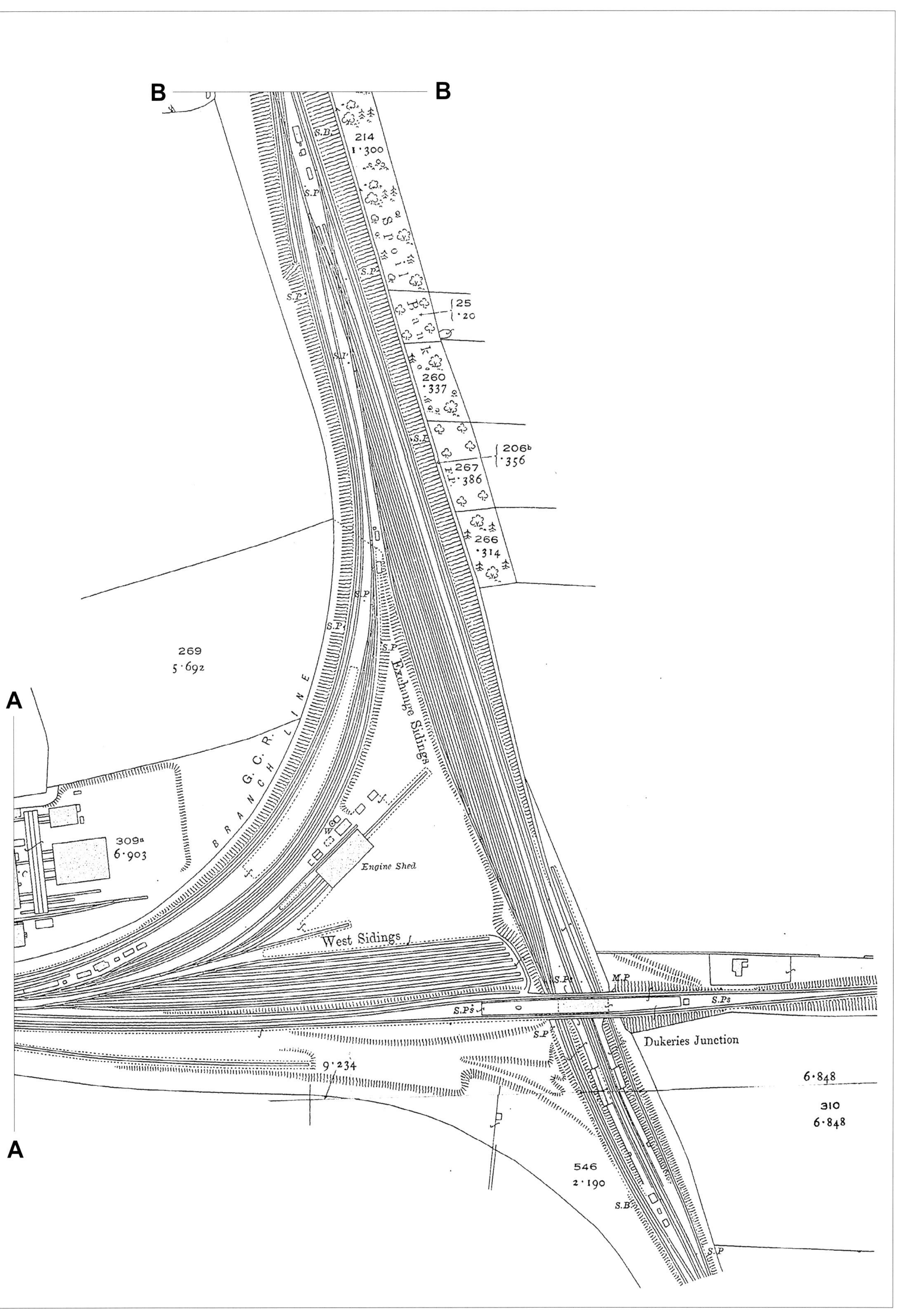
B
B
A
A
214
1·300
Spoil Bank
25
·20
260
·337
206b
·356
267
·386
266
·314
269
5·692
G.C.R. BRANCH LINE
Exchange Sidings
309a
6·903
Engine Shed
West Sidings
Dukeries Junction
9·234
6·848
310
6·848
546
2·190

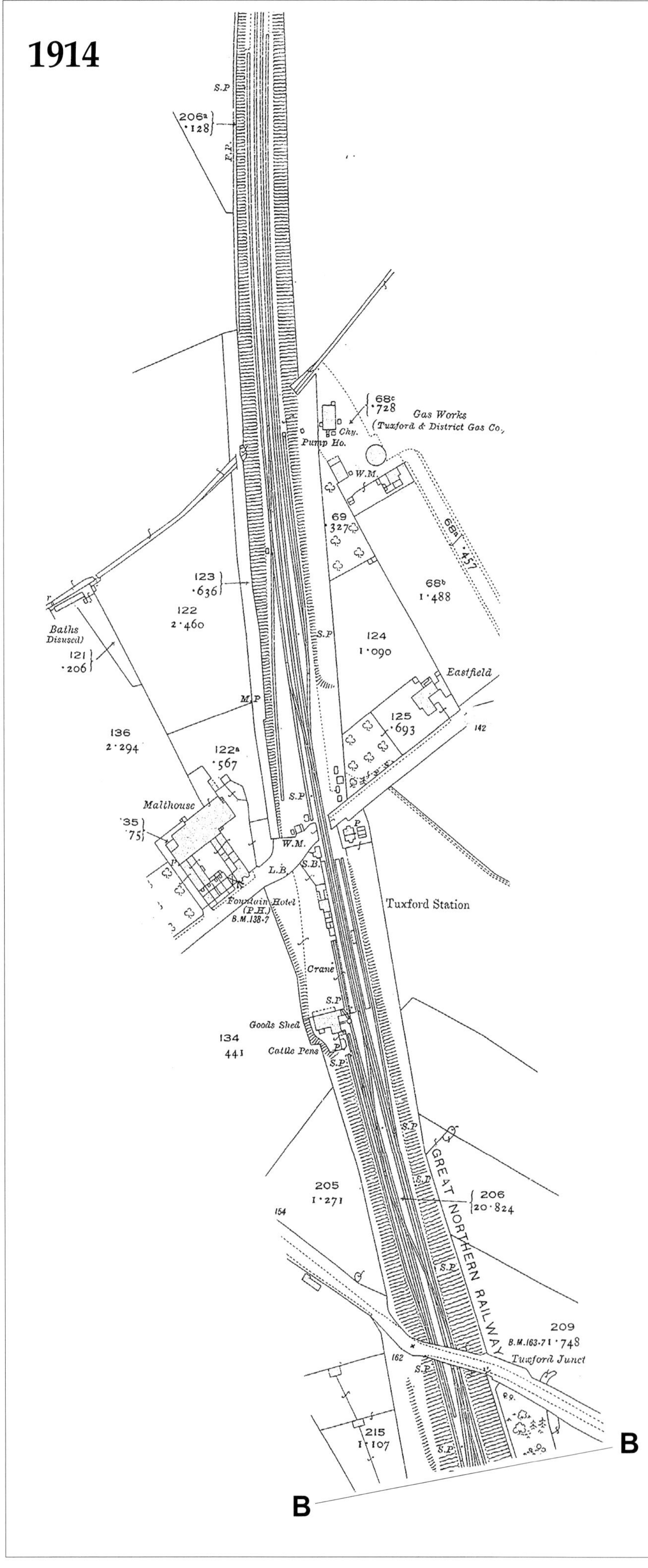

of CWR was more costly, and the transition to the cost-conscious railway with an army of accountants was inevitable. Eventually with improved plant and practices we learnt to achieve good track more economically. In more recent years, the cost of a large stock of service rails, that would otherwise have been sold for scrap, told against prefab relaying, and relaying has returned to the days of building up in situ, although now with mechanical plant to expedite the process.

The installation of CWR usually leads to the question of expansion. Expansion was one of the devices used by physics teachers to bewilder hapless students, and it has always been a conceptual problem. When CWR was first installed, the adjacent jointed track was protected against the expansion of the welded track by sliding switches, called breather switches. As the mileage of CWR increased breather switches were removed, which posed the question, whither expansion?

The answer is that expansion is constrained, firstly by extremely robust fastenings between rail and sleeper, secondly by the weight of 28-30 12 cwt (600kg) concrete sleepers per 60ft length, and thirdly by the weight and friction resistance of the ballast bed beneath the sleepers and the heaped and consolidated ballast shoulders. In fact only 200-250 yards at each end of the early individual lengths expanded, the rest being constrained by weight, etc. as above.

When the rail is installed, it is de-stressed; that is, its length is adjusted with hydraulic tensors so that it is stress-free at 65-75 degrees Fahrenheit. Below that range the rail is in tension, above, it is in compression. Before the hydraulic tensor was introduced some relatively crude de-stressing arrangements were used which were of questionable effectiveness. In the late 1960s and early 1970s there were a number of derailments caused by CWR buckling or distorting. The cause was the loss of stress in the CWR due to inadequate de-stressing or inadequate ballasting. The stress-free temperature of the CWR had fallen through rolling-out under traffic and, in hot weather the weight of ballast was inadequate to prevent buckling. As a result lengths of CWR were re-stressed, and the specification for ballasting was increased substantially. One major derailment occurred near Sandy, when the Deltic-hauled down Tees-Tyne Pullman was derailed at high speed on a distortion. What could have been a major disaster was avoided due to the design of the Mk1 Pullmans and the use of robust buckeye couplers.

At Tuxford the main line passes beneath the former LD&ECR, later GCR line to Lincoln, one of the major freight routes from the former Nottinghamshire coalfield, connected to the main line from Dukeries

Two views of Retford crossing taken on 5th April 1944. The considerably less robust nature of the bullhead assembly can be seen by comparison with the Newark crossing illustrated earlier.

Retford GN shed yard on 3 August 1963 with two local B1s, 61127 and 61055. The GN and GC sheds, although separated from each other by something like half a mile, shared the same code 36E, an unusual, maybe unique circumstance. B. Bailey.

Retford

1914

Note the sharp Whisker Hill curve north of the station and the entrance to the GN engine shed crossing it. This no doubt called for some unusual signal arrangements!

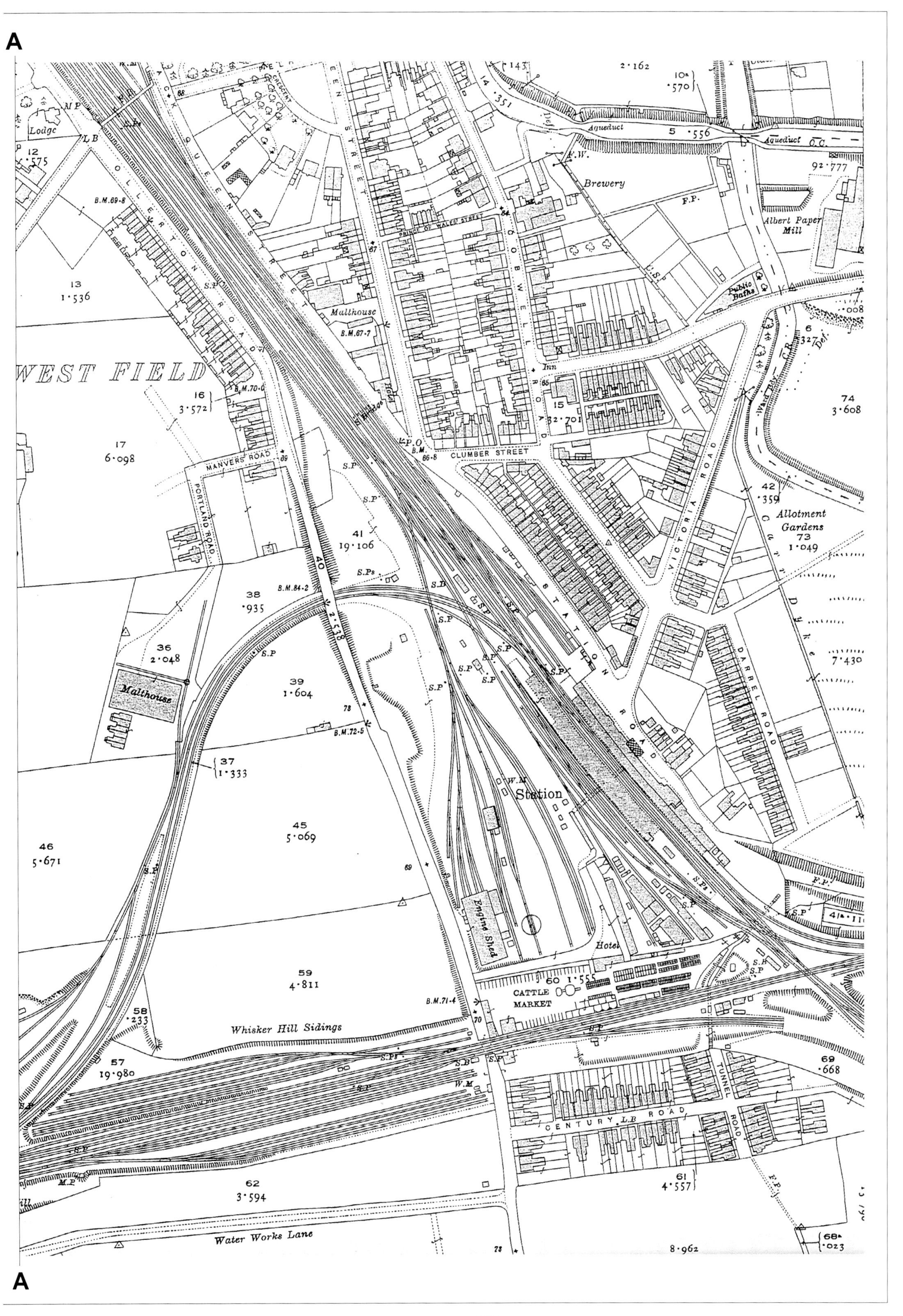
A
Lodge
WEST FIELD
OLLERTON ROAD
QUEEN STREET
Malthouse
PRINCE OF WALES STREET
COBWELL ROAD
Aqueduct
Brewery
Albert Paper Mill
Public Baths
Inn
CLUMBER STREET
MANVERS ROAD
PORTLAND ROAD
STATION ROAD
VICTORIA ROAD
DARREL ROAD
Allotment Gardens
Station
Engine Shed
Hotel
CATTLE MARKET
Whisker Hill Sidings
CENTURY ROAD
TUNNEL ROAD
Water Works Lane
A

A view of the southern half of the junction at Retford about 1964-1965, from the up bracket signal looking south. The flat crossing can be seen in the distance and one can see that the crossing itself is straight, no doubt simplifying the task of casting components. The up curve towards Lincoln is to the left. What takes the eye is the sweetness of line of the down curves through five diamond crossings; the work of a master. I imagine that the connection from the platform and the diamonds were all special castings due to the proximity to the flat crossing itself and the need to maintain a good line.

Junction. Just past the summit at MP133¾ the line passes under a high ridge through Askham Tunnel referred to earlier, which, at 57 yards of conventional tunnel construction must be the shortest tunnel on the UK system. The 4-5 miles from Retford was a hard pull for steam hauled up expresses. Just before Retford the railway crossed the River Idle on a short viaduct, but the river swung north to meet the main line again at Bawtry.

At Retford the main line crossed one of the principal routes of the old GCR, from Sheffield to Lincoln, on the level. The crossing was limited to 65mph, and unlike its neighbour at Newark, the crossing route carried considerably more freight. It is a convenient connecting point for Sheffield and Lincoln with main line services. The passenger services to Sheffield departed from the down platform and turned west to join the line to Worksop and Sheffield via the acute Whisker Hill curve north of the station. The curve was seven chains radius, approximately 140m, very roughly 15-20% of the radius of the old Offord curves. Services to Lincoln came off the Whisker Hill curve and swung across to the main line to the up platform road. The up platform road rejoined the up main before the flat crossing, and a curve off the up platform road turned east to join the GCR route to Lincoln, and the platform edge followed it part way round the curve. The down platform was an island, with the down main and down platform lines either side. In 1965 the crossing was replaced by an underpass for the GCR line, with separate platforms for the Sheffield-Lincoln line. There was also a down goods line, and a GN engine shed beyond. There was also a shed at Thrumpton, to the east of the main line on the Lincoln line.

The GN shed had only a small allocation for local passenger and freight, and the provision of main line pilots. Latterly it became well-known due to the sporadic appearances of one of its handful of B1s, the 'Retford Pacifics'. Drivers needing a replacement locomotive knew that Pacific pilots stood at Doncaster and Grantham, but with a more urgent need south of Doncaster and the loco unlikely to make Grantham without serious consequences, the Retford pilot was the only option. In GN days a 4-4-0 or smaller might have been the pilot or even an Atlantic. The GC shed was at Thrumpton, round the curve on to the Lincoln line, housing 2-8-0s, 0-8-0s and 0-6-0s of several types for work mainly on the Sheffield-Lincoln route.

North of Retford the line crossed the Chesterfield Canal, and travelled north through flat country past Ranskill on to Scrooby water troughs. At one time Ranskill had a wagon works, then a wartime ordnance factory. The loops remained in the 1950s but all else had gone. There was a farm crossing just north of the station which was the scene of an accident reminiscent of some of the more fanciful scenes in early films of the Wild West. A farm worker, using his farm crossing, unprotected by signals, drove his tractor and hay-wain on to the railway without prior notification to the signalman, then left them in order to close one gate and open the other. His attention to agricultural detail was superb, but his awareness of railway requirements was not. I suppose Bert Green and SIR RALPH WEDGWOOD with the up 'Tees-Tyne Pullman' would have been travelling at about 60-70mph when they struck the trailer loaded with hay. The tractor was upside down in a ditch several hundred yards farther south, while the wooden trailer and its load disintegrated explosively and utterly, wooden fragments here and there, and hay everywhere, even in the pole route telegraph wires. The A4 had her front brake hose dislodged but was otherwise none the worse for the encounter. Although humorous, it must have been terrifying to those involved. I wonder whether the farmer adjusted his crossing procedure afterwards. I hope so.

In the 1950s, much of the track on the Retford-Doncaster section was still laid in ash, and although it was not a fast section, the PSR in steam days was, I believe, 70mph; 60mph over the troughs. Scrooby water troughs were fed from the River Idle and treated, as all GN water trough supplies were. They were 705 yards long, the fourth set on the GN main line. It was important to fill right up here if one was going beyond York or even through to Edinburgh. The

The flat crossing seen from the Sheffield-Lincoln bracket signals, about 1964-1965 (all this sequence of pictures dates from that period). The point rodding from Retford South, itself a sign of the past, is a signal fitter's nightmare.

Retford looking north. Peering closer at the track, it looks as though renewal is not far away. The line through the crossing could be better. Indeed it was not, as these pictures were taken prior to the replacement of the flat crossing with an underpass for the Sheffield-Lincoln line. The lookout man phlegmatically draws on his Woodbine, as they almost all did.

Retford, from the south. Construction work for the underpass has started, to the left. A WD 2-8-0, looking in much same weary state as the crossing, thumps and wheezes it way west about 1965.

D9008 roars through Retford with the up Tees Thames non-stop York to Kings Cross on 2 August 1963. Coming to terms with diesel and electric power was a shade difficult for permanent way staff. With steam, one had visible and audible warning of proximity and speed. With the new forms of traction, it was wiser to move to a 'place of safety' first. B. Bailey.

B1 61225 arrives with down Sheffield train from Grimsby on 2 August 1963; 61251 has an up Class D. B. Bailey.

9F 92145 with a Class E freight on the down main at Retford, 2 August 1963. We can see where the connection to Sheffield went off; it led to the acute 7 chain Whisker Hill curve by means of which departing trains travelled first north, then south-west and then north-west to head for Worksop and Sheffield. Services from Sheffield followed the same circuitous route in the opposite direction; indeed the up Sheffield to up main lead looks even sharper in curvature. I am not familiar with the detailed operating at Retford but cannot call to mind any regular services that would use this later connection; perhaps others know better. In the foreground is a scissors crossing, the two leads at the north end being replaced with two single slips. A scissor crossing is a particular form of outside slip in itself, with a central diamond crossing. Mercifully there were not too many about, since they could be a continual maintenance problem. All S&C was prone to rail cracking from the sheer number of boltholes involved, if nothing else. It was layouts such as these that were provided at the operators' request which made maintenance so onerous. Trade union refusal to allow the use of contract labour made life many times worse. The Master Cutler service called at Retford and I wonder how much the EE Type 4s damaged the complicated layout just off the platform. In my experience they tended to bend or even knock the point off the vee of the common crossings at first; very dangerous. It may be that greater lateral play was allowed on the leading wheels subsequently. B. Bailey.

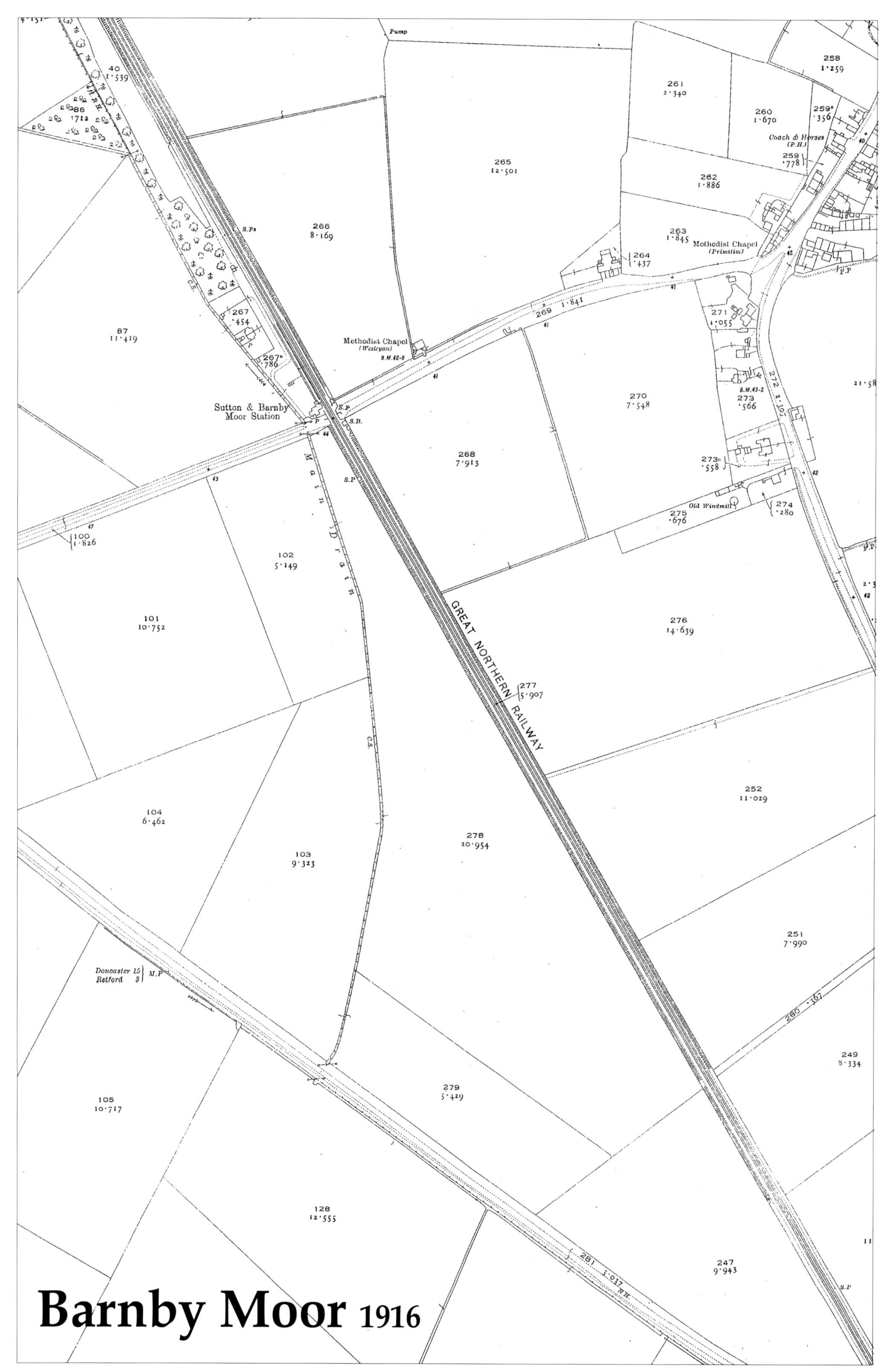
Barnby Moor 1916
Pump
Coach & Horses (P.H.)
Methodist Chapel (Primitive)
Methodist Chapel (Wesleyan)
B.M.42·8
Sutton & Barnby Moor Station
S.B.
S.P.
Main Drain
GREAT NORTHERN RAILWAY
Old Windmill
B.M.43·2
Doncaster 15
Retford 8
M.P.
265 12·501
266 8·169
87 11·419
101 10·752
102 5·149
104 6·462
103 9·323
105 10·717
128 12·555
278 20·954
279 5·429
268 7·913
270 7·548
276 14·639
252 11·029
251 7·990
249 8·334
247 9·943
261 2·340
260 1·670
262 1·886
263 1·845
258 1·259

Ranskill 1916

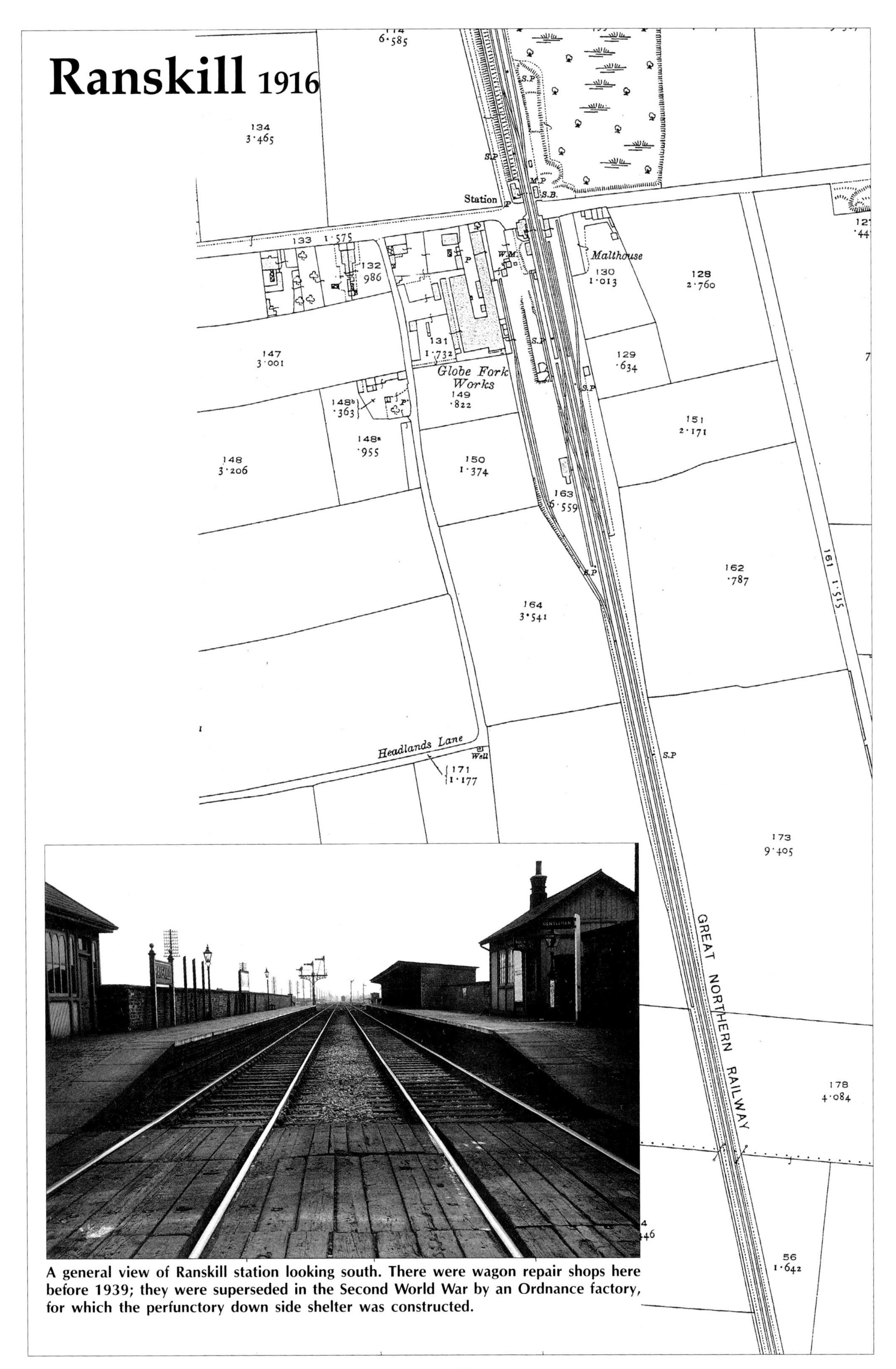

A general view of Ranskill station looking south. There were wagon repair shops here before 1939; they were superseded in the Second World War by an Ordnance factory, for which the perfunctory down side shelter was constructed.

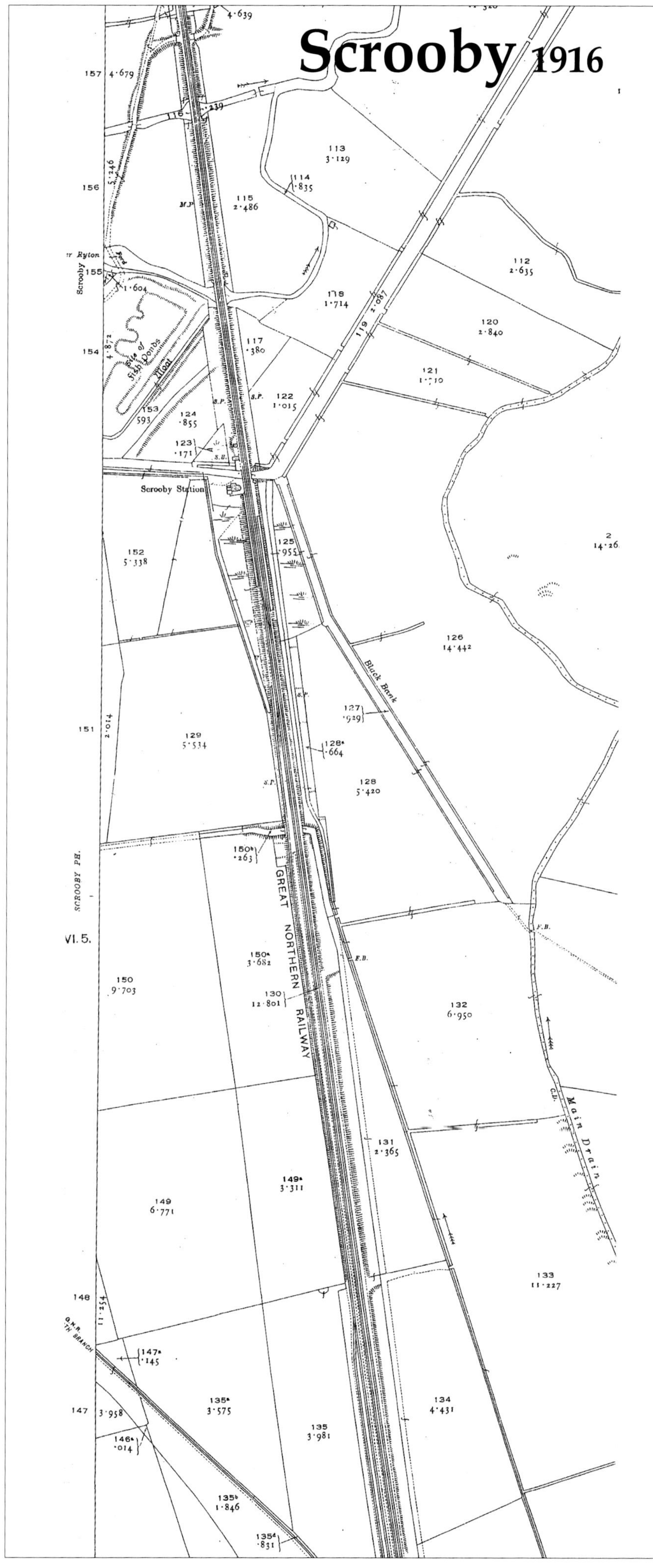

next set was at Wiske Moor, over 70 miles to the north. The troughs were the last set to be removed, in 1969, their last few years serving to replenish train heating boilers of the Type 4 and Deltic diesels. There was a station at Scrooby until 1931, and a junction serving the coal mines in the Harworth area that survived into the diesel era.

Bawtry is on a curve, first right-hand then left, and as the line crosses the long brick viaduct it crosses a loop in the River Idle, now joined by the River Ryton. The land is low lying and in recent years the viaduct foundation has needed reinforcement, partly to ensure structural security and also to allow higher speeds. Currently I believe the PSR is 110mph. The Idle valley was low-lying with fertile farm land, and the station was provided with all of the facilities that were required for dealing with agricultural traffic. North of the station on the up side, the Misson branch curved in from the east. Originally the branch reached farther east, but as agricultural traffic atrophied it died back. It was used for the storage of wagons in the 1950s, but it was not until 1965 that it closed completely.

Beyond Bawtry, the left-hand curve straightens as the line climbs to the Yorkshire boundary at MP 149½. At one time there was a signalbox at the summit, variously known as Pipers Wood or Bawtry Forest, replaced as another pre-war IBS scheme. From here the main line dropped down into the Don Valley through Rossington into Doncaster. Rossington was a familiar name in railway circles since the large colliery outside the village supplied good coal for the principal express steam locomotives.

Doncaster was a very large railway centre, possibly the largest on the whole main line. Apart from the large junction station, it was the location of the largest works on the old LNER for both locomotives and rolling stock. Although the junction with the North Eastern was at Shaftholme Junction, just over four miles to the north, Doncaster marked the northern passenger boundary of the GNR on the East Coast main line. Passenger traffic from Leeds, Bradford and the West Riding towns joined with that from Hull for the journey south behind larger locomotives. For that reason Doncaster for many years had a fleet of the largest express locomotives allocated to the engine shed south of the station, fondly known as 'Carr Loco'. Doncaster was a concentration point for coal traffic from the South Yorkshire coalfield, requiring a large number of sidings. It was also a staging point for fast freight from the West and East Ridings, as they used to be known, where heavy locomotives replaced the lighter classes for the run up to London. In addition there was the growing encrustation of industry, associated with or living off

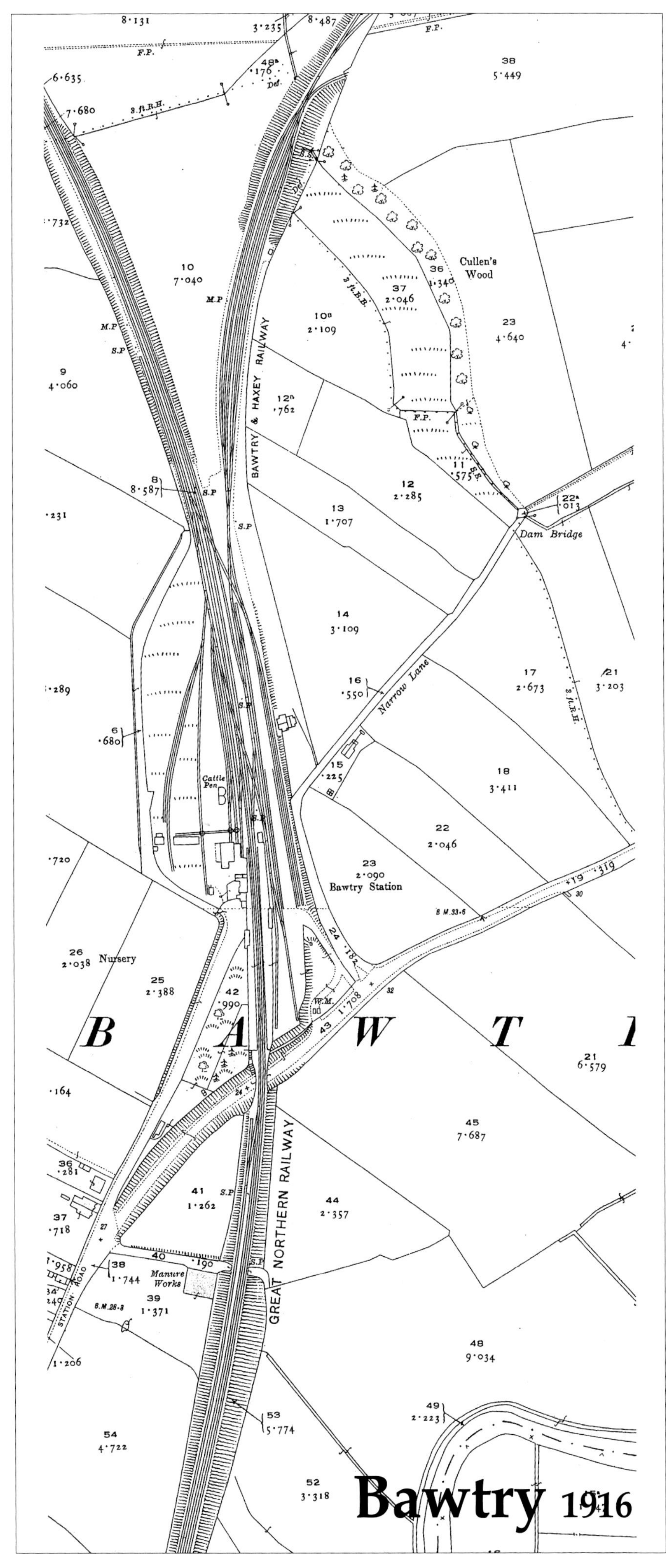

the availability of skilled labour on the railway.

Doncaster had a further complication arising from its location, with the GNR to the south, the NER to the north, the GCR, Hull & Barnsley criss-crossing, and the L&Y, MR and LNWR attempting to tap the lucrative mineral traffic. Freight routes were built avoiding Doncaster, and at its peak, the Doncaster area must have been bewildering to understand and control. Services to and from the collieries meant branches going off all over South Yorkshire, and at the peak referred to above, dozens of freight trips were being worked in the area to the west and north of Doncaster. The town is the location of the third and largest power box controlling the old GNR main line, completed in 1974. Whereas Kings Cross and Peterborough control 85 and 70 route miles respectively, Doncaster controls 156. The southern boundary is north of Stoke Tunnel, and the northern boundary with York, now controlled from Leeds IECC, is short of Temple Hirst Junction before the Selby Diversion. Control also extends down the branches, principally to Gainsborough, Hull, Scunthorpe, Leeds, and Sheffield. A measure of the flat nature of the terrain is that in 1990 there were 52 level crossings in the area.

The station comprised a down island platform and an up platform. Between the two platforms there were four tracks. There were two platform roads and two main lines between them, and another down slow platform road on the outer side of the down island. The platforms are linked with a subway, with the buildings on the up side. The station was rebuilt just before the war, when the up platform became an island with the construction of a second up platform road. The signalling was modernised and completed after the war. Now the station is much the same but the signalling has been replaced by the power box.

Carr Loco was one of the largest depots on the GNR, with a long history of service on many of the principal services on the GN main line, including parcels and fast freight. The services to West and East Riding were worked to the south of Doncaster by Doncaster or Kings Cross in the main. With the introduction of Pacifics, which were precluded from Leeds and normally from Hull, Doncaster's leading role on express work continued. Copley Hill shed at Leeds continued to work through to London with the Pullman trains using superheated Ivatt Atlantics, and the standard of work achieved was excellent. The Pullman services started in 1923 when the newly created LNER took the Pullman cars inherited from the old GER, and used them on a new service from London to Newcastle via Leeds and Harrogate. The

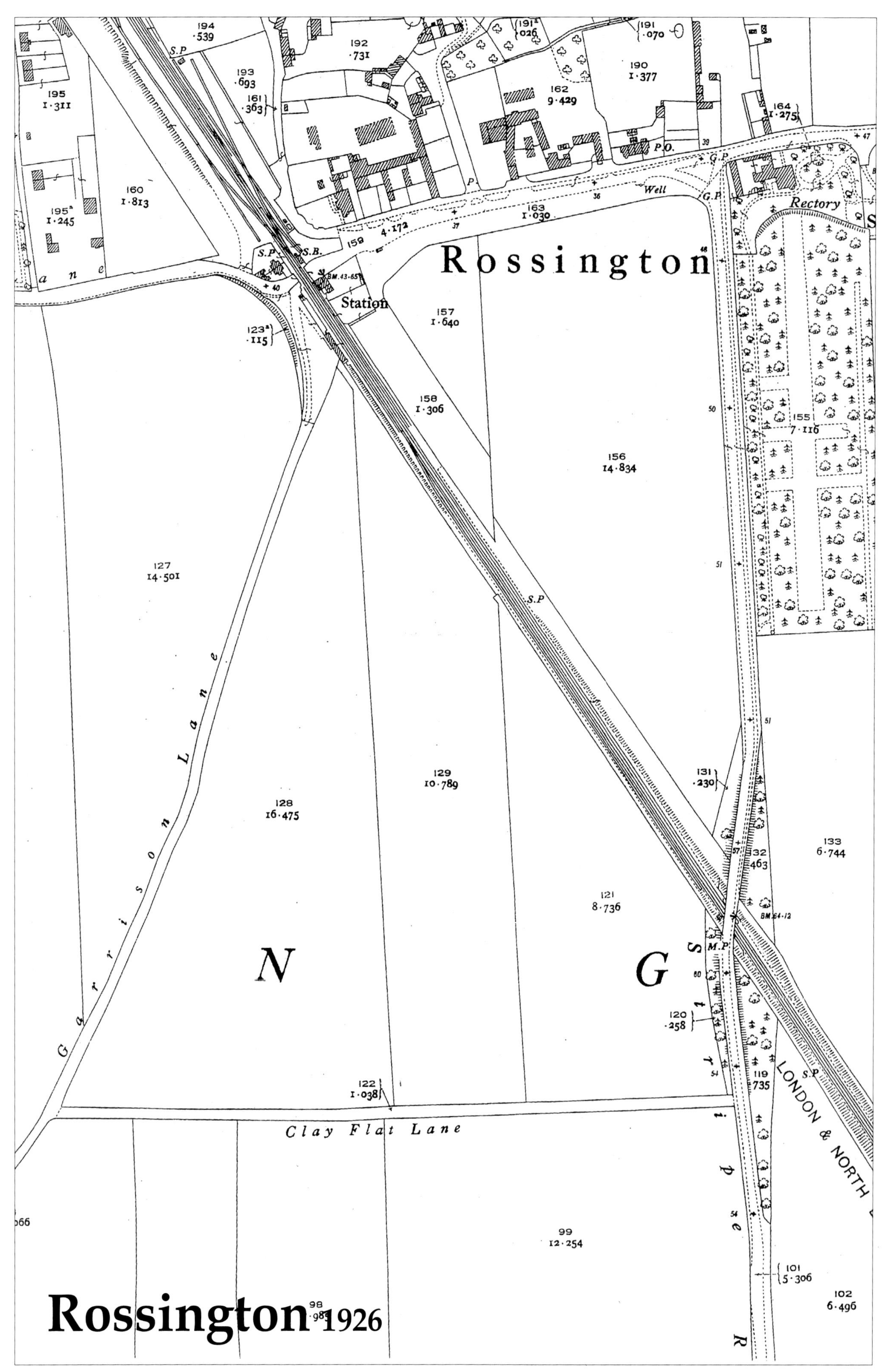
Rossington
Station
Rectory
Well
P.O.
Garrison Lane
Clay Flat Lane
LONDON & NORTH
N
G
Rossington 1926

The approach to Doncaster was through the mass of Balby Road overbridge. It can be seen on the Ordnance Survey, page 212. A V2 2-6-2 waits in the distance. The signalbox on the right was Sand Bank.

The southbound Elizabethan passing Doncaster on 9th August 1956. The A4 is No.60010 DOMINION OF CANADA, still with her presentation CPR bell and a single chimney. She was not often on the Non-stop, and when she was, there was often a Haymarket replacement on the up run. Stephen Gradidge.

A heavy down service for the Bergen Line passes through Doncaster in August 1960, headed by A3 No.60107 ROYAL LANCER. D.H. Beecroft, www.transporttreasury.co.uk

Harrogate Pullman was hauled between Kings Cross and Leeds by Ivatt Atlantics. In 1925 it was extended to Edinburgh. In the winter timetable it was diverted north of Doncaster via Shaftholme Junction, Knottingley, Ferrybridge and Church Fenton, to run non-stop to Harrogate, 198¾ miles. This was to avoid the new West Riding Pullman serving Leeds and Bradford, later named the Yorkshire Pullman. In May 1928 the train was re-equipped with all-steel cars and renamed the Queen of Scots.

Doncaster had seven of the original twelve A1s in the early 1920s, and gained a further eight of those built by the LNER, far more than was needed, although in those days the number of relief services at holiday times was considerable. Once the Pacifics were allowed to run to Leeds in the mid-1930s, Doncaster's role on the main line lessened. With the introduction of the class A4 Pacifics, Doncaster were allocated Nos.4468, 4900 and 4903, which were often seen on the Yorkshire Pullman. On a few occasions Doncaster were obliged to lend Copley Hill a Pacific for the up West Riding Limited. Probably the best work was in hauling the 7.50 from Leeds to Kings Cross, unofficially known as The Breakfast Flyer. From summer 1932 the schedule was cut, the Grantham-Kings Cross time being reduced to 100 minutes, while the load on this popular service grew larger. Towards the end of the 1930s some of the new Green Arrow V2 2-6-2s were sent to Doncaster, and their impressive turn of speed quickly led to their use on the down Yorkshire Pullman.

Through the 1939-45 war, Doncaster's fleet of V2s increased considerably. Post-war, Doncaster must have been responsible for at least half the fast freight and parcels on the main line. One of the tasks at Carr loco was running-in newly overhauled locomotives from Doncaster Plant. The locomotives were sent, light, to Lincoln or Retford and then Barkston, before working freight or parcels to Peterborough or even London. The most famous inhabitant of Carr Loco was indubitably MALLARD. The first Kylchap A4, she was sent to Doncaster, and within a few months went to Kings Cross for a braking trial, to test the use of quick service application valves of the coaching stock of the Coronation. The result was a world speed record of 125mph, usually quoted at 126mph.

Perhaps history has concentrated overmuch on the machine and its designer, and not enough on the skill and, frankly, the bravery of Driver Joe Duddington and Fireman Tom Bray. Without doubt the A4 was carefully examined and prepared, but nobody could be absolutely sure that all would be well at such an enormous speed with a steam engine. There was simply no previous experience, and earlier high speed runs had not been achieved without considerable risk. In 1935 SILVER LINK had reached 112½mph with ease and held more than 100mph for 25 miles, but her driver was forced to make a heavy brake application at the last minute to avoid risk of derailment at excessive speed in 1936. SILVER FOX and her driver were not prepared, and disaster was not far away. On the LMSR in 1937, Driver Clarke on CORONATION had come within a whisker of wiping out the entire LMSR management team on the approach to Crewe station. Almost certainly the overheating of the big end of MALLARD was caused by the sudden relaxation of the supreme effort to reach the highest possible speed. The German high speed 4-6-4s showed the same tendency, and drivers were instructed that the locomotive should be progressively eased when travelling at high speed rather than abruptly shutting off steam. Speed was a dangerous game, as the LMSR management would have endorsed a year earlier. Nevertheless it was a wonderful achievement, and a very brave one too.

I have not referred to the Plant, the popular local name for Doncaster Works, since there are others far more knowledgeable and better acquainted with its history and the work of the people there. Suffice it to say that until diesel traction appeared, a Doncaster overhauled locomotive sounded good, certainly looked good and was good to ride behind or on if one was lucky. But the world of railways has moved on. At the end of steam Doncaster became host to an inflated stud of express and mixed traffic types for a while before mass withdrawals took place. With diesel traction, Doncaster's role diminished very much, although the works continued to bring locomotives in numbers for repair. There remained considerable freight work for the massive power stations in South Yorkshire, but general freight diminished as well. Fish traffic was an early loss as both the rail and fishing industries changed. The advent of HST sets moved the East Coast's passenger services farther away, with greater acceleration, higher speeds and increased service frequency. The acceleration of the Deltics was astonishing compared with steam traction only a few years before but, electrification apart, that of the HSTs was unprecedented. On one of my first trips in the cab, the speed had reached 60mph with the station that we had just left still visible in the distance.

With electrification, the London suburban area was the first to experience the rapidity of electric traction that passengers on the Southern Railway and Region had enjoyed for 70 years or so. Main line electrification transformed the service still further, with slightly increased speeds, but a greater service frequency. The rapid acceleration of electric traction made station calls easier in terms of total journey times, and the principal services make more station calls than in the days of steam. Indeed, for many stations, the timetable has lost its importance, as there will be a train calling within half an hour at the worst. The Class 90 and 91 electric locomotives, coupled to fixed formations, are in effect electric HSTs.

So, in 1922 some five hours later and almost 156 miles north of Kings Cross, our imaginary inspection saloon would have drawn to a halt at Doncaster station, the gleaming Klondyke at the head no doubt attracting the attention of the many small lads always at Doncaster station. Brief farewells to colleagues would soon follow, before getting back to their various offices. We return to Kings Cross behind one of the new LNER A1 Pacifics from Doncaster shed which has taken over from one of Copley Hill's Ivatt Large Atlantics.

Over 80 years later, the return journey would be made with a BR Mk4 set, propelled by an AC electric locomotive of Cl.90 or more likely, Cl.91, in half the time. Almost everything has changed, especially the lineside, and one can see where the GNR expanded to its maximum extent before contracting again, even if wayside stations and yards have transformed into housing or industrial estates.

However, the GNR route itself, the railway of the Cubitts, Brassey, Denison, Bury and others, the railway of the many engineers and operators that have since followed, remains largely as it was built over 150 years ago.

The rebuilt station at Doncaster nears completion in June 1940. Over the brackets awaiting the veranda at the entrance a simple sign says TO BOOKING OFFICE AND TRAINS. Many big building projects were ruthlessly abandoned on the outbreak of war (Plymouth North Road station is a famous example) but Doncaster was finished off, even if the work was somewhat protracted.

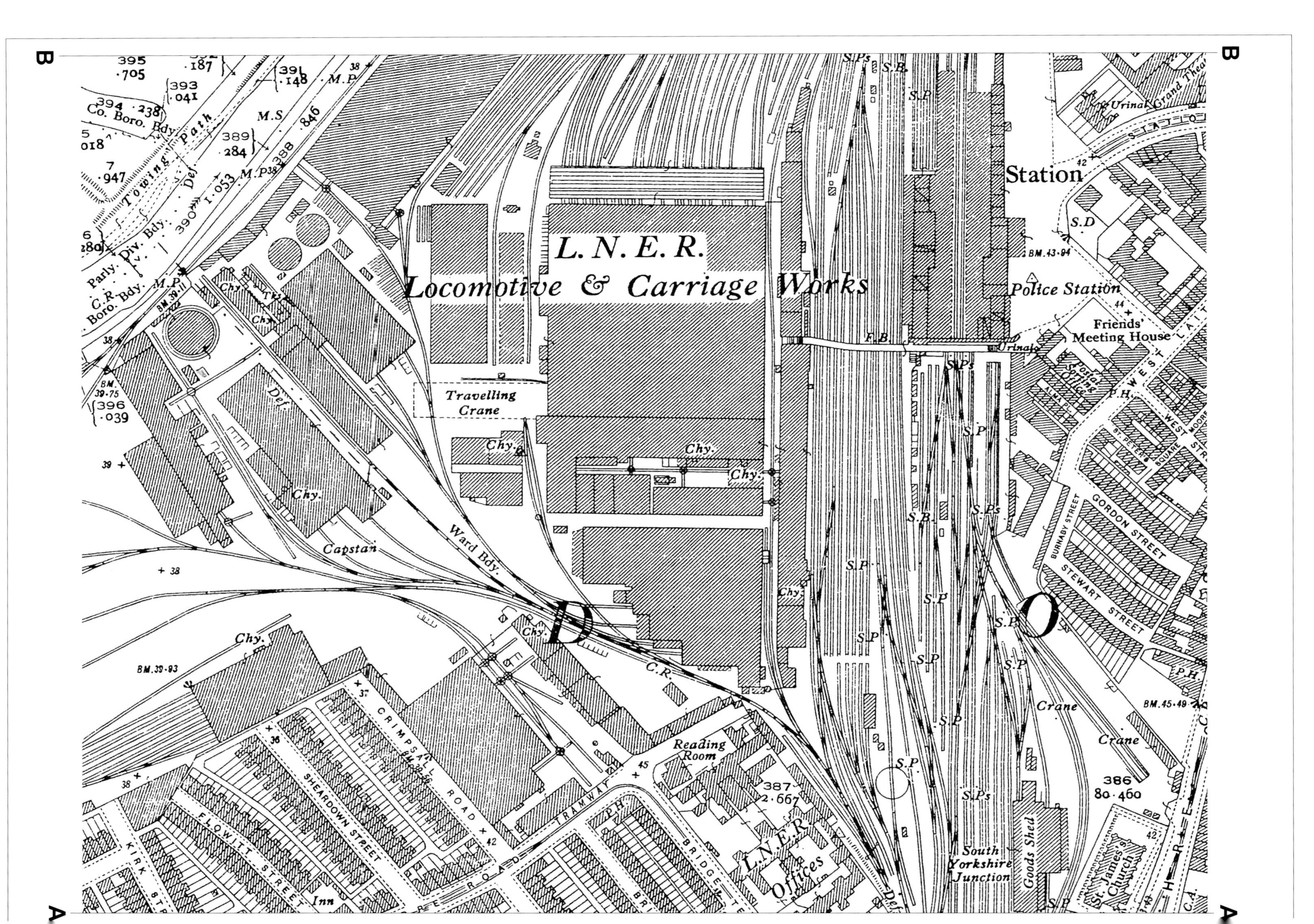

B
B
L. N. E. R.
Locomotive & Carriage Works
Station
Police Station
Friends' Meeting House
Postal Sorting Office
Urinal
Grand Theatre
Travelling Crane
Ward Bdy.
Capstan
Reading Room
L.N.E.R. Offices
South Yorkshire Junction
Goods Shed
St. James's Church
Crane
Crane
GORDON STREET
STEWART STREET
BURNABY STREET
WEST STREET
ST. PETER'S SQUARE
CRIMPSALL ROAD
SHEARDOWN STREET
FLOWITT STREET
KIRK STREET
TRAMWAY
BRIDGE
Inn
Towing Path
Co. Boro. Bdy.
Parly. Div. Bdy.
C.R. Boro. Bdy.
A
A

A

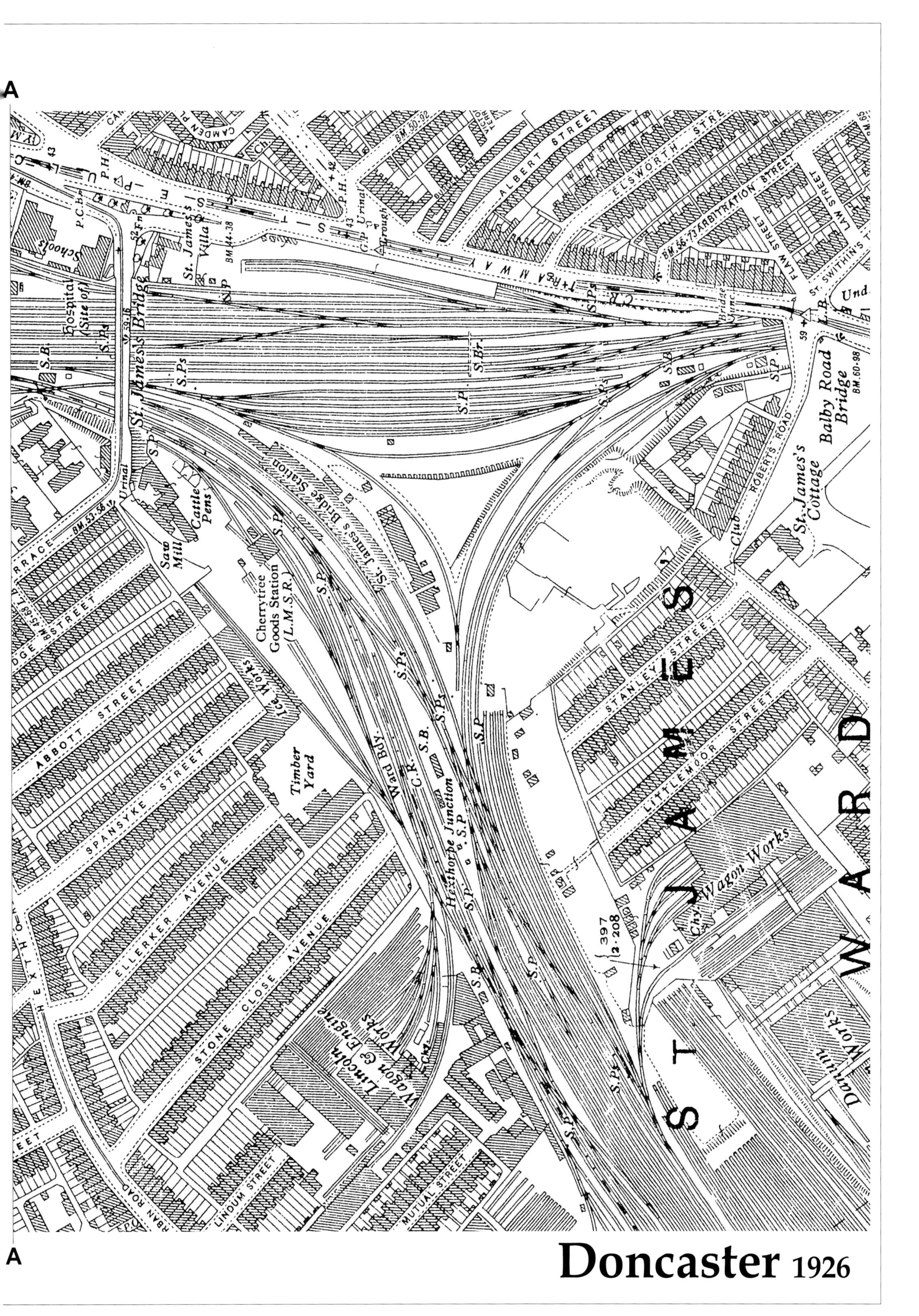

A

Doncaster 1926

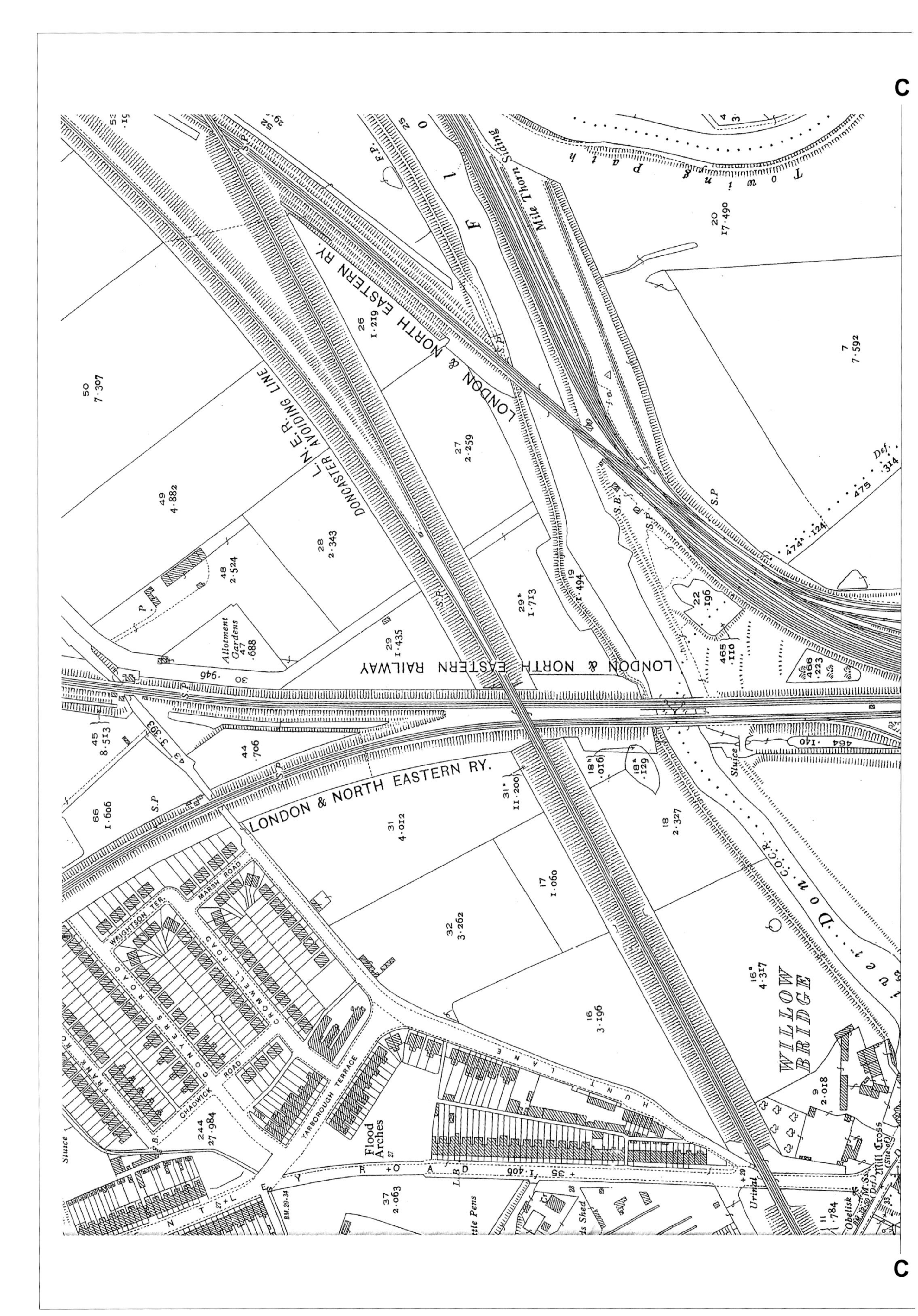
C
LONDON & NORTH EASTERN RY.
L.N.E.R. DONCASTER AVOIDING LINE
LONDON & NORTH EASTERN RAILWAY
LONDON & NORTH EASTERN RY.
Mile Thorn Siding
Allotment Gardens
WILLOW BRIDGE
Flood Arches
YARBOROUGH TERRACE
MARSH ROAD
CROMWELL ROAD
CHADWICK ROAD
WEIGHTSON TER.
Sluice
Urinal
Mill Cross
Obelisk
C

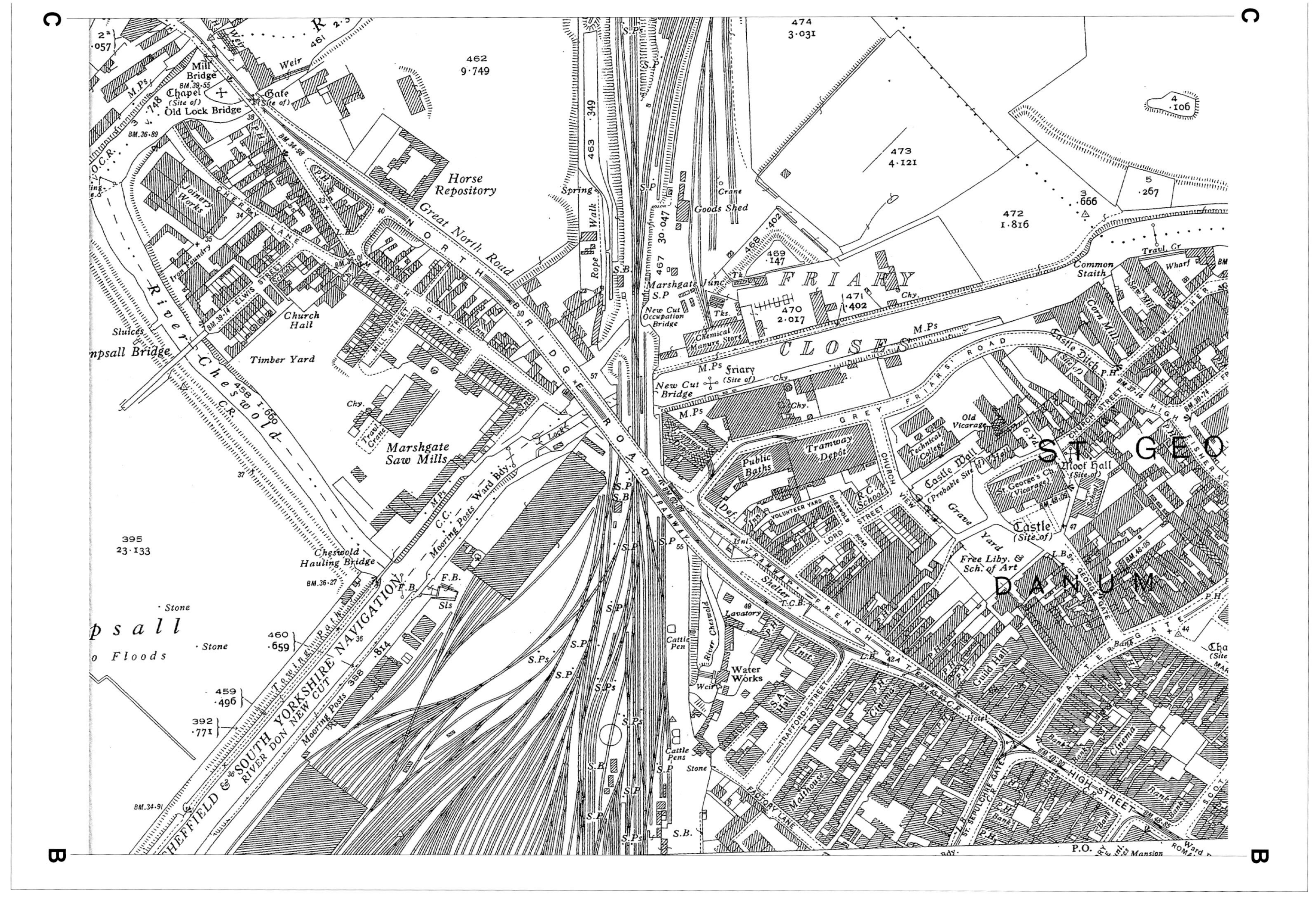

FRIARY
CLOSES
ST GEO
DANUM
Great North Road
NORTH BRIDGE ROAD
MARSH GATE
FRENCH GATE
GREY FRIARS ROAD
CHURCH VIEW
ST. GEORGE GATE
BAXTER GATE
HIGH STREET
TRAFFORD STREET
FACTORY LANE
MILL STREET
Horse Repository
Marshgate Saw Mills
Timber Yard
Church Hall
Joinery Works
River Cheswold
Public Baths
Tramway Depot
Technical College
Water Works
Goods Shed
Rope Walk
Corn Mill
Common Staith
Castle Ditch
Castle (Site of)
Castle Wall (Probable Site of)
Moot Hall (Site of)
Grave Yard
Free Liby. & Sch. of Art
Guild Hall
Old Vicarage
Friary (Site of)
New Cut Bridge
New Cut Occupation Bridge
Chemical Manure Store
Marshgate Junc.
Cattle Pens
Cheswold Hauling Bridge
Mill Bridge
Chapel (Site of)
Old Lock Bridge
Weir
Sluices
Cinema
Malthouse
Lavatory
Shelter
Mooring Posts
SHEFFIELD & SOUTH YORKSHIRE NAVIGATION
RIVER DON NEW CUT
Floods

C C

B B

Doncaster station, now *en fête* under BR ownership and looking more like a cinema than a station. The Festival of Britain year, 1951, suggests itself as the year in question.

The south end of Doncaster station in 1940 with the new second up platform, widened bay and new parting wall. The white rail ends were a wartime precaution. The footbridge in the distance gave access to the Works on the down side, and the main span was subsequently renewed as a lattice span.

V2 2-6-2 No.60946 coasts into the platform road at Doncaster with a down express while another V2, No.60852, heads for the shed tender first. Curiously, both V2s were involved in relieving A4s due to failure, and made exceptionally fast runs to London.

One of the magnificent Ivatt Atlantics in old age, LNER No.2849, at Doncaster with an up stopping service. She was fitted with a booster to assist in starting, in which the tender was powered by a two small steam cylinders which cut out once the train was on the move. It was unsuccessful and was removed later. Originally GNR No.1419, then LNER No.4419, she was also fitted with an improved cab similar to the A1/A3 design in place of the rudimentary GN cab. A.G. Forsyth, Initial Photographics.

An unidentified V2 arrives at Doncaster from the south with a relief, carrying its reporting number 367. The south pilot is another V2, which suggests to me that the date is shortly after nationalisation. The stock of the relief would have hardly inspired confidence to a knowledgeable traveller!

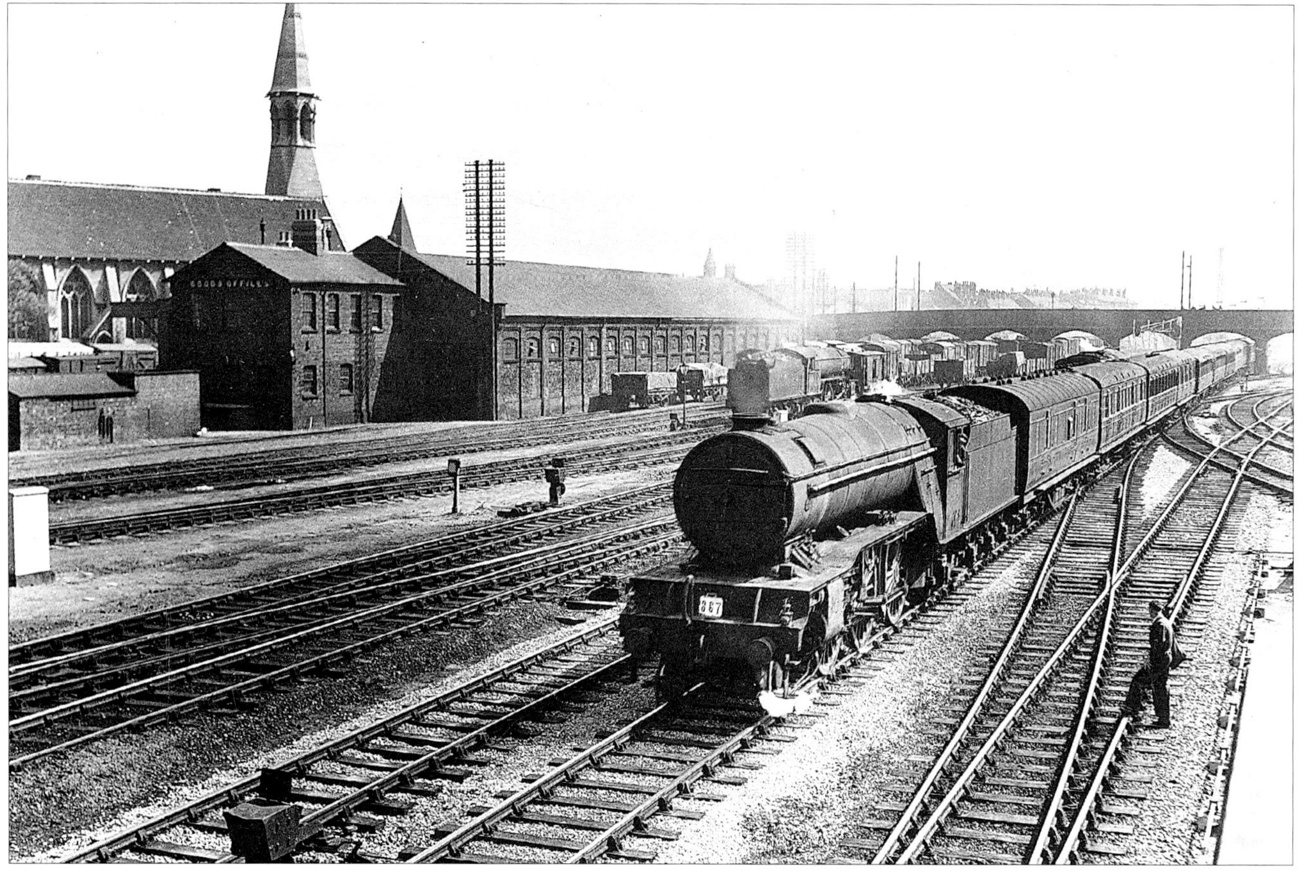

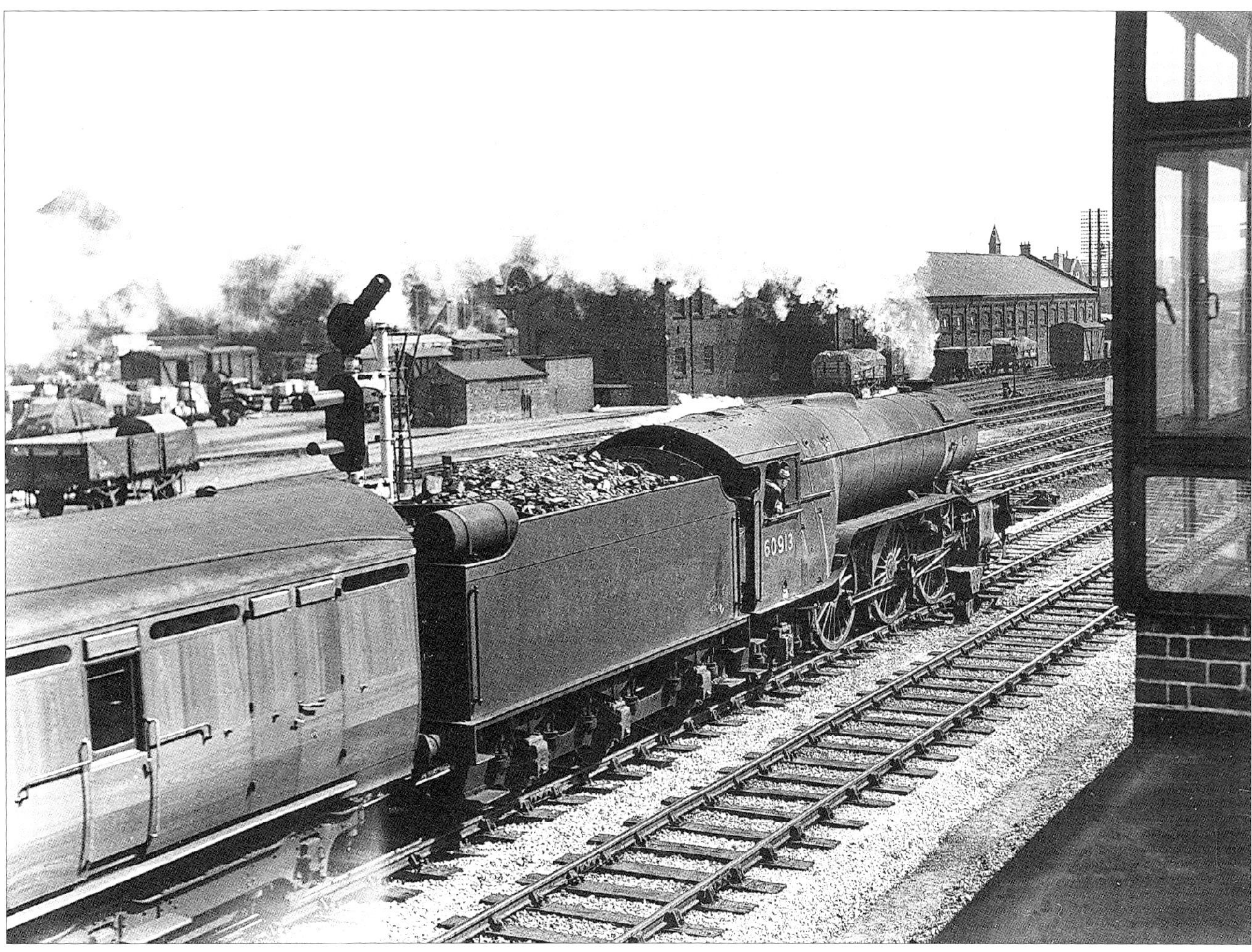

V2 No.60913 sets off from Doncaster with an up express.

The up bulk cement service in August 1960 passing through Doncaster behind the Haymarket favourite, A3 No.60043 BROWN JACK. The A3 is fresh from general overhaul at the Plant. D.H. Beecroft, www.transporttreasury.co.uk

O4 No.63593, tender first, with a train of coal bound for the yard at Doncaster Decoy, south of the Doncaster station area, on 8th February 1964. The vast Works – 'The Plant' to many – lies to the west of the station. A.H. Lucas, www.transporttreasury.co.uk

A southbound Newcastle service calls at Doncaster, headed by the last A4, No.60034 LORD FARINGDON, in August 1960. D.H. Beecroft, www.transporttreasury.co.uk

An up freight comes through the station on 8th February 1964, behind K1 No.62058. A.H. Lucas, www.transporttreasury.co.uk

A4 No.60015 QUICKSILVER backs through Doncaster station towards the shed south of the station in August 1960. D.H. Beecroft, www.transporttreasury.co.uk

Doncaster

Yards, engine shed ('Carr Loco') and repair shops south of the station. The smaller engine shed was once owned by the LNW, and latterly used by the Great Eastern.

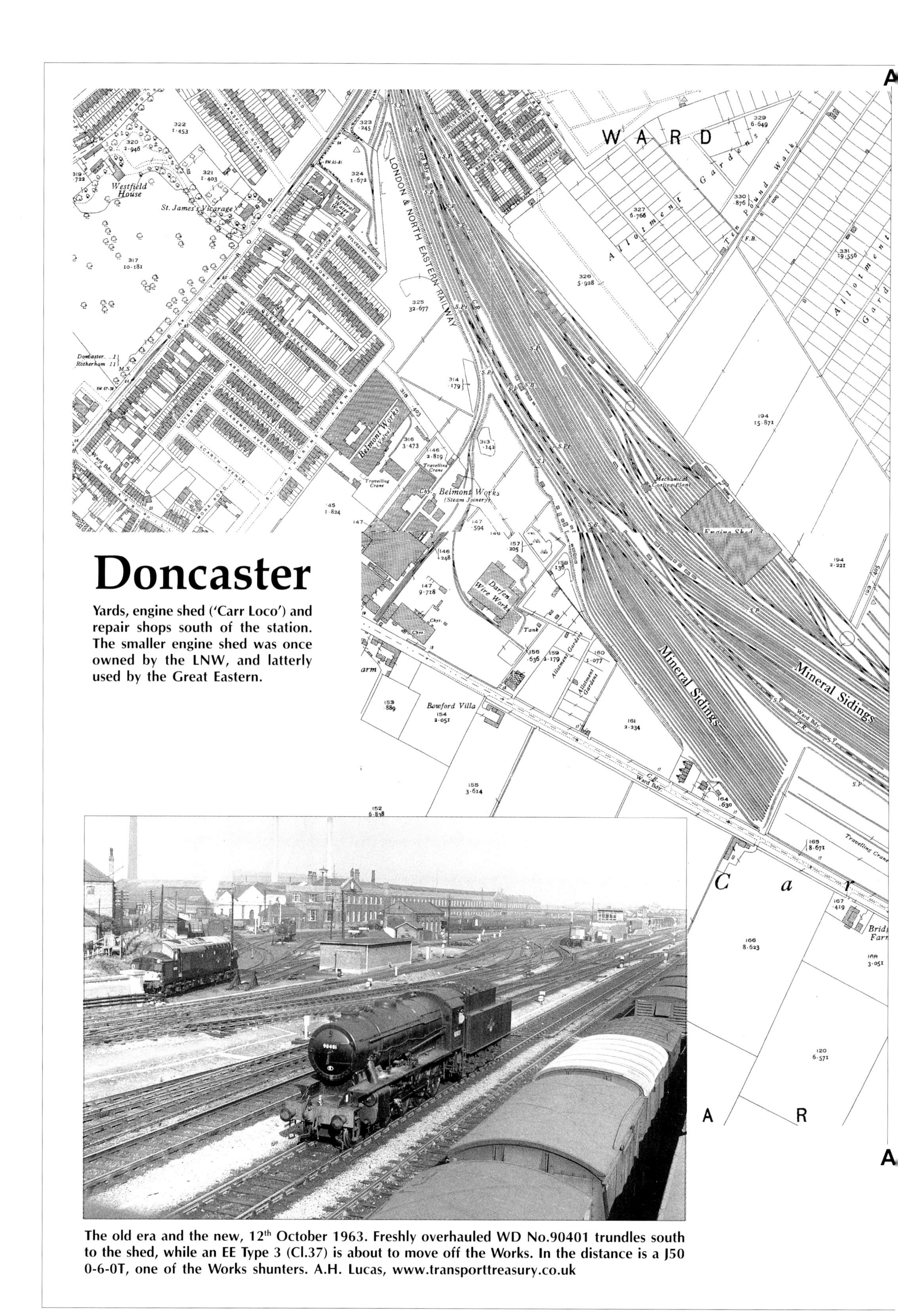

The old era and the new, 12th October 1963. Freshly overhauled WD No.90401 trundles south to the shed, while an EE Type 3 (Cl.37) is about to move off the Works. In the distance is a J50 0-6-0T, one of the Works shunters. A.H. Lucas, www.transporttreasury.co.uk

A pre-war Doncaster station, around 1937/38. A3 No.2550 (BR No.60051) BLINK BONNY pulls away with an up service, while an Ivatt Atlantic waits on the up main and an A1 or A3 on the down main. A down train stands in the down platform. A.G. Forsyth, Initial Photographics.

A4 No.60030 GOLDEN FLEECE in the up platform at Doncaster on 23rd May 1959. The Works footbridge central span has recently been renewed. A.G. Forsyth, Initial Photographics.

K3 No.61976 with a stopping service at Doncaster on 23rd May 1959.

B1s Nos.61250 A HAROLD BIBBY and **61249 FITZHERBERT WRIGHT** double head a stopping service from Doncaster on 19th April 1952. Doncaster had a batch of named B1s, and the pairing was not as coincidental as it may appear. It seems to have been a requirement of LNER Directors to have an eccentric name. This photograph shows the station before the platform canopies were replaced and their supporting columns removed, and the footbridge span renewed. A.G. Forsyth, Initial Photographics.

J39/2 No.64962 at Doncaster on 2nd August 1954 on the 12.32 Cleethorpes-Sheffield service. A.G. Forsyth, Initial Photographics.

On a grey, wet day, A3 No.60061 PRETTY POLLY starts away from Doncaster. The period would be 1961-63.

The Doncaster station of yore, in March 1936 and prior, obviously, to rebuilding. Passengers, if unaware of it, were advised of their rightful place at the heart of things, for the giant sign (compare with the later dim placard on the new station) proclaims: BOOKING OFFICE FOR LONDON AND WEST OF ENGLAND, NOTTINGHAM, EREWASH VALLEY, ILKESTON, DERBY, BURTON, LEICESTER, MELTON MOWBRAY, MARKET HARBOROUGH, NORTHAMPTON, KETTERING AND THE EASTERN COUNTIES. Underneath is a comprehensive list of destinations available by bus. In the left centre are the 'Dining and Tea Rooms' with access from the up platform. Observe the little building at the right, visible through the far corner of the canopy advertising BOVRIL, a room for cab men probably and looking for all the world like a signal box.

How stations could never look now; a line of rooms with afterthoughts added at every turn, disappearing into the distance northwards. Just *how* many fireplaces did it have?

Craven 'A', amongst the strongest fags known to man will not, nevertheless, 'affect *your* throat'. Under the hoarding is the entrance to the 'Plant', firmly closed up now and open only for clocking-on, clocking-off and lunch times. Probably not many of those trudging over the bridge ever enjoyed a Cunard White Star cruise! One of the smaller posters inform us that ONLY THE WISE BOVRILISE.

The soon to be demolished Stationmasters house at Doncaster in 1936, opposite the main entrance. Station Road is ahead of us, with the 'Grand Theatre & Empire Electric Picture Palace' beyond.

South end of the down platform, March 1936.

The down main platform, now looking north; at this time it was Platform 4 and the western platform No.7 while the north end Bays were 5 and 6.

The down platform, reminding us that the place was called Doncaster Central. It bore this title from 1923 to 1951 to distinguish it from the Doncaster York Road on the Great Central/Hull & Barnsley Joint Line – though this didn't have a passenger service!

The up platform at Doncaster in 1936, looking south.

Middle part of the up platform, looking south on 31st March 1936. The *Illustrated London News* was still in its pomp – regard the huge sign for that week's issue, featuring the *Queen Mary* leaving the Clyde...

London end of the up platform, 31 March 1936.

The south end with the South Box beyond the station footbridge. It was removed and replaced by a subway with the new station.

The Works footbridge in 1936.

An ancestor of BR's Travellers-Fare and the myriad train catering outlets of today, a Tea Bar on the up platform at Doncaster in March 1945. The photograph positively reeks of post-war austerity, gloom and neglect, with a dull wet day to complete the impression!

Doncaster up platform in happier days. The date is unknown, but I would put it no later than 1960. In the days of porterage and the carriage of mail, platform barrows were a commonplace, together with the fenders protecting platform buildings from damage and demolition by careless handling.

The second up platform was a 1930s addition, seen here with an approaching V2 hauled express in the early 1950s.

The down slow platform in the early 1950s, seen from the south end with the Works to the left of the carriage sidings.

A general view from the south through the station at Doncaster in the early 1950s. The up platform canopy is being renewed, while the down has yet to be started.

60022 GANNET with the Elizabethan headboard reversed, heads the up Sunday service on July 3rd 1960.

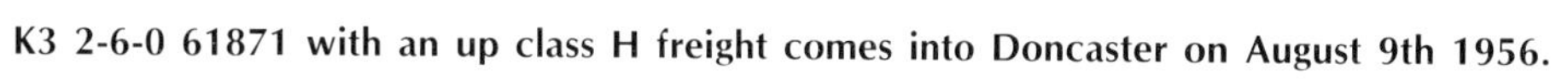
K3 2-6-0 61871 with an up class H freight comes into Doncaster on August 9th 1956.

Haymarket's 60011 EMPIRE OF INDIA heads the down Elizabethan through Doncaster on August 9th 1956. This A4 was used for three quarters of the season that year.

One of the later O2 2-8-0s with Gresley cab and group standard tender, 63974, on an up coal train, bound for Decoy Yard in August 1956.

K3 mogul 61942, just out of a General overhaul, at Doncaster on August 9th 1956.

J39 0-6-0 64732 with a miniscule down freight, August 1956.

A visitor from the old NER, D20 4-4-0 62378, arrives from Selby on August 9th 1956.

Grantham's B12/3 61574, off a down service, backs down towards Doncaster shed on August 9th 1956.

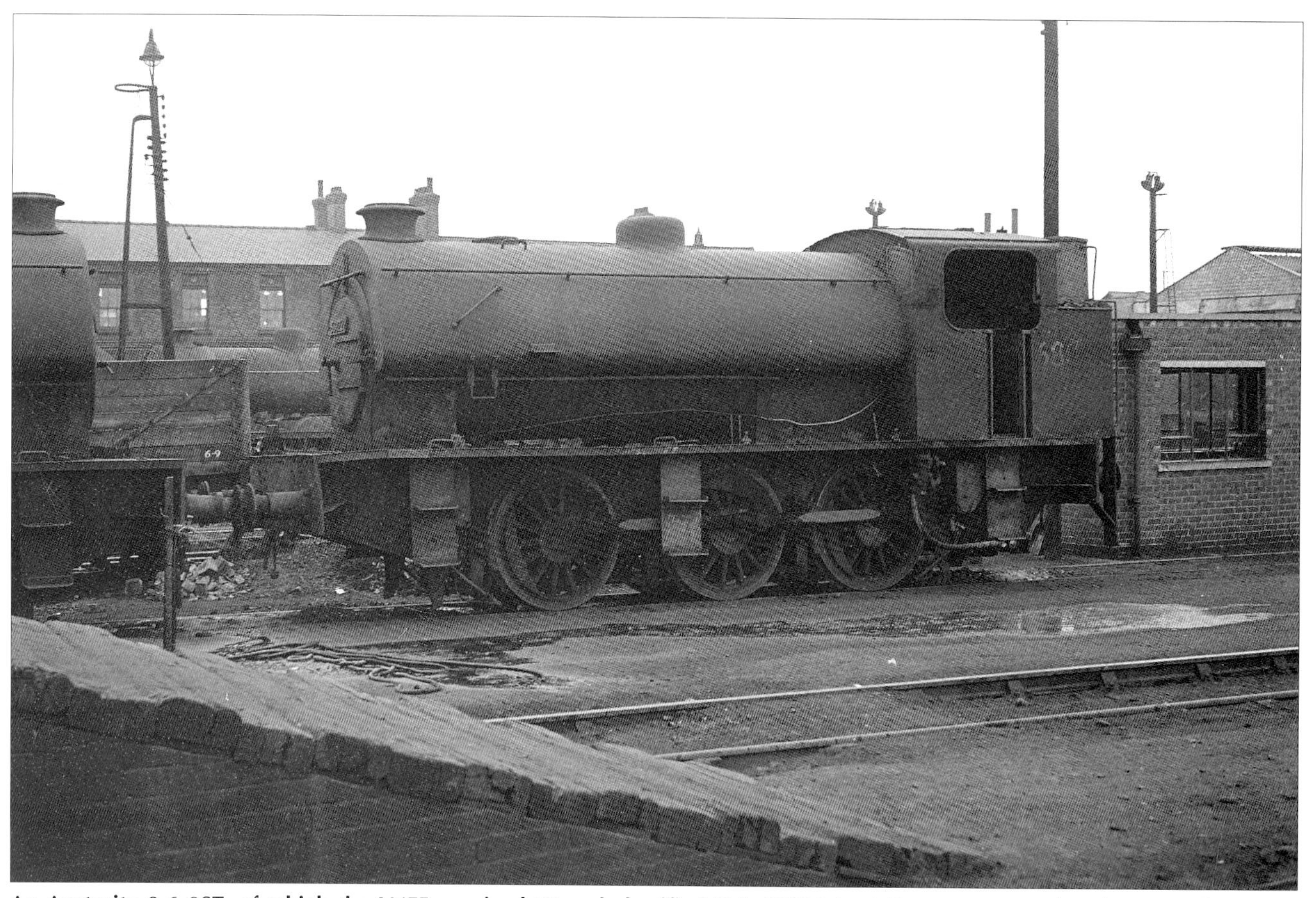

An Austerity 0-6-0ST, of which the LNER received 75 and classified J94. 68022 is at Doncaster on July 7th 1960. They were simple but light and inclined to slip with a good load.

60008 DWIGHT D EISENHOWER, fresh from overhaul, on July 2nd 1960 at the shed – 'Carr Loco'.

Another K3, 61887, brings a fast freight through Doncaster, bound for Decoy Yard, on August 9th 1956.

B1 4-6-0 61408 freshly repainted, at the shed on July 2nd 1960.

ENTERPRISE in for repair.

Doncaster was of course the place see newly shopped locos – this is recently overhauled K1 2-6-0 62024 rolling an up class H freight through the station on August 9th 1956.

A3 60048 DONCASTER herself with tender in for attention, at Carr Loco about 1960.

Appendices

MILEAGE FROM KINGS CROSS

LOCATION (Stations in capitals)	MILES	NOTES (prior to power operation)
KINGS CROSS	0.00	
Belle Isle Up	0.97	
Goods & Mineral Jct	1.03	
Copenhagen Jct	1.05	
Holloway South Dn	1.65	
Holloway South Up	1.66	
HOLLOWAY (closed 1913)	1.67	
Holloway North Up	1.69	
Holloway North Dn	1.77	
East Goods	2.09	
Finsbury Park No.3	2.41	
Finsbury Park No.4	2.42	
FINSBURY PARK	2.50	
Finsbury Park No.6	2.63	
Finsbury Park No.5	2.65	
Harringay West	3.35	
HARRINGAY	3.40	
Harringay Up Goods	3.43	
Ferme Park South Dn	3.58	
Ferme Park South Up	3.62	
Ferme Park North Up	3.83	
Ferme Park North Dn	3.88	
Hornsey No.1	4.01	
HORNSEY	4.05	
Hornsey No.2	4.16	
Wood Green No.1	4.84	
Wood Green No.4	4.94	
WOOD GREEN	4.95	
Wood Green No.3	5.03	
Wood Green No.4	5.12	
Wood Green Tunnel	5.43	
New Southgate	6.39	
NEW SOUTHGATE	6.45	
Cemetery	7.42	
Oakleigh Park	8.24	
OAKLEIGH PARK	8.35	
New Barnet South	9.03	
NEW BARNET	9.15	
New Barnet North	9.26	
Greenwood	10.08	
HADLEY WOOD	10.60	
Hadley Wood	10.60	Replaced with IBS: GF until 1959
Ganwick	11.20	Replaced with IBS, 1930s
Mimms Hall	12.11	Replaced with IBS, 1930s
POTTERS BAR	12.70	
Potters Bar	12.73	
Hawkshead	14.03	Replaced with IBS
BROOKMANS PARK*	14.53	
Marshmoor	15.71	
Red Hall	16.47	
Hatfield No.1	17.51	
HATFIELD	17.70	
Hatfield No.3	17.77	
Hatfield No.2	17.81	
WELWYN GARDEN CITY	20.30	
Welwyn Garden City	20.34	
Digswell	21.37	Replaced with IBS
Welwyn North	21.90	

MILEAGE FROM KINGS CROSS (cont)

LOCATION (Stations in capitals)	MILES	NOTES (prior to power operation)
WELWYN NORTH	22.00	
Woolmer Green	23.45	
Knebworth	25.04	
KNEBWORTH	25.05	
Langley Jct	26.99	Troughs
Stevenage South	28.27	
STEVENAGE	28.55	
Stevenage North	28.59	
Wymondley	29.78	Replaced with IBS
Hitchin South	31.52	
HITCHIN	31.90	
Hitchin Yard	31.94	
Hitchin Midland	32.15	Bedford branch box
Cambridge Junction	32.18	
Cadwell	33.26	
Three Counties	35.58	
THREE COUNTIES	35.70	
ARLESEY	37.00	
Arlesey	37.03	
Langford Bridge	38.56	
Biggleswade South	40.87	
Biggleswade North	41.12	
BIGGLESWADE	41.15	
Sandy	43.81	
SANDY	44.15	
Sandy North	45.18	1913 wartime addition, later disused.
Everton	46.31	
Tempsford	47.41	
TEMPSFORD	47.50	
Great Barford	49.41	Replaced with IBS
St.Neots	51.41	
ST NEOTS	51.75	
Paxton	53.73	
Offord	55.84	
OFFORD	55.95	
Ouse	57.40	Removed
Huntingdon No.1	58.66	
HUNTINGDON NORTH	58.85	
Huntingdon No.2	58.97	
Stukeley	61.03	
Leys	62.00	Replaced with motored connections
Abbots Ripton	63.44	
ABBOTS RIPTON	63.50	
Wood Walton	64.99	
Connington South	67.32	
Connington North	68.25	
Holme	69.26	
HOLME	69.35	
Stilton Fen	71.01	Removed
YAXLEY & FARCET	72.60	
Yaxley	72.60	
Fletton Junction	74.92	
Crescent Junction	76.15	
PETERBOROUGH	76.35	
Peterborough North	76.39	
Spital Junction	76.57	
Eastfield	76.98	
Westwood	77.01	
New England South	77.31	
New England East	77.44	
New England North	77.81	
Walton	78.62	
Werrington Jct	79.44	Troughs
Helpston	81.82	
Lolham	83.34	
Tallington	84.74	
TALLINGTON	84.85	
Greatford	87.06	
Essendine South	88.47	
ESSENDINE	88.65	
Essendine North	88.68	
Monkswood	90.53	Replaced with IBS
Little Bytham	92.22	
LITTLE BYTHAM	92.25	
Counthorpe	94.60	Replaced with IBS
Corby Glen	97.09	
CORBY GLEN	97.10	
Burton Dn	97.83	Replaced with IBS
Stoke	100.05	
Highdyke	101.26	
Great Ponton	102.02	Rebuilt at 102.15
GREAT PONTON	102.10	
Saltersford	103.56	Replaced with IBS
Grantham South	105.04	
Grantham Yard	105.33	
GRANTHAM	105.45	
Grantham North	105.55	
Barrowby Road Junction	106.40	Main line signalling replaced by IBS
Peascliffe	107.20	Replaced with IBS

MILEAGE FROM KINGS CROSS (cont)

LOCATION (Stations in capitals)	MILES	NOTES (prior to power operation)
Barkston South Junction	109.64	
BARKSTON	109.70	
Barkston North Junction	110.09	
Hougham	111.47	
HOUGHAM	111.50	
Westborough	113.66	
Claypole	115.29	
CLAYPOLE	115.35	
Balderton	116.82	
Barnby	118.98	
Newark South	119.87	
NEWARK	120.10	
Newark North	120.27	
Midland Crossing	120.73	
Trent	121.57	Troughs at Muskham
Bathley Lane	122.92	
Cromwell	124.64	
Carlton	126.26	
CARLTON	126.30	
Crow Park	127.38	
CROW PARK	127.45	
Egmanton	130.31	
DUKERIES JUNCTION	131.15	
Dukeries	131.16	
Tuxford North Junction	131.61	
Tuxford	131.89	
TUXFORD	131.90	
Lincoln Road	133.00	
Gamston	135.44	
Grove Road	137.38	
Retford South	138.46	
RETFORD	138.60	
Retford North	138.68	
Babworth	139.11	
Canal	139.54	
Botany Bay	140.61	
Barnby Moor	141.64	
BARNBY MOOR & SUTTON	141.75	
Ranskill	143.94	
RANSKILL	143.95	
Scrooby	145.11	
Scrooby Junction	145.89	Troughs at 146.25
Bawtry	147.70	
BAWTRY	147.70	
Pipers Wood	149.37	
Rossington	151.31	
ROSSINGTON	151.35	
Loversall Carr	152.33	
Black Carr Junction	153.12	
Childers Drain	153.49	
Potteric Carr	153.55	
Decoy No.1 Down	153.74	
Decoy No.2 Up	153.86	
Red Bank	154.14	
Carr	154.17	
Balby Junction	154.73	
Sand Bank	154.90	
Bridge Junction	155.09	
Doncaster South	155.42	
DONCASTER	155.95	

*no box

COMPARISON BETWEEN GN MAIN LINE TIMETABLES; 1922, 1938, 1953

1922		1938		1953	
				0055	ED
		0329	GM (Papers)	0234	GM (Papers)
445	York & Leeds	445	York & Leeds	0350	LDS
505	Doncaster & Sheffield	502	Doncaster & Sheffield	0545	DR
		610	GM & Derby	0645	GM
		718	CB	0714	BK
715	York & Leeds	725	York & Leeds		
		730	ED		
745	Peterborough	745	DR		
				0750	LDS & BD
				0800	YK
845	NC	845	DR		
				0900	NC
				0910	LDS
		935	CB	0922+E39	CB
				0935	ED
				0940	NC
950	ED	1000	ED & AB	1000	ED & AB
1000	ED & AB	1005	ED	1005	ED & GG
1010	LDS	1010	ED & HL		
1025	Peterborough	1015	LDS & HL	1018	LDS & HL
		1040	DR	1040	GM
		1100	SCA & NC	1120	SCA
1120	SCA & GG	1120	Queen of Scots Pulman	1205	Queen of Scots Pulman
1130	SCA	1130	York		
				1210	NC
				1218	NC
				1235	YK (Parcels)
		1240	CB	1205	CB
				1305	LDS
		1310	NC		
				1318	LDS
				1345	ED
1320	ED	1320	ED	1400	ED
1330	LDS & HL	1330	LDS & HL	1418	LDS & HL
1340	RP	1340	RP & YK		
1350	NC		RP (SO)		
1355	PE	1355	PE		
		1410	CB	1405	CB
		1420	NC	1500	NC
1500	Cromer	1500	PE		
		1530	NC	1510	NC
1600	NC	1600	Coronation		
				1545	LDS
		1600	LDS & YK	1550	LDS
		1605	Cleethorpes	1600	Cleethorpes
1615	GM	1615	GM	1610	PE
		1645	Yorkshire Pulmn	1730	Yorkshire Pulmn
1700	ES	1700	PE & CB	1700	PE & CB
1710	PE	1710	BK	1710	BK
1730	NC	1730	Silver Jubilee	1645	Tees-Tyne Pulmn
1735	YK & SUN	1735	BK	1739	BK
		1745	NC & HL	1735	NC
1745	LDS	1750	HGT & LDS	1818	LDS
		1754	BK		
		1800	ED (Cars)		
		1802	BK		
				1805	HL
				1810	LDS
1815	HN	1815	CB & PE	1752	CB & PE
		1830	BK	1825	ROY
		1855	CB	1840	ROY
		1910	LDS		
		1915	LDS & HL		
		1925	AB	1900	AB
1930	AB				
		1933	ED	1915	AB
		1940	AB		
				1915	YK (Parcels)
1942	HN	1950	PE	1921	PE
		2010	CB	2002	CB
				2010	DR
2025	ED	2025	ED	2020	ED
		2110	BK		
		2138	YK (Parcels)		
		2155	CB		
2220	AB			2215	AB & ED
		2225	ED & AB		
2230	ED	2235	ED	2235	ED
2245	NC	2245	NC	2245	NC & BD
		2250	LDS	2300	LDS
		2253	YK	2345	NC
		2303	Letchworth		
		2340	CB		

KEY
AB Aberdeen, BD Bradford, BK Baldock, CB Canbridge, DR Doncaster, ED Edinburgh, ES Essendine, GG Glasgow, GM Grantham, HGT Harrogate, HL Hull, HN Hitchin, LDS Leeds, NC Newcastle, PE Peterborough North, ROY Royston, RP Ripon, SCA Scarborough, SUN Sunderland, YK York

GNR CHAIRMEN

Wiliiam Astell	1846-47
Edmund Denison	1847-64
GeorgeHussey Packe	1865-74
Hon.Octavius Duncombe	1874-79
Lord Colville	1879-95
W I Jackson	1895-1917
Sir Frederick Banbury	1917-22

GENERAL MANAGER

Seymour Clarke	1850-70
Henry Oakley	1870-98
C Steel	1898-1902
Oliver Bury	1902-13
C.B.D Dent	1913-22

SUPERINTENDENT OF THE LINE

John Denniston	1849-53
Waiter Leith	1853-63
John Currey	1863-65
Francis Cockshot	1865-95
J Alexander	1895-1902
(Vacant)	*1902-10*
W H Hills	1910-14
C J Selway	1914-22

LOCOMOTIVE ENGINEER

Benjamin Cubitt	1846-48
Edward Bury	1848-50
Archibald Sturrock	1850-66
Patrick Stirling	1866-95
Henry Ivatt	1895-1911
H Nigel Gresley	1911-22

ENGINEER (CIVIL & SIGNALLING)

John Miller	1846-47
Joseph Cubitt	1848-55
Waiter Marr Brydone	1856-61
Richard Johnson	1861-96
A Ross	1896-1911
C J Brown	1911-22

LOCAL TIMETABLES COMPARED: GNR DOWN SUBURBAN 1922 (10.00-12.00)

Moorgate	952			1000	1006	1010	1024			1042							1143
Kings Cross arr						1021				1052							1157
Kings Cross dep	1004			1012	1020	1050	1036	1025		1105	1120		1130	1137		1145	1204
Broad St		955							1011						1127		
Finsbury Park arr	1010	1008		1018	1026	1057	1042	1031	1024	1111			1136	1143	1140	1151	1210
Finsbury Park dep	1011	1029		1019	1029	1058	1043	1032	1030	1112			1137	1144	1144	1152	1212
Alexandra Palace				1036			1100			1129					1201		
Finchley		1043	1043								1148	1215					
High Barnet		1058				1128					1159						
Edgware		1059										1225					
New Barnet	1031															1212	
Potters Bar																	
Hatfield													1201				
Gordon Hill									1056					1207			
Cuffley					1059												1248
Hitchin								1134					1222				
													Scarborough				

LOCAL TIMETABLES COMPARED: DOWN SUBURBAN 1938 (10.00-12.00)

						LMS				LMS									LMS SO					LMS SO
Moorgate	951		1000	1006			1024							1100										
Kings Cross arr	1001		1010	1016			1034							1110										
Kings Cross dep	1002	1009	1012	1017	1020		1036		1040	1050		1054		1111		1130	1130			1137		1145	1155	
Broad St						1011		1028																
Finsbury Park arr	1008	1015	1017	1023	1026	1024	1042	1042	1046	1055		1100		1117			1136			1142		1150	1201	
Finsbury Park dep	1010	1017	1019	1024	1028	1030	1045	1044	1048	1056	1058	1102	1112	1118	1126		1137		1144	1143	1153	1152	1202	1210
Alexandra Palace			1036				1102						1129						1201					
Finchley																								
High Barnet					1059						1129					1207					1223			1240
Edgware																								
New Barnet								1105							1145							1223		
Potters Bar																								
Hatfield arr												1147					1201							
Hatfield dep																	1202	1209						
Gordon Hill						1056				1121				1143										
Cuffley																					1207			
Hertford North	1055		1112																				1250	
Hitchin		1122							1130								1222	1238						
									Don								York	C'bge						

LOCAL TIMETABLES COMPARED: DOWN SUBURBAN 1953 (10.00-12.00)

Moorgate										
Kings Cross arr										
Kings Cross dep	1000	1021	1030	1040	1054	1121	1130	1154		1205
Broad St										
Finsbury Park arr	1006	1027	1036	1046	1100	1127	1136	1200		
Finsbury Park dep	1007	1029	1037	1047	1102	1128	1137	1201	1202	
Alexandra Palace									1219	
Finchley										
High Barnet										
Edgware										
New Barnet										
Potters Bar										
Hatfield arr		1053		1115	1147	1153				
Hatfield dep		1054		1117		1154				
Welwyn Gar. City								1252		1236
										1237
Gordon Hill										
Cuffley										
Hertford North	1057		1127				1227			
Hitchin		1125		1138		1224				1251
		C'bdge		P'borough						C'bdge

Doncaster on 9 August 1956; 76068 is brand new, 43096 has been overhauled.

KINGS CROSS-DONCASTER
TRACKS AND SIGNALBOXES in 1950

SIGNALBOX NAME	Control Area	Tracks at Location								
		Up Lines				Down lines				
Kings Cross			US	UM	UI	DM1	DM2	DS		
Belle Isle Up	U		US	UM	UI					
Goods & Mineral Jct	GL								UG	DG
Copenhagen Jct	D					DM1	DM2	DS		
Holloway South Down	D					DM	DS	DG		
Holloway South Up	U		UG	US	UM					
Holloway North Up	U	UG	UECS	US	UM					
Holloway North Down	D					DM	DS	DG	D ECS	
Holloway Carriage Sdgs	D SIdings								D ECS	
East Goods	U	UG/Bch								
Canonbury Jct	Bch				UBch	DBch				
Highbury Vale	U Sidings									
Ashburton Grove	D Sidings									
Clarence Yard	D Sidings							DG		
Finsbury Park No.1	Bch				UBch	DBch				
Finsbury Park No.2	D							DG	D ECS	
Finsbury Park No.3	D					DM	DS1	DS2	DG	
Finsbury Park No.4	U	UG	UC/ECS	US	UM					
Finsbury Park No.5	D					DM	DS1	DS2	D Bch	DG
Finsbury Park No.6	U	UBch	UG	US	UM					
Finsbury Park No.7	Bch									
Harringay	DG		UG	US	UM	DM	DS	DS2	DG	
Harringay Goods	UG		UG							
Ferme Park Sth Dn	DYD							DG		
Ferme Park Nth Dn	DYD							DG		
Ferme Park Sth Up	UYD		UG							
Ferme Park Nth Up	UYD		UG							
Hornsey No.1		UG/ECS	UG	US	UM					
Hornsey No.2						DM	DS1	DS2	DG	
Wood Green No.1	D					DM	DS1	DS2	DG	
Wood Green No.2	U	UG/ECS	UG	US	UM					
Wood Green No.3	D					DM	DS1	DS2	DG	
Wood Green No.4	U	UBch	UG	US	UM					
Wood Green Tunnel	D					DM	DS	DG		
Bounds Green	Bch/ECS				U Bch	D Bch				
New Southgate		UR	UGstop	US	UM	DM	DS			
Cemetery		UR	UGstart	US	UM	DM	DS			
Oakleigh Park			UGstop	US	UM	DM	DS	DGstart		
Barnet South			UG	US	UM	DM	DS	DG		
Barnet North			UGstart	US	UM	DM	DSstop	DG		
Greenwood				USstart	UM	DM	DGstop			
Hadley Wood IBS					U	D				
Ganwick IBS					U	D				
Mimms Hall IBS					U	D				

KINGS CROSS-DONCASTER
TRACKS AND SIGNALBOXES in 1950

SIGNALBOX NAME	Control Area	Tracks at Location								
		Up Lines				Down lines				
Potters Bar				USstop	UM	DM	DSstart			
Hawkshead IBS				US	UM	DM	DS			
Marshmoor				US	UM	DM	DS			
Red Hall				US	UM	DM	DS			
Hatfield No.1				US	UM	DM	DS			
Hatfield No.3				US	UM	DM	DS			
Hatfield No.2			SBch	US	UM	DM	DS	SBch		
Welwyn Gar City			SBch	US	UM	DM	DSstop	SBch		
Digswell				USstart	UM	DM	DGstop			
Welwyn North					U	D				
Woolmer Green				UGstop	UM	DM	DSstart			
Knebworth			UGstop	UGstart	UM	DM	DS			
Langley Jct			UBch	US	UM	DM	DS	DBch		
Stevenage South				US	UM	DM	DS			
Stevenage North				US	UM	DM	DGstart	DSstop		
Wymondley IBS				US	UM	DM	DG			
Hitchin South				US	UM	DM	DGstop			
Hitchin Yard				US	UM	DM	DS			
Cambridge Jct			Ugstop	US	UM	DM	DS			
Hitchin Midland	Bch							Bch	(Bedford)	
Cadwell			USstop	UGstart	UM	DM	DSstop	DGstart		
Three Counties					UM	DM	DG			
Arlesey	B'neck/LX		UGstop	USstart	UM	DM	DG			
Langford Bridge				UG	UM	DM	DG			
Biggleswade South			USstop	UGstart	UM	DM	DG			
Biggleswade North				US	UM	DM	DG			
Sandy	B'neck			US	UM	DM	DSstart	DGstop		
Sandy Jct				US	UM	DM	DS		Bch	
Everton	LX			US	UM	DM	DS			
Tempsford	LX			US	UM	DM	DS			
St.Neots				US	UM	DM	DSstop	DGstart		
Paxton			UGstop	USstart	UM	DM	DG			
Offord	LX			UG	UM	DM	DG			
Huntingdon No.1			Bch	UGstart	UM	DM	DSstart	DGstop		
Huntingdon No.2	3T				UM	DM	DSstop	DGstart		
Stukeley					UM	DM	DG			
Leys				UGstop	UM	DM	DG			
Abbots Ripton				UG	UM	DM	DG			
Connington South				UGstart	UM	DM	DG			
Connington North					UM	DM	DGstop			
Holme	LX			Bch	UM	DM				
Stilton Fen IBS					UM	DM				

KINGS CROSS-DONCASTER
TRACKS AND SIGNALBOXES in 1950

SIGNALBOX NAME	Control Area	Tracks at Location								
		Up Lines				Down lines				
Yaxley			Brick loops	UGstop	UM	DM	DGstart	Brick loops		
Fletton Jct				UG	UM	DM	DG	Bch		
Crescent Jct		UBch	USstop	UGstart	UM	DM	DG	Bch		
Peterborough North.				US	UM	DM	Dplat	DG		
Spital Jct		UGstop	USstart	DG	UM	DM				
Eastfield	GL		UG	DG	UM	DM			* Up side	
Westwood Jct			UG	DG	UM	DM		Bch		
NWE South	GL		UG	DG	UM	DM				
NWE East	GL		UG	DG	UM	DM				
NWE North	GL		UG	DG	UM	DM				
Walton	LX		UG	DG	UM	DM				
Werrington Jct.		Bch	UG	DG stop	UM	DM	DSstart			
Helpston	LX			UG	UM	DM	DS			
Lolham	LX			UG	UM	DM	DS			
Tallington	LX		UG start	US stop	UM	DM	DS stop/start			
Greatford	LX			US	UM	DM	DS stop	DG start		
Essendine		(Bourne)	Bch	US	UM	DM	DG	Bch	(Stamford)	
Little Bytham				US	UM	DM	DG			
Corby Glen				US	UM	DM	DG			
Stoke				US start	UM	DM	DG stop			
Highdyke					U	D		Bch	(Stainby)	
Gt. Ponton				UG	UM	D				
Grantham South				UGstart	UM	DM	DS			
Grantham Yard	U				U	D				
Grantham North					U	D	DS			
Barrowby Road Jct					U	D	Bch		(Nott'm)	
Barkston Sth Jct		(Sleaford)	Bch		U	D				
Barkston Nth Jct				U loop	U	D				
Hougham					U	D	D loop			
Westborough					U	D				
Claypole					U	D	D loop			
Balderton					U	D	D loop			
Barnby					U	D				
Newark Sth				U loop	U	D	Bch			
Newark Nth				U loop	U	D	Bch			
Midland Crossing					U	D				
Trent					U	D	D loop			
Bathley Lane					U	D				
Cromwell					U	D				

KINGS CROSS-DONCASTER
TRACKS AND SIGNALBOXES in 1950

SIGNALBOX NAME	Control Area	Tracks at Location								
		Up Lines				Down lines				
Carlton					U	D				
Crow Park					U	D				
Egmanton					U	D				
Dukeries Jct					U	D				
Tuxford Nth Jct					U	D	D &U Bch			
Tuxford					U	D				
Lincoln Road					U	D	D loop			
(Markham Siding)					U	D				
Gamston					U	D				
Grove Road				U loop	U	D				
Retford Sth					U	D	DS	DG		
Retford Nth		(Lincoln)	Bch	U loop	U	D	DS	Bch	(Sheffield)	DG
Babworth				U loop	U	D	D loop			
Barnby Moor					U	D				
Ranskill			Bch	U loop	U	D	D loop			
Scrooby					U	D	Bch			
Bawtry			Bch	U loop	U	D	D loop			
Pipers Wood					U	D				
Rossington				UG stop	U	D		Bch		
Black Carr Jct		(Lincoln)	Bch	UG	U	D				
Potteric carr Jct				US/UG	U	D				
Doncaster			U plat	US	U	D	DS	D plat	Bch	(Sheffield)
Marshgate Jct			(H & G	Bch	U	D	Bch	(Leeds)		
Bentley					U	D				
Arksey					U	D	D loop			
Shaftholme Jct					U	D	U Bch	D Bch		

SYMBOLS USED SINGLY OR TOGETHER

Control Area	U-up lines, D-down lines, Blank-all lines.
U	Up
D	Down
UM	Up main
DM	Down main
UI	Up Independent
US	Up slow
DS	Down slow
UG	Up goods
DG	Down goods
UECS	Up empty carriage (slow) line
DECS	Down empty carriage (slow) line
BCH	Branch or location off the main route
US or UGstart	Start of US or UG:i.e. change of signalling regime
US or Ugstop	Stop of US or UG:i.e. change of signalling regime
UR	Up reception
SBCH	Single line branch
B'neck	Bottleneck i.e. 4 to 2 tracks and back to 4
LX	Level crossings
Dplat	Platform line
DG(U)	Down goods (on up side)
S	Single
3T	Three tracks in station
H & G	Hull and Grimsby

GNR TIMETABLES

A comparison between the timetables just over a century apart illustrates the enormous shift that has taken place in rail travel. We know that with greatly increased power, together with investment in the infrastructure to allow higher speeds, the number of trains that can be operated is far greater. We know also that the freight traffic has metamorphosed into a small number of relatively fast services. We can see from the timetables of 1922, 1938 and 1953 that the rather basic GNR timetable grew before the 1939-45 war, but the reorganisation in the mid-1950s increased and accelerated passenger services. In 1922 there were really just two trains, or groups of trains, to Scotland, plus the overnight sleeping car services. Eighty years later the service is *hourly*.

The change from steam traction brought increased service levels and speeds, but the overwhelming increase in passenger travel that has occurred with electrification is catered for by a service that is unrecognisable by comparison with that of 1922. The philosophy underlining timetabling has changed radically. The RailAir service from London to Gatwick Airport of the 1980s was, I think, the first on which the service frequency was increased to a level that made understanding the timetable no longer necessary. A service was never more than a cup of tea away. This philosophy now underpins timetabling on all the electrified routes, the former GNR main line being one of the most important.

In the comparison between the three timetables only the down service has been shown as an example. The arrival times at Kings Cross for individual up services varied over the years and hence comparison is much less clear. Two things stand out in the 1922 timetable. Firstly, the very few services that ran were large, and although a number of portions were carried on some trains, with an abundance of branch lines and connecting services, passengers were expected to change to reach their destination. Travelling to places off the main line therefore took longer, waiting for a connecting service which was inevitably slower. The number of stops was considerable; for example, the 8.45 Newcastle called not only at all of the principal stations but also at Finsbury Park, Hatfield, Hitchin, Huntingdon and Bawtry. The 1922 down timetable started gently, unless that is, one was travelling to the Leeds area, since there was nothing between the 7.15 and 10.10 departures. Newcastle travellers were more kindly treated with an 8.45 departure. The 1922 businessman, without Internet, mobile telephone and all the trappings of the present day, would eventually arrive at Newcastle at 15.18. His consolation would have been that he had been sumptuously fed with a fine breakfast and lunch as well. One might speculate as to his ability to discuss complex business issues after that! Or even stay awake.

Secondly, one can see that much of the time the railway was given over to freight, and passenger services were despatched in blocks so that the line could be kept clear of slow freight until the last of each group had passed. As No.272 down, the 8.45 made its way up to Potters Bar, a braked goods, No.271 down, was waiting at Greenwood to follow it into the bottleneck. In fact a number of freight services remained reasonably constant, for obvious reasons related to their nature such as evening and overnight fish traffic to Billingsgate, and returning empties several hours later. Even the celebrated Scots Goods, which ran post-war in the early afternoon in two parts, Nos.262 and 266 down, were established much earlier as Nos.527 and 562 down, using the pre-war working timetable numbers.

One of the most popular services in the up direction was the 7.50 from Leeds. The link between the Yorkshire wool and coal industries and the City of London's financial centres was critical, and the train became known as 'The Breakfast Flyer'. It loaded well, and punctual running was a high priority. In the early 1930s it became one of the hardest turns on the old GN main line, worked with distinction by Doncaster – 'Carr Loco'. Train catering in those days was a serious business, despite my light hearted remarks above. People were used to the traditional (and challenging) breakfast, lunch and supper, and that was an important consideration in the planning of the Silver Jubilee in 1934/35. The reaction, particularly of North Country passengers, on being faced with a Continental breakfast on a high speed diesel multiple unit (DMU) was considered likely to be explosive, and Wedgwood and Gresley opted for a wiser course of action.

In 1928 the Flying Scotsman was run non-stop between London and Edinburgh during the three summer months, and the successful running continued until 1961, broken by the eight years of war and its aftermath. A feature of GNR and LNER operating was that at holiday and summer periods the major services were duplicated or even triplicated. By 1938 a number of those extra services had become timetabled. The early morning services had hardly changed. The blocs of services of 1922 had increased in number, and the three streamliners were additions rather than replacements. The introduction of the Coronation caused the Newcastle service to move to 15.30, likewise the Silver Jubilee caused the 17.30 Newcastle to move to 17.45, and the West Riding Limited was inserted ahead of the evening Leeds and overnight services.

The dedication of the timetablers, to what always seemed to me to be spurious accuracy, was a feature of all timetables, adding greatly their volume and making reading more difficult. No.315 down, the 10.00 Flying Scotsman, was given two independent paths depending on the date – the difference being whether the train was the non-stop or the regular calling pattern and therefore the loading changed. The two paths differed by 1½ minutes as far as Doncaster! Would that trains ran that closely to time.

By the 1950s people, especially on business, were getting up and about earlier. The early morning Leeds and Bradford service was an innovation in the 1952/53 winter book, and after a slow start, became popular, so much so that it was extended to Newcastle. The early morning revolution continued with the introduction of a service to Edinburgh, the Morning Talisman. The original blocks of passenger services had broadened and increased in number to the stage that there were only two lengthy quiet periods in the working day. These varied with location but 11.00 to noon, and 14.30 to 1530 in the London suburbs were the only times when one might indulge in a little shunting, etc. During the summer book they almost disappeared.

Later in the 1950s and into the 1960s, train lengths were shortened as the number of services steadily increased, and at the end of steam traction on what had now become the East Coast Main Line, trains no longer than the pre-war streamliners were commonplace. With underpowered diesel traction and smaller trains, train speeds increased and were maintained both up hill and down.

The small excerpt from the 2007 timetable is given to illustrate the enormous change compared with the steam age timetables. The whole timetable is quite different, and services that remained from GNR days up to the end of steam traction in some cases have entirely disappeared. The services start even earlier since not everyone lives near London, Leeds, Newcastle, or Edinburgh. Our memories are of a very different world.

Looking at the suburban service from Kings Cross in 1922, I have compared the 10-12.00 window in the timetables for 1922, 1938 and 1953, again in the down direction. To anyone who knows what used to be Middlesex and South Hertfordshire before it became swallowed up in Greater London, the first two are interesting. The services linked the outlying villages of Barnet, Finchley, Enfield, Palmers Green and what were outer London suburbs of Highgate, Muswell Hill and Wood Green with the capital. The emphasis lay on the services to High rather than New Barnet, and Alexandra Palace, presumably in the latter case for Muswell Hill since nobody actually lived at the Palace! The development down the New Line had hardly started in 1922, and trains went only as far as Gordon Hill, which might have been called Enfield North, and occasionally, Cuffley.

By the 1938 service, the spaces between were being filled in steadily. The Highgate – Barnet branches were still very busy, and although better, the service down the main line was not terribly good. The LMS contribution from Broad Street was quite significant, and even in 1938 the Piccadilly Line extension from Finsbury Park to Cockfosters had not yet had a significant effect. The New Line was now open to Hertford North, and estates were growing up alongside the stations throughout the GN suburban area. In those days, Saturday was a working day for most people, and after 12.00 the service was considerably increased. Broad Street, Moorgate and the Widened Lines were used far more before the 1939 war, and a number of services that began at Kings Cross or Finsbury Park were started from Moorgate and Broad Street instead.

A feature of those far-off days fondly remembered by commuters of those times, many now gone from us, alas, occurred at about 17.25. The 17.18 from Kings Cross to Cuffley, No.617 down, probably with its N2 0-6-2T hauling a quad-art set, reached Finsbury Park at 17.24, alongside the LMS 'Jinty' 0-6-0T on the 17.12 from Broad Street for Potters Bar, No.618 down. Although the New Line train was scheduled to leave at 17.26 and the other at 17.27, one can be sure that there was often a contest between the two as far as the parting at Wood Green. However, there was a 17.30 Newcastle departure from the main line station, No.619 down which added spice to the occasion – the Silver Jubilee – and there were tales of diminutive LMS tanks being urged up to speed to keep up with SILVER LINK and her sisters. As it was booked non-stop to New Barnet where it waited for the A4 to pass at 17.42 , the sharp bend through New Southgate on the down slow must have taxed the normally serene riding of the quad-arts.

Looking at the suburban service from Kings Cross in 1922, I have compared the 10-12.00 window in the timetables for 1922, 1938 and 1953, again in the down direction. To anyone who knows what used to be Middlesex and South Hertfordshire before it became swallowed up in Greater London, the first two are interesting. The services linked the outlying villages of Barnet, Finchley, Enfield, Palmers Green and what were outer London suburbs of Highgate, Muswell Hill and Wood Green with the capital. The emphasis lay on the services to High rather than New Barnet, and Alexandra Palace, presumably in the latter case for Muswell Hill since nobody actually lived at the palace! The development down the New Line had hardly started in 1922 and trains went only as far as Gordon Hill, which might have been called Enfield North, and occasionally Cuffley.

By the 1938 service, the spaces between were being filled in steadily. The Highgate-Barnet branches were still very busy and although better, the service down the main line was not terribly good. The LMS contribution from Broad Street was quite important but even in 1938 the Piccadilly Line extension from Finsbury Park to Cockfosters had not yet had a significant effect. The New Line was now open to Hertford North, and estates were growing alongside the stations throughout the GN suburban area. In those days, Saturday was a working day for most people and after 12.00 the service was considerably increased. Broad Street, Moorgate and the Widened Lines were used far more before the 1939 war, and a number of services that started at Kings Cross or Finsbury Park began at Moorgate and Broad Street instead.

A feature of those far off days fondly remembered by commuters of those times, many now gone from us, alas, occurred at about 17.25. The 17.18 from Kings Cross to Cuffley, No.617 down, probably with its N2 0-6-2T hauling a quad-art set, reached Finsbury Park at 17.24, where it found itself alongside the LMS 3F 0-6-0T on the 17.12 from Broad Street for Potters Bar, No.618 down. Although the New Line train was scheduled to leave at 17.26 and the other at 17.27, one can be sure that there was often a contest between the two as far as the parting at Wood Green. However, there was a 17.30 Newcastle departure from the main line station, No.619 down – the Silver Jubilee – which added spice to the occasion and there were tales of the diminutive LMS tanks being urged up to speed to keep up with SILVER LINK and her sisters. As it was booked non-stop to New Barnet where it waited for the A4 to pass at 17.42, the sharp bend through New Southgate on the down slow must have taxed the normally serene riding of the quad-arts.

Looking back, both timetables in 1922 and 1938 lacked any systematic pattern. Whereas after the war freight was discouraged during the commuter periods, apart obviously from the bottlenecks, freight was moved between yards to pick up or deliver traffic. After the war, things were very different. The transfer of the line to Finchley and Barnet to the Northern Line had removed a great deal of traffic and although the Alexandra Palace service was retained most of it went to LT at Highgate, and the branch was closed in 1954. Apart from coal for some years, the line was disused, and the flyover at Finsbury Park was used for the transfer of empty carriage stock. The Piccadilly Line extension also took a great deal of traffic off the old GNR between Finsbury Park and New Southgate. The service provided an hourly off-peak frequency on the inner and outer main line stations and on the New Line, which was strengthened during the peaks. Both Moorgate and Broad Street were by now only rush hour terminals and both York Road and platform 16 at Kings Cross were deserted outside these periods. Later, some strengthening of the service was made and further improvements came with the use of DMU and diesel locomotives.

With electrification the service was intensified quite dramatically, with three trains per hour on the main and New lines. The change over nearly a century has been astonishing. The 10-12.00 window enclosed 24 down services in 1922, which fell to a mere 13 in the early 1950s as the Piccadilly and Northern Lines took the weight of commuting in from the north.

It says much for the foresight of the GNR in fostering the infant Underground system, which ironically siphoned off the GNR's commuter business. These were the days of Gresley's N2s and the quad-arts of immortal memory. GNR No.1744 is gloriously restored to her GNR livery and a quad-art is superbly preserved by the North Norfolk Railway. To the commuters of yesteryear, however, they rarely looked so splendid in normal service!

A few years ago, the 2007 timetable showed no less than 33 services in the two hour window, but there are important differences. High Barnet and Potters Bar no longer mark the edge of civilisation. That is now defined at Peterborough and Kings Lynn and the policy of putting more stops on main line services mean that each hour there are four services to Peterborough in addition to the stopping services terminating there. Cambridge has four trains an hour instead of something near four hours between trains, and the rural settlements north of Hitchin have two services an hour.

The class 313 dual voltage units are now over 30 years old, and before long thoughts must turn to the nature of their successors. Broad Street is long gone, as is Moorgate on the Widened Lines, replaced by the Northern City station of the same name. Before long, services from south of the Thames will link to GNR destinations, recalling the 1860s when SER services were seen on Holloway Bank.

Class O2/3 2-8-0 63980 with a down goods at Doncaster. The loco has recently had a General overhaul and has not had time to acquire its usual livery of matt black.